Ritchie   Fo

Diagnosis and Improvement of

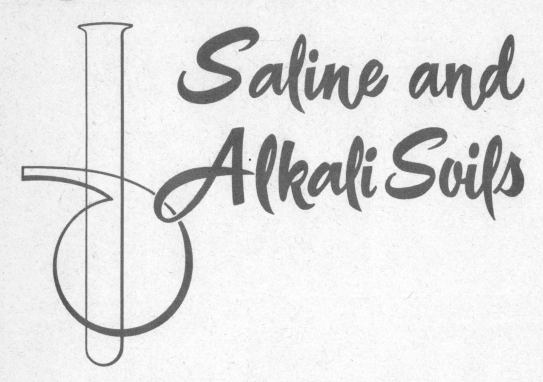

Saline and Alkali Soils

United States Salinity Laboratory Staff

Contributing Authors:

L. E. Allison	L. Bernstein	C. A. Bower
J. W. Brown	M. Fireman	J. T. Hatcher
H. E. Hayward	G. A. Pearson	R. C. Reeve
L. A. Richards	L. V. Wilcox	

L. A. Richards, Editor
Soil and Water Conservation Research Branch
Agricultural Research Service

Agriculture Handbook No. 60   Issued February 1954
UNITED STATES DEPARTMENT OF AGRICULTURE

Preface

The Bankhead-Jones Act adopted by Congress in 1935 made funds available for agricultural research on a regional basis. At a meeting of representatives of the United States Department of Agriculture and the directors of the Agricultural Experiment Stations of 11 Western States, the decision was made to establish a salinity laboratory to conduct research on problems connected with the success and permanence of agriculture on saline and alkali soils. In 1937 the United States Regional Salinity Laboratory was established by the then Bureau of Plant Industry on grounds adjacent to its Rubidoux Laboratory in Riverside, Calif. A memorandum of understanding, providing for official collaborators, was entered into with these 11 Western States and Hawaii.

The Rubidoux Laboratory had been established by the Bureau's Division of Western Irrigation Agriculture in 1928 primarily to conduct research relating to the quality of water, with special emphasis on the toxicity of boron to plants. It was combined with the United States Regional Salinity Laboratory in 1948.

In 1951 official cooperation and collaborator representation was extended to include the 17 Western States, and the name of the Laboratory modified to United States Salinity Laboratory.

Close cooperative relations are maintained with the State Agricultural Experiment Stations and Hawaii through the official collaborators who meet annually to review the Laboratory's research program.

The United States Salinity Laboratory is administered in the Agricultural Research Service.

Introduction

Saline and alkali soil conditions reduce the value and productivity of considerable areas of land in the United States. The problem is an old one, and there is much information on this subject in the technical literature. It is the purpose of this handbook to bring together and summarize information that will be useful, particularly to professional agricultural workers, for the diagnosis and improvement of saline and alkali soils.

The nomenclature for these problem soils is still in a formative stage. This is illustrated by the diversity of usage of such prominent investigators as Gedroiz (1917), Hilgard (1906), Hissink (1933), Kelley (1948, 1951), and De Sigmond (1938). Ultimate agreement on nomenclature will depend on the role of exchangeable potassium. The facts now available on this subject are meager, but they suggest that the undesirable physical properties that are characteristic of alkali soils are caused by excessive exchangeable sodium. Other elements of the alkali metal group either do not occur in significant quantities or do not appear to have similar action in soils.

It is not the purpose of the writers to emphasize the definition of terms or to influence the usage of others; but, for clarity in the presentation of the subjects treated in this handbook, it was necessary to consider terminology, and a glossary of special terms has been included. In deference to past usage, the term "alkali soil" is employed to refer to soils that have a high exchangeable-sodium-percentage; and "saline soil" is used in connection with soils having a high value for the electrical conductivity of the saturation extract.

This handbook was first issued in multilithed form in 1947, and it has been widely distributed in this country and abroad.

No attempt is made to present a comprehensive review of the literature, because the handbook is intended primarily as a practical guide for those who are confronted with soil, plant, and water problems involving salinity and alkali. The first five chapters provide a basis for the evaluation and interpretation of measurements. The procedures and measuring methods given in chapters 6, 7, and 8 are those with which the Laboratory has had experience, and they are believed to have general applicability in the diagnosis and improvement of saline and alkali soils.

There are other measuring methods in current use in various localities that have not been included, but no particular significance should be attached to this omission. It is not possible to cover all special methods, and it is always advisable to consult with the State agricultural experiment stations for detailed information on local problems.

There is need for continued research on problems of saline and alkali soils and the many complicated interrelations to crop production on these soils. The close cooperative relations of the Salinity Laboratory and the agricultural experiment stations of the 17 Western States and Hawaii have provided an efficient arrangement for conducting investigational work with a minimum of duplication of effort and for exchanging and disseminating research information.

This handbook is the result of the combined efforts of the entire staff of the Salinity Laboratory. Those listed as authors have carried responsibility for writing various sections. Former staff members C. H. Wadleigh and A. D. Ayers were among the authors of the earlier draft and assisted in reviewing the present one. The illustrations were prepared by Miles S. Mayhugh and R. H. Brooks.

The writers are indebted to many reviewers, not all of whom are mentioned, who have offered helpful criticisms and suggestions. The sections relating to leaching and drainage in chapter 3 were reviewed by F. M. Eaton, Vaughn E. Hansen, O. W. Israelsen, and Dean F. Peterson, Jr. W. C. Cooper, W. P. Cottam, F. M. Eaton, W. G. Harper, and W. J. Leighty reviewed chapter 4 and contributed suggestions relating to salt tolerance and indicator plants. Chapter 5 on quality of irrigation water was given special consideration by the collaborators, and this chapter was also reviewed by C. S. Scofield. Chapters 6, 7, and 8, dealing with methods, were reviewed by L. T. Alexander, B. J. Cooil, E. E. Frahm, J. C. Hide, A. J. MacKenzie, C. D. Moodie, A. H. Post, R. F. Reitemeier, and others.

Special acknowledgment is made to the official collaborators of the Salinity Laboratory for their many helpful suggestions and for their cooperation and encouragement. The preliminary drafts of all sections of the handbook were made available to all collaborators, and the great majority of them responded with constructive criticisms and comments.

H. E. HAYWARD
Director

United States Salinity Laboratory
Riverside, Calif.
May 1953.

Contents

Chapter 1

Origin and Nature of Saline and Alkali Soils

The soils under consideration in this handbook owe their distinctive character to the fact that they contain excessive concentrations of either soluble salts or exchangeable sodium, or both. For agricultural purposes, such soils are regarded as a class of problem soils that requires special remedial measures and management practices. Soluble salts produce harmful effects to plants by increasing the salt content of the soil solution and by increasing the degree of saturation of the exchange materials in the soil with exchangeable sodium. The latter effect occurs when the soluble constituents consist largely of sodium salts and is of a more permanent nature than the salt content of the soil solution, since exchangeable sodium usually persists after the soluble salts are removed.

In discussing these problem soils it is convenient to use terms that refer specifically to the two principal causes of the problem. "Saline soil," as used in this handbook, refers to a soil that contains sufficient soluble salts to impair its productivity. Similarly, alkali soils can be defined in terms of productivity as influenced by exchangeable sodium. In accordance with this usage, alkali soils may or may not contain excess soluble salts. Probably the most common problem involves soils that contain an excess of both soluble salts and exchangeable sodium, and, in agreement with the terminology of De Sigmond (1938),[1] these soils will be referred to as saline-alkali soils.

The salt content of soils above which plant growth is affected depends upon several factors, among which are the texture of soil, the distribution of salt in the profile, the composition of the salt, and the species of plant. Several arbitrary limits for salinity have been suggested for distinguishing saline from nonsaline soils. Kearney and Scofield (1936), in discussing the choice of crops for saline lands, considered that plants begin to be adversely affected as the salt content of the soil exceeds 0.1 percent. De Sigmond (1938) was in agreement with this limit. In the report of the United States National Resources Planning Board (1942, *pp. 263–334*) relative to the Pecos River investigation, Scofield considered a soil to be saline if the solution extracted from a saturated soil paste had an electrical conductivity value of 4 mmhos/cm. or more. The electrical conductivity of the saturation extract was adopted by the Salinity Laboratory as the preferred scale for general use in estimating soil salinity. The Soil Survey Staff (1951) of the United States Department of Agriculture now uses either this method or the earlier method based on the electrical resistance of a sample of soil paste, the latter reading being converted to the dry-weight percentage of soluble salt in the soil.

The decision regarding what level of exchangeable sodium in the soil constitutes an excessive degree of saturation is complicated by the fact that there is no sharp change in the properties of the soil as the degree of saturation with exchangeable sodium is increased. In the past an exchangeable-sodium-percentage of 15 has been used at the Laboratory as a boundary limit between nonalkali and alkali soils. Insufficient data and experience are available to justify a change, but this limit must be regarded as somewhat arbitrary and tentative. In some cases, for example, 2 or 3 milliequivalents of exchangeable sodium per 100 gm. of soil has equal or even greater usefulness as a critical limit.

There has been uncertainty in the past regarding the effect of exchangeable potassium on the physical properties of soils and if, as De Sigmond (1928) and Magistad (1945) have proposed, exchangeable sodium and potassium should be considered as additive in defining alkali soils. It has been observed in several instances that alkali soils high in exchangeable potassium have better physical properties and are more readily reclaimable than other alkali soils containing similar amounts of exchangeable sodium but low amounts of exchangeable potassium. The view that exchangeable potassium has only a slight or no adverse effect upon the physical properties of soils is supported by the results of measurements made recently at the Laboratory [2] on samples of seven soils adjusted to various levels of exchangeable sodium and exchangeable potassium (fig. 1).

The magnitude of the air:water permeability ratio is a measure of the extent to which soil structure deteriorates when water is applied, a high ratio indicating a high degree of deterioration. The data for

---

[1] References to Literature Cited (p. 148) are herein indicated by the name of the author (or authors) followed by the year of publication.

[2] Unpublished data by R. C. Reeve, C. A. Bower, R. H. Brooks, and F. B. Gschwend.

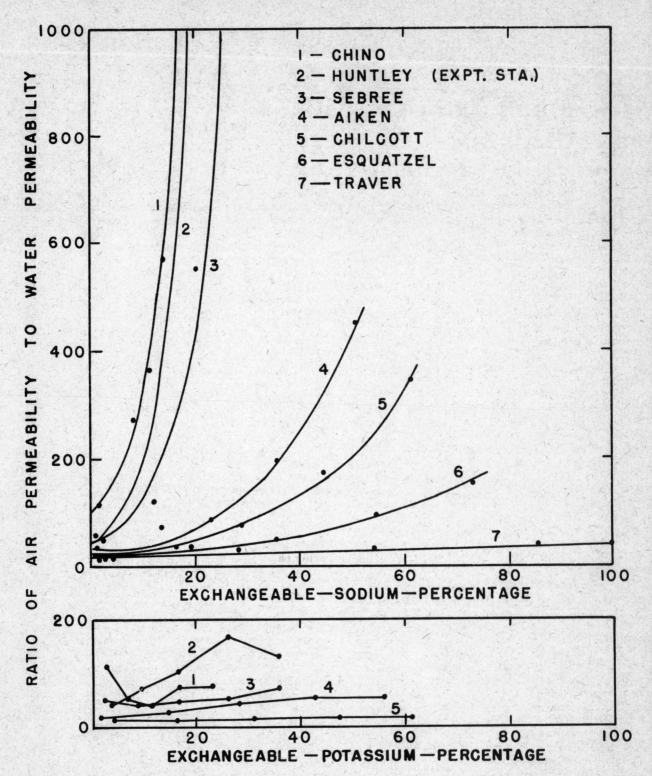

FIGURE 1.—Relative effect of exchangeable sodium and exchangeable potassium on the ratio of the air permeability to the water permeability of soils.

two soils are not plotted in the graph showing the effect of the exchangeable-potassium-percentage, because they nearly coincide with the lower curve. In general, the increase in ratio with increase in exchangeable sodium is directly related to the total specific surface of the soils.

Improvements are being made in methods of appraising both the susceptibility and the status of soils with respect to the injurious effects of exchangeable sodium. For these reasons, both the terminology and the classification limits for alkali soils must be regarded as being in a transitional stage.

Sources of Soluble Salts

The soluble salts that occur in soils consist mostly of various proportions of the cations sodium, calcium, and magnesium, and the anions chloride and sulfate. Constituents that ordinarily occur only in minor amounts are the cation potassium and the anions bicarbonate, carbonate, and nitrate. The original and, to some extent, the direct source of all the salt constituents are the primary minerals found in soils and in the exposed rocks of the earth's crust. Clarke (1924) has estimated that the average chlorine and sulfur content of the earth's crust is 0.05 and 0.06 percent, respectively, while sodium, calcium, and magnesium each occur to the extent of 2 or 3 percent. During the process of chemical weathering, which involves hydrolysis, hydration, solution, oxidation, and carbonation, these constituents are gradually released and made soluble.

Bicarbonate ions form as a result of the solution of carbon dioxide in water. The carbon dioxide may be of atmospheric or biological origin. Water containing carbon dioxide is a particularly active chemical weathering agent that releases appreciable quantities of the cation constituents as the bicarbonates. Carbonate and bicarbonate ions are interrelated, the relative amounts of each present being a function of the pH value of the solution. Appreciable amounts of carbonate ions can be present only at pH values of 9.5 or higher.

While the above-mentioned salt constituents are of most importance in saline soils, there are places, as in parts of Colorado, Utah, and Washington, where high concentrations of nitrate are found. Various theories (Kelley, 1951) have been proposed to explain the origin of excessive nitrate salts in soils. Boron, owing to its marked toxicity to plants when present even in low concentrations, also deserves mention (Eaton and Wilcox, 1939). The principal source of this element is the mineral tourmaline, which is a rather widespread but minor constituent of primary rocks.

Although weathering of primary minerals is the indirect source of nearly all soluble salts, there are probably few instances where sufficient salts have accumulated in place from this source alone to form a saline soil. Saline soils usually occur in areas that receive salts from other locations, and water is the primary carrier. The ocean may be the source of salts as in soils where the parent material consists of marine deposits that were laid down during earlier geologic periods and have since been uplifted. The Mancos shales occurring in Colorado, Wyoming, and Utah are typical examples of saline marine deposits. The ocean is also the source of the salts in low-lying soils along the margin of seacoasts. Sometimes salt is moved inland through the transportation of spray by winds and is called cyclic salt (Teakle, 1937). More commonly, however, the direct source of salts is surface and ground waters. All of these waters contain dissolved salts, the concentration depending upon the salt content of the soil and geologic materials with which the water has been in contact. Waters act as sources of salts when used for irrigation. They may also add salts to soils under natural conditions, as when they flood low-lying land or when ground water rises close to the soil surface.

Salinization of Soils

Saline soils occur for the most part in regions of arid or semiarid climate. Under humid conditions the soluble salts originally present in soil materials and those formed by the weathering of minerals generally are carried downward into the ground water and are transported ultimately by streams to the oceans. Saline soils are, therefore, practically nonexistent in humid regions, except when the soil has been subjected to sea water in river deltas and other low-lying lands near the sea. In arid regions leaching and transportation of soluble salts to the ocean is not so complete as in humid regions. Leaching is usually local in nature, and soluble salts may not be transported far. This occurs not only because there is less rainfall available to leach and transport the salts but also because of the high evaporation rates characteristic of arid climates, which tend further to concentrate the salts in soils and in surface waters.

Restricted drainage is a factor that usually contributes to the salinization of soils and may involve the presence of a high ground-water table or low permeability of the soil. The high ground-water table is often related to topography. Owing to the low rainfall in arid regions, surface drainageways may be poorly developed. As a consequence, there are drainage basins that have no outlet to permanent streams. The drainage of salt-bearing waters away from the higher lands of the basin may raise the ground-water level to the soil surface on the lower lands, may cause temporary flooding, or may form permanent salty lakes. Under such conditions upward movement of saline ground water or evaporation of surface water results in the formation of saline soil. The extent of saline areas thus formed may vary from a few acres to hundreds of square miles. Many of the saline soils in the Great Basin were formed in this manner. Similar areas occur throughout the Western States. They are often referred to as playas or dry lakes.

Low permeability of the soil causes poor drainage by impeding the downward movement of water. Low permeability may be the result of an unfavorable soil texture or structure or the presence of indurated layers. The latter may consist of a claypan, a caliche layer, or a silica hardpan. De Sigmond (1924) considered the presence of an impermeable soil layer essential for the formation of the saline soils found in Hungary.

The salinity problem of principal economic importance arises when previously nonsaline soil becomes saline as the result of irrigation. Such soils are often located in valleys adjacent to streams, and, because of the ease with which they can be irrigated, the more level areas are usually selected for cultivation. While such soils may be well drained and nonsaline under natural conditions, the drainage may not be adequate for irrigation. When bringing new lands under irrigation, farmers have frequently failed to recognize the need for establishing artificial drains to care for the additional water and soluble salts. As a result, the ground-water table may rise from a considerable depth to within a few feet of the soil surface in a few years. During the early development of irrigation projects, water is frequently plentiful and there is a tendency to use it in excess. This hastens the rise of the water table. Waters used for irrigation may contain from 0.1 to as much as 5 tons of salt per acre-foot of water, and the annual application of water may amount to 5 feet or more. Thus, considerable quantities of soluble salts may be added to irrigated soils over relatively short periods of time. When the water table rises to within 5 or 6 feet of the soil surface, ground water moves upward into the root zone and to the soil surface. Under such conditions, ground water, as well as irrigation water, contributes to the salinization of the soil.

Alkalization or Accumulation of Exchangeable Sodium in Soils

Soil particles adsorb and retain cations on their surfaces. Cation adsorption occurs as a consequence of the electrical charges at the surface of the soil particles. While adsorbed cations are combined chemically with the soil particles, they may be replaced by other cations that occur in the soil solution. The reaction whereby a cation in solution replaces an adsorbed cation is called cation exchange. Sodium, calcium, and magnesium cations are always readily exchangeable. Other cations, like potassium and ammonium, may be held at certain positions on the particles in some soils so that they are exchanged with great difficulty and, hence, are said to be fixed.

Cation adsorption, being a surface phenomenon, is identified mainly with the fine silt, clay, and organic matter fractions of soils. Many different kinds of minerals and organic materials occurring in soils have exchange properties and together are referred to as the exchange complex. The capacity of a soil to adsorb and exchange cations can be measured and expressed in chemical equivalents and is called the cation-exchange-capacity. It is commonly expressed in milliequivalents per 100 gm. of soil. Various chemical and physical factors interact to make the measured value depend somewhat on the method of determination, but, nevertheless, the cation-exchange-capacity is a reasonably definite soil property that has considerable practical significance. In view of the fact that the adsorbed cations can interchange freely with adjacent cations in the soil solution, it is to be expected that the proportion of the various cations on the exchange complex will be related to their concentrations in the soil solution.

Calcium and magnesium are the principal cations found in the soil solution and on the exchange complex of normal soils in arid regions. When excess soluble salts accumulate in these soils, sodium frequently becomes the dominant cation in the soil solution. Thus, sodium may be the predominant cation to which the soil has been subjected, or it may become dominant in the soil solution, owing to the precipitation of calcium and magnesium compounds. As the soil solution becomes concentrated through evaporation or water absorption by plants, the solubility limits of calcium sulfate, calcium carbonate, and magnesium carbonate are often exceeded, in which case they are precipitated with a corresponding increase in the relative proportion of sodium. Under such conditions, a part of the original exchangeable calcium and magnesium is replaced by sodium.

From a practical viewpoint, it is fortunate that the calcium and magnesium cations in the soil solution are more strongly adsorbed by the exchange complex than sodium. At equivalent solution concentrations, the amounts of calcium and magnesium adsorbed are several times that of sodium. In general, half or more of the soluble cations must be sodium before significant amounts are adsorbed by the exchange complex. In some saline soil solutions, however, practically all of the cations are sodium, and in these sodium is the predominant adsorbed cation.

Characteristics of Saline and Alkali Soils

The term "soil" is used in several senses by agriculturists. In one sense a soil is considered to be a three-dimensional piece of landscape having shape, area, and depth (Soil Survey, 1951). The concept of a soil as a profile having depth but not necessarily shape or area is also a common use of the term. In another sense, often used in this handbook, the term is applied to samples representing layers or points in the profile. Saline and alkali soils are defined and diagnosed on the basis of determinations made on soil samples, and the significance of information thus obtained contributes substantially to scientific agriculture. The extension and harmonization of these definitions to the problems and purposes of soil survey and soil classification have not been attempted, because it lies somewhat beyond the scope of the present work.

To facilitate and clarify this discussion, the problem soils under consideration have been separated into three groups: Saline, saline-alkali, and nonsaline-alkali soils.

Saline Soils

Saline is used in connection with soils for which the conductivity of the saturation extract is more than 4 mmhos/cm. at 25° C. and the exchangeable-sodium-percentage is less than 15. Ordinarily, the pH is less than 8.5. These soils correspond to Hilgard's (1906) "white alkali" soils and to the "Solonchaks" of the Russian soil scientists. When adequate drainage is established, the excessive soluble salts may be removed by leaching and they again become normal soils.

Saline soils are often recognized by the presence of white crusts of salts on the surface. Soil salinity may occur in soils having distinctly developed profile characteristics or in undifferentiated soil material such as alluvium.

The chemical characteristics of soils classed as saline are mainly determined by the kinds and amounts of salts present. The amount of soluble salts present controls the osmotic pressure of the soil solution. Sodium seldom comprises more than half of the soluble cations and hence is not adsorbed to any significant extent. The relative amounts of calcium and magnesium present in the soil solution and on the exchange complex may vary considerably. Soluble and exchangeable potassium are ordinarily minor constituents, but occasionally they may be major constituents. The chief anions are chloride, sulfate, and sometimes nitrate. Small amounts of bicarbonate may occur, but soluble carbonates are almost invariably absent. In addition to the readily soluble salts, saline soils may contain salts of low solubility, such as calcium sulfate (gypsum) and calcium and magnesium carbonates (lime).

Owing to the presence of excess salts and the absence of significant amounts of exchangeable sodium, saline soils generally are flocculated; and, as a consequence, the permeability is equal to or higher than that of similar nonsaline soils.

Saline-Alkali Soils

Saline-alkali is applied to soils for which the conductivity of the saturation extract is greater than 4 mmhos/cm. at 25° C. and the exchangeable-sodium-percentage is greater than 15. These soils form as a result of the combined processes of salinization and alkalization. As long as excess salts are present, the appearance and properties of these soils are generally similar to those of saline soils. Under conditions of excess salts, the pH readings are seldom higher than 8.5 and the particles remain flocculated. If the excess soluble salts are leached downward, the properties of these soils may change markedly and become similar to those of nonsaline-alkali soils. As the concentration of the salts in the soil solution is lowered, some of the exchangeable sodium hydrolyzes and forms sodium hydroxide. This may change to sodium carbonate upon reaction with carbon dioxide absorbed from the atmosphere. In any event, upon leaching, the soil may become strongly alkaline (pH readings above 8.5), the particles disperse, and the soil becomes unfavorable for the entry and movement of water and for tillage. Although the return of the soluble salts may lower the pH reading and restore the particles to a flocculated condition, the management of saline-alkali soils contin-

ues to be a problem until the excess salts and exchangeable sodium are removed from the root zone and a favorable physical condition of the soil is reestablished.

Saline-alkali soils sometimes contain gypsum. When such soils are leached, calcium dissolves and the replacement of exchangeable sodium by calcium takes place concurrently with the removal of excess salts.

Nonsaline-Alkali Soils

Nonsaline-alkali is applied to soils for which the exchangeable-sodium-percentage is greater than 15 and the conductivity of the saturation extract is less than 4 mmhos/cm. at 25° C. The pH readings usually range between 8.5 and 10. These soils correspond to Hilgard's "black alkali" soils and in some cases to "Solonetz," as the latter term is used by the Russians. They frequently occur in semiarid and arid regions in small irregular areas, which are often referred to as "slick spots." Except when gypsum is present in the soil or the irrigation water, the drainage and leaching of saline-alkali soils leads to the formation of nonsaline-alkali soils. As mentioned in the discussion of saline-alkali soils, the removal of excess salts in such soils tends to increase the rate of hydrolysis of the exchangeable sodium and often causes a rise of the pH reading of the soil. Dispersed and dissolved organic matter present in the soil solution of highly alkaline soils may be deposited on the soil surface by evaporation, thus causing darkening and giving rise to the term "black alkali."

If allowed sufficient time, nonsaline-alkali soils develop characteristic morphological features. Because partially sodium-saturated clay is highly dispersed, it may be transported downward through the soil and accumulate at lower levels. As a result, a few inches of the surface soil may be relatively coarse in texture and friable; but below, where the clay accumulates, the soil may develop a dense layer of low permeability that may have a columnar or prismatic structure. Commonly, however, alkali conditions develop in such soils as a result of irrigation. In such cases, sufficient time usually has not elapsed for the development of the typical columnar structure, but the soil has low permeability and is difficult to till.

The exchangeable sodium present in nonsaline-alkali soil may have a marked influence on the physical and chemical properties. As the proportion of exchangeable sodium increases, the soil tends to become more dispersed. The pH reading may increase, sometimes becoming as high as 10. The soil solution of nonsaline-alkali soils, although relatively low in soluble salts, has a composition that differs considerably from that of normal and saline soils. While the anions present consist mostly of chloride, sulfate, and bicarbonate, small amounts of carbonate often occur. At high pH readings and in the presence of carbonate ions, calcium and magnesium are precipitated; hence, the soil solutions of nonsaline-alkali soils usually contain only small amounts of these cations, sodium being the predominant one. Large quantities of exchangeable and soluble potassium may occur in some of these soils.

The effect of excessive exchangeable potassium on soil properties has not been sufficiently studied.

Nonsaline-alkali soils in some areas of western United States have exchangeable-sodium-percentages considerably above 15, and yet the pH reading, especially in the surface soil, may be as low as 6. These soils have been referred to by De Sigmond (1938) as degraded alkali soils. They occur only in the absence of lime, and the low pH reading is the result of exchangeable hydrogen. The physical properties, however, are dominated by the exchangeable sodium and are typically those of a nonsaline-alkali soil.

Chapter 2

Determination of the Properties of Saline and Alkali Soils

This chapter discusses determinations that give information on the chemical and physical properties of saline and alkali soils and thus serve as a basis for their diagnosis, treatment, and management. The status of knowledge on this subject is such that it is not yet possible to prepare a brief handbook containing a few simple measurements that will give all the necessary information. A number of different types of measurements are presented. Some of these must be regarded as tentative and subject to change and improvement. In some cases alternate procedures are proposed, and the individual worker will need to decide what kind and how many measurements will be required for the problem at hand. The purpose, application, and interpretation of the various determinations are discussed in this chapter. Detailed directions for making the measurements are given in chapter 6.

Soil Sampling

There is no standard procedure for obtaining soil samples for appraising salinity and alkali. Usually the details of procedure will depend upon the purpose for which the sample is taken. If the objective is to obtain a general evaluation of salinity in a given area, the average salt content of a number of samples provides an index for the over-all appraisal. The variation among samples gives an index of the variation in salt content that may be encountered in the field. The larger the number of samples, the more accurate the appraisal will be. Too few samples may give a completely erroneous index of the salinity status. The deviation between the actual conditions existing in an area and the evaluation of the situation from the sampling procedure is designated as the "sampling error." It is evident that the larger the number of samples and the more carefully they are selected, the smaller the sampling error will be.

Salt concentration in soils may vary greatly with horizontal or vertical distance and with time. The nature of the soil, microrelief, and the cause and source of salinity should be considered. Factors that cause migration of salt, such as seasonal precipitation, irrigation, and phase in the crop cycle, should be taken into account in relation to the time of sampling. In cultivated areas, soil management history may be the most

important single factor in determining salinity status, and field boundaries may enter the problem of where to sample and how to composite the samples.

The interpretation and use of salinity and alkali measurements necessarily depend on the completeness and accuracy of observational data recorded at the time of sampling. A record of the species and condition of the plant cover is of particular importance. When attempting to correlate crop conditions in the field with soil-salinity measurements, it is necessary to take samples from the active root zone of the plants.

The following suggestions are offered on where and how to sample:

(a) Visible or suspected salt crusts on the soil surface should be sampled separately and the approximate depth of sample recorded.

(b) If the soil shows evidence of profile development or distinct stratification, samples should be taken by horizons or layers.

(c) In the absence of profile development or distinct stratification, the surface samples (excluding the surface crust) should be taken to the plow depth, usually to a depth of 6 or 7 inches.

(d) Succeeding samples may be taken at intervals of 6 to 18, 18 to 36, and 36 to 72 inches, or other convenient depths, depending on the depth of the root zone, the nature of the problem, and the detail required.

(e) Sometimes soil samples taken for salinity and alkali determinations may be composited to reduce analytical work.

(f) The size of samples will depend on the measurements that are to be made.

Detailed suggestions on taking and handling soil samples along with a sample of the field data sheet used at the Salinity Laboratory are given in Method 1.

Estimation of Soluble Salts From Electrical Conductivity

The choice of a method for measuring salinity depends on such things as the reason for making the measurements, the number of samples to be handled, and the time and effort available for doing the work. Accurate

7

methods usually require more time and, therefore, limit the number of determinations.

Electrical-resistance measurements can be made quickly and accurately and have long been used for estimating soluble salts in soil (Whitney and Means, 1897); however, electrical conductance, which is the reciprocal of resistance, is more suitable for salinity measurements, because it increases with salt content, thus simplifying the interpretation of readings. Moreover, expressing results in terms of specific conductance or conductivity makes the determination independent of the size and shape of the sample.

Electrical conductance is expressed in mhos, i. e., reciprocal ohms, while electrical conductivity has the dimensions of mhos per centimeter. In this handbook, the symbol "EC" is used to represent electrical conductivity.[3]

The salt content of the soil can be estimated roughly from an electrical-conductivity measurement on a saturated soil paste or a more dilute suspension of soil in water. A better estimate of soluble salts can be obtained from the conductivity of a water extract of the soil. In general the higher the moisture content, the easier it will be to obtain the extract, but the less representative the extracted solution will be of the solution to which plant roots are exposed in the soil.

Soil solutions in the field-moisture range can be extracted for study and analysis by the displacement method (White and Ross, 1937) or with the pressure-membrane apparatus (Method 3d). These methods are used mainly for research and special chemical studies.

Plants in saline soil are responsive to the concentration of the soil solution, and the relation of concentration to the normal field-moisture range is sometimes overlooked. There is more than a tenfold range in the wilting percentage of various soils. Consequently, the field-moisture range may vary greatly from one soil to another. For example, a sand and a clay could have the same soluble-salt content expressed as percent, dry-weight basis, but the soil-solution concentration when near the wilting percentage could be 10 times as high for the sand as for the clay.

---

[3] The standard unit for conductivity (mho/cm.) is a large unit, so that most solutions have a conductivity that is much less than one unit. For instance, a measurement on one sample of water from the Rio Grande at the Elephant Butte Dam gave $EC=$ 0.000694 mho/cm. For such cases, with physical and chemical measurements, it is customary to choose a small subunit that gives a more convenient location of the decimal point when recording or expressing data. For example, the unit $EC \times 10^3$ is called the millimho per centimeter. This is a convenient, practical conductivity unit for most soil salinity work. Until recently $EC \times 10^5$ (or $K \times 10^5$) has been in common use. $EC \times 10^6$ designates conductivity expressed in micromhos per centimeter. This is the unit most generally used for expressing the conductivity of waters. The conductivity of the Rio Grande sample mentioned above, when expressed in these various units, is:

$EC = 0.000694$ mho/cm.
$EC \times 10^3 = 0.694$ millimho/cm.
$EC \times 10^5 = 69.4 \ (= K \times 10^5)$
$EC \times 10^6 = 694$ micromhos/cm.

Conductivity of the Saturation Extract and the Saturation Percentage

The conductivity of the saturation extract is recommended as a general method for appraising soil salinity in relation to plant growth. The method is somewhat less rapid than a resistance measurement of the soil paste, but the result is easier to relate to plant response. The procedure involves preparing a saturated soil paste by stirring, during the addition of distilled water, until a characteristic endpoint is reached. A suction filter is then used to obtain a sufficient amount of the extract for making the conductivity measurement.

The special advantage of the saturation-extract method of measuring salinity lies in the fact that the saturation percentage is directly related to the field-moisture range. In the field, the moisture content of the soil fluctuates between a lower limit represented by the permanent-wilting percentage and the upper, wet end of the available range, which is approximately two times the wilting percentage. Measurements on soils indicate that over a considerable textural range the saturation percentage (SP) is approximately equal to four times the 15-atmosphere percentage (FAP), which, in turn, closely approximates the wilting percentage. The soluble-salt concentration in the saturation extract, therefore, tends to be about one-half of the concentration of the soil solution at the upper end of the field-moisture range and about one-fourth the concentration that the soil solution would have at the lower, dry end of the field-moisture range. The salt-dilution effect that occurs in fine-textured soils, because of their higher moisture retention, is thus automatically taken into account. For this reason, the conductivity of the saturation extract (EC_e) can be used directly for appraising the effect of soil salinity on plant growth.

Table 1 gives some of the experimental data supporting the foregoing statements. Since the 15-atmosphere percentage appears to be the most significant moisture property that can be readily measured, this retentivity value was used to separate soil samples into three textural groups: Coarse, medium, and fine (table 1). The FAP ranges arbitrarily selected to designate these textural groups were: Coarse, 2.0–6.5; medium, 6.6–15.0; and fine, greater than 15.1. The numbers in the FAP column of table 1 are the actual FAP values for the available samples in the various textural groups. The SP/FAP ratio of the medium-textured group, which is largest in number, is approximately 4 and the standard deviation is small; whereas the ratios for the fine-textured and high organic matter groups are somewhat lower (Campbell and Richards, 1950).

The saturation percentage for sands, when determined by the standard procedure, gives values that, relative to the field-moisture range, are higher than for other soils. This occurs because in sands the large pores that are filled with water at the saturation-paste condition do not correspondingly retain water under field conditions. Consequently, $EC_e \times 10^3$ for sands, when referred to the regular saturation-extract scale, gives an

TABLE 1.—*Relation of saturation percentage (SP) to 15-atmosphere percentage (FAP) as influenced by soil texture*

Soil group	Soil samples	FAP			SP			SP/FAP			
		Minimum	Maximum	Average	Minimum	Maximum	Average	Minimum	Maximum	Average	Standard deviation
	Number										
Coarse............	10	3.4	6.5	5.0	16.0	43.1	31.8	4.68	8.45	6.37	1.15
Medium..........	23	6.6	14.2	10.8	26.4	60.0	42.5	3.15	5.15	3.95	.48
Fine..............	11	16.1	21.0	18.5	41.8	78.5	59.5	2.03	4.26	3.20	.60
Organic..........	18	27.6	51.3	37.9	81.0	255	142	2.53	4.97	3.66	.75

optimistic index of salinity, i. e., underrates the salinity condition. Method 3b gives a tentative procedure for estimating the upper limit of the field-moisture range. From this, a moisture content for extraction is determined and a procedure for obtaining a conductivity value that can be used on the regular saturation-extract scale is suggested. This new procedure is tentative because it has not been subjected to extensive testing, but it has given good results for soils with *SP* values of approximately 25 or less.

It would be more reliable to appraise salinity by using measurements of extracts of the soil solution in the field-moisture range. However, difficulty of obtaining such extracts would make them prohibitive for routine use. The next higher feasible moisture content appears to be the saturation percentage. The following scale is recommended for general use in appraising the effect of soluble salts on crops. It shows the relation of crop response to soil salinity expressed in terms of the conductivity of the saturation extract.

Use of the conductivity of the saturation extract as an index of soil salinity was introduced at the Rubidoux Laboratory in 1939 for the Pecos River Joint Investigation. The salinity scale given in the earlier draft of this handbook was substantially the same as the scale originally proposed by Scofield in his report on the Pecos River Joint Investigation (United States National Resources Planning Board, 1942, *pp. 263–334*). The scale given here has been modified somewhat from those previously used.

It is often desirable, because of the extra information provided on soil texture and moisture retention, to determine the soil-moisture content at saturation, i. e., the saturation percentage (*SP*) when saturated soil paste is prepared for salinity measurements. A rapid procedure for *SP* determination based on the weight of a known volume of saturated paste has been described by Wilcox (1951) and is included as Method 27c.

The endpoint for mixing a saturated soil paste is reasonably definite; and, with a little training, good agreement can be obtained among various operators. Slight variations in technique, such as adding practically all the water to the soil sample before stirring or adding the air-dry soil to a known amount of water, do not appreciably affect the saturation percentage of most soils. Special precautions, however, must be taken with very fine and very coarse textured soils. For example, in some clay soils the amount of water that must be added to bring about saturation can be varied 10 percent or more, depending upon the rate of adding water and the amount of stirring. The more rapid the rate of water addition in relation to stirring, the lower the saturation percentage may be. The lower value is desirable to reduce the time and effort during mixing and also to minimize puddling of the soil. Campbell and Richards (1950) found that the conductivity of the saturation-extract method is applicable also for the measurement of salinity in peat soils. With air-dried peats, an overnight wetting period is necessary to obtain a definite endpoint for the saturated paste.

Relation of Conductivity to Salt Content and Osmotic Pressure

The relation between the electrical conductivity and the salt content of various solutions is shown graphically in several figures. The curves (fig. 2) for the chloride salts and Na_2SO_4 almost coincide, but $MgSO_4$, $CaSO_4$, and $NaHCO_3$ have lower conductivities than the other salts at equivalent concentrations. When the concentration is given in percent salt or parts per million, the curves (fig. 3) are more widely separated.

Salinity effects mostly negligible	Yields of very sensitive crops may be restricted	Yields of many crops restricted	Only tolerant crops yield satisfactorily	Only a few very tolerant crops yield satisfactorily

0   2   4   8   16

Scale of conductivity (millimhos per centimeter at 25° C.)

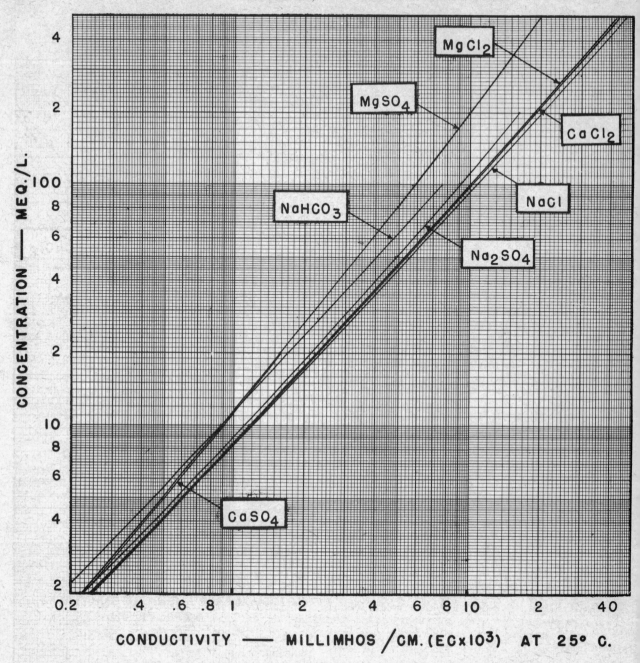

FIGURE 2.—Concentration of single-salt solutions in milliequivalents per liter as related to electrical conductivity.

With soils from widely separated areas in western United States, the concentration range was higher (fig. 4) than that shown in figures 2 and 3; consequently, the electrical conductivity is expressed in millimhos per centimeter. This is a convenient unit to use for extracts from saline soils. Soils represented by points that are considerably above the average line usually contain a relatively high amount of calcium or magnesium sulfate. Information on the salt content of irrigation water in relation to electrical conductivity is given in chapter 5.

Experimental work conducted at the Salinity Laboratory by Hayward and Spurr (1944), Wadleigh and Ayers (1945), and workers elsewhere indicates that the osmotic pressure of the soil solution is closely related to the rate of water uptake and growth of plants in saline soils. The osmotic pressure (OP) of solutions expressed in atmospheres is usually calculated from the freezing-point depression, in degrees C., $\triangle T$, in accordance with the relation, $OP = 12.06 \triangle T - 0.021 \triangle T^2$, given in the International Critical Tables. The relation between osmotic pressure and electrical

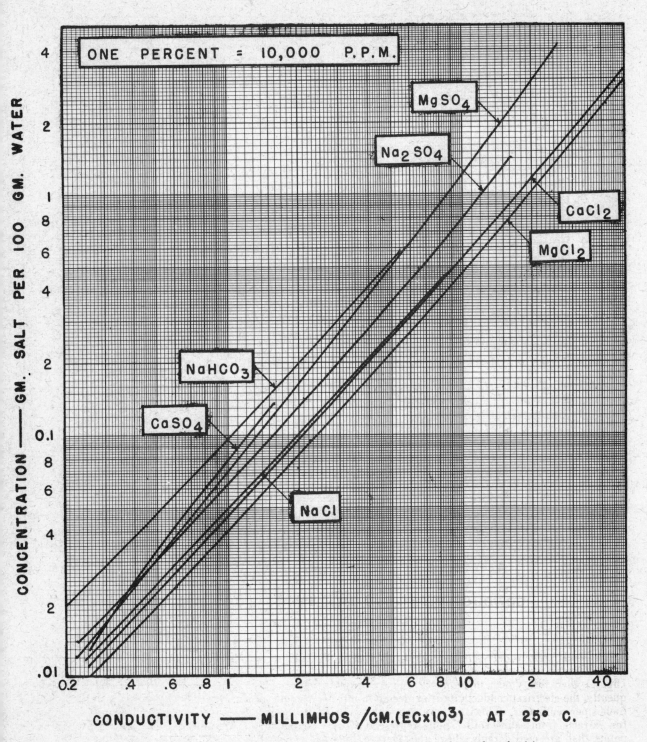

FIGURE 3.—Concentration of single-salt solutions in percent as related to electrical conductivity.

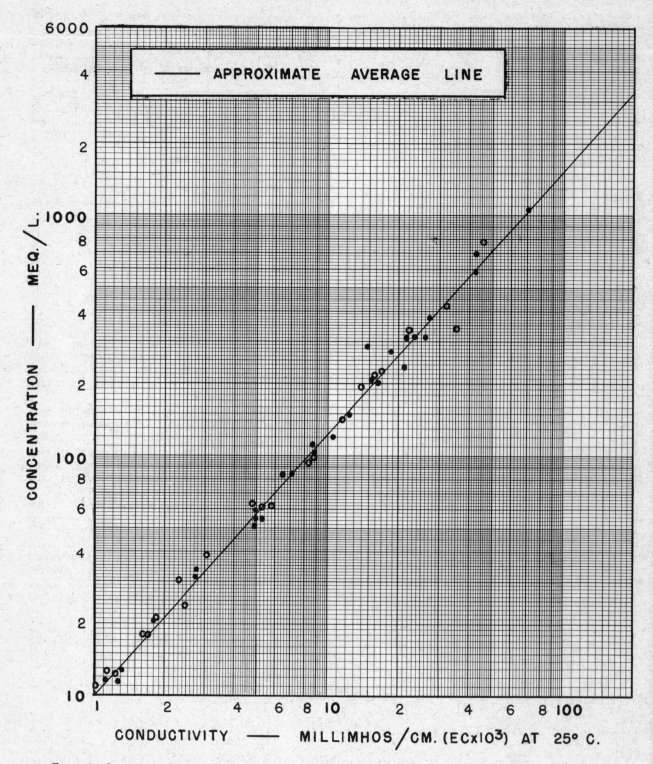

FIGURE 4.—Concentration of saturation extracts of soils in milliequivalents per liter as related to electrical conductivity.

conductivity (fig. 5) is useful for some agricultural purposes. This measurement is in general use and can be more readily measured than freezing-point depression. The relation between OP and EC for salt mixtures found in saline soils is indicated in figure 6 from data reported by Campbell and coworkers (1949). The OP values were calculated from freezing-point measurements. In the range of EC that will permit plant growth, the relation $OP = 0.36 \times EC_e \times 10^3$ can be used for estimating the osmotic pressure of soil solutions from conductivity measurements.

Conductivity of 1:1 and 1:5 Extracts

For soil:water ratios of 1:1 and 1:5, the extract is obtained by filtering without the use of vacuum or pressure. The conductivity of these extracts is sometimes used for estimating salinity from the line in figure 4 or, preferably, from special curves that apply for the salts and soil in question.

Salinity estimates based on the conductivity of 1:1 and 1:5 extracts are convenient for rapid determinations, particularly if the amount of soil sample is limited, or when repeated samplings are to be made in the same soil to determine the change in salinity with time or treatment. The reliability of such estimates depends upon the kind of salts present. For chloride salts, the results will be only slightly affected by moisture content, but, if sulfate or carbonate salts, which have relatively low solubility, are present in appreciable quantities, the apparent amount of soluble salt will depend on the soil : water ratio (table 2). In an experiment conducted by Wadleigh, Gauch, and Kolisch (1951) to determine the salt tolerance of orchardgrass, the salts shown in the table were individually added to a loam soil. During the course of the experiment, many samples were taken to check distribution of the salt in the soil and conductivity measurements were made of the saturated soil (EC_s), the saturation extract (EC_e), the 1:1 extract (EC_1), and the 1:2 extract (EC_2). The regression coefficients, which are the slopes of the best fit straight lines, were calculated for various comparisons among the data (table 2).

The theoretical values given in the table are based on the saturation percentage of 30 for the soil used. Except for small changes in the activity coefficients of the ions with dilution, the conductivity ratios should be inversely proportional to the moisture contents of the soil at extraction if the total dissolved salt is independent of the moisture content at which the extraction is made. The average measured conductivity ratios were always greater than the theoretical. The differences were not large for the chloride salts, but when $NaHCO_3$, Na_2SO_4, or $MgSO_4$ were added to this soil, in which the exchange complex was largely saturated with calcium, some $CaSO_4$ and $CaCO_3$ were precipitated. It is evident from the table that the regression coefficients are quite different for extracts obtained at high moisture contents if the less soluble salts are present in the soil. This example illustrates why the estimation of salinity from the conductivity of the extract at 1:1 or at higher moisture contents is not recommended for general use. These higher moisture contents may be used to advantage in certain cases, but the limitations of the method should be clearly understood.

Salinity Appraisal From the Electrical Resistance of Soil Paste

Salinity determinations based on the electrical resistance of a standard sample of wet soil have been in use for many years (Whitney and Means, 1897; Briggs, 1899). The Bureau of Soils cup and the data published by Davis and Bryan (1910) have been widely used by various agencies in this country for estimating the percentage of soluble salts in soils. The apparatus is simple and rugged, the measurements can be quickly made, and the results are reproducible.

To obtain the relation between wet-soil resistance and percent salt, Davis and Bryan made measurements using 4 soil samples representing the textural groups of sand, loam, clay loam, and clay. These samples of soil were composited from various types of nonsaline soils. A mixture of chloride and sulfate salts was used to obtain 5 levels of added salt ranging from 0.2 to 3 percent, and resistance values were obtained on the saturated pastes. Making use of these 20 readings on the synthetic soil and salt mixtures, Davis and Bryan used graphical interpolation to obtain the relation of soil-cup resistance to percent salt for mixed sulfates and chlorides. The Davis and Bryan procedure for the Bureau of Soils method of determining soluble salt in soil is given in Method 5. The method is also described in the Soil Survey Manual (1951, p. 343).

TABLE 2.—*Regression coefficients* (b) *between various criteria for evaluating soil salinity by a conductance procedure*

Soils containing—	$b_{EC_1 \cdot EC_e}$	$b_{EC_2 \cdot EC_e}$	$b_{EC_2 \cdot EC_1}$	$b_{EC_s \cdot EC_e}$
NaCl	0.359 ± 0.0070	0.185 ± 0.0037	0.514 ± 0.0069	0.235 ± 0.0066
CaCl₂	.356 ± .011	.191 ± .0028	.534 ± .0046	.242 ± .0078
MgCl₂	.376 ± .010	.192 ± .0042	.507 ± .012	.237 ± .019
NaHCO₃	.379 ± .027	.227 ± .017	.589 ± .011	.222 ± .013
Na₂SO₄	.590 ± .023	.355 ± .010	.600 ± .011	.217 ± .015
MgSO₄	.600 ± .068	.471 ± .060	.780 ± .027	.226 ± .0054
Theoretical	.333	.167	.5	

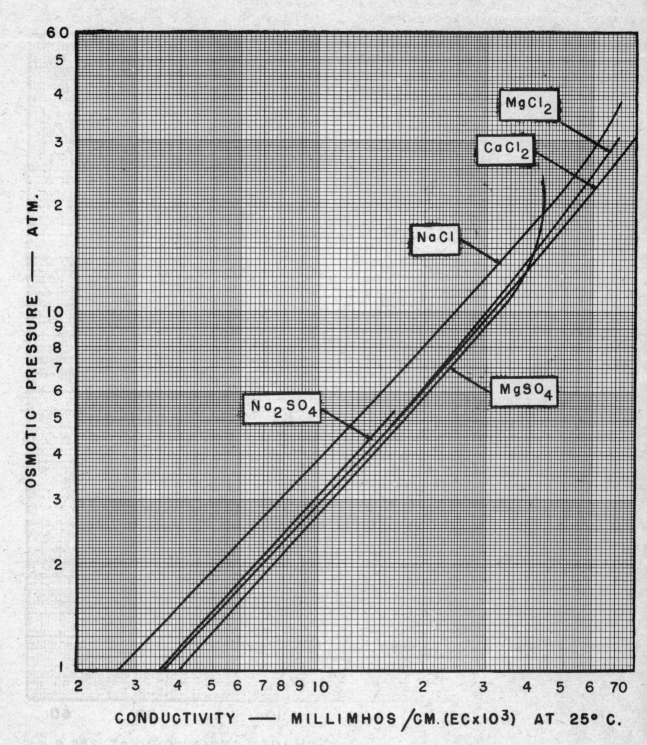

FIGURE 5.—Osmotic pressure of single-salt solutions as related to electrical conductivity.   (Data from International Critical Tables.)

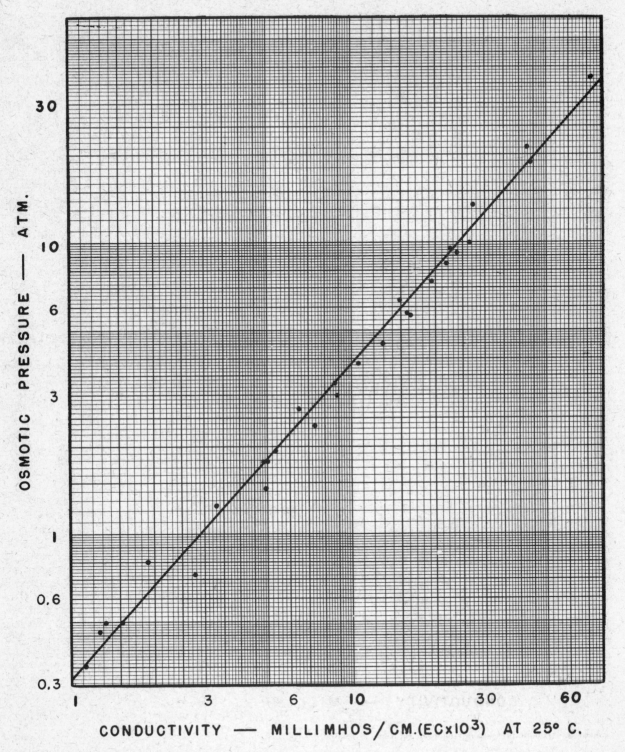

FIGURE 6.—Osmotic pressure of saturation extracts of soils as related to electrical conductivity.

TABLE 3.—*Comparison of measured and calculated values of* EC_e *after correcting for effect of* SP

Soils from—	Number of samples	Average $EC_e \times 10^3$ at 25° C.		Difference	Standard deviation of differences
		Measured	Calculated		
Lower Rio Grande Valley, Texas	6	9.93	11.10	1.17	1.30
Grand Junction district, Colorado	12	8.64	9.45	.81	.85
Tucumcari district, New Mexico	11	9.63	11.85	2.22	1.16
Gem County, Idaho	7	5.73	16.24	10.51	2.90
Four Western States	12	10.25	13.05	2.80	1.76

A similar procedure was used by Davis and Bryan to obtain calibration data for "carbonate" salts, presumably sodium carbonate. Tests at the Laboratory, however, indicate that table IV of Davis and Bryan for carbonate salts is unreliable and should not be used. The unreliability of the calibration data for these salts is a result of cation-exchange reactions that were not generally understood at the time the original work was done.

The conductivity of the saturation extract (EC_e) is recommended in this handbook as a measurement for general use for indicating soil salinity, but the method based on the soil-paste resistance (R_s) is still commonly used. The electrical conductivity of the soil paste (EC_s) is related to paste resistance by the relation $EC_s = 0.25/R_s$, where 0.25 is the constant for the Bureau of Soils electrode cup. In a study by Reitemeier and Wilcox (1946), it was found that the relation between EC_e and EC_s is markedly influenced by variations in the saturation percentage, the salinity, and the conductivity of the soil minerals. From unpublished work at the Laboratory, Bower concluded that there is no easy method for simplifying the relation of EC_s (or R_s) to EC_e. He equilibrated a group of western soils with various concentrations of a 1:1 mixture of sodium and calcium chloride and found that on the average $EC_e/EC_s = 5.4 - 0.07(SP)$. Using this average relationship and SP values calculated from the weight of the soil paste as described by Wilcox (1951), he calculated values for EC_e based on R_s measurements. The degree of correspondence between measured and calculated values is indicated by the data in table 3.

The calculated average values for EC_e are somewhat high but are acceptable except for the soils from Gem County, Idaho. These soils had a low salinity level but were high in exchangeable sodium. The large discrepancy here and for some other locations apparently is owing to conduction by the clay minerals, when they contain exchangeable sodium. Bower found, for example, that the electrical conductivity of a 5-percent suspension of calcium-saturated montmorillonite was 0.072 mmhos/cm., but when saturated with sodium, the conductivity was 0.446 mmhos/cm.

No method has been found for improving the reliability of the paste-resistance method that does not destroy its simplicity. The method may be acceptable for estimating salinity for purposes of soil classification, but for soils like those of Gem County, Idaho, it does not have acceptable reliability.

Conversion of Conductivity Data to a Standard Reference Temperature

The electrical conductivity of solutions and of soils containing moisture increases approximately 2 percent per degree centigrade increase in temperature. To simplify the interpretation of salinity data, it is customary either to take the measurements at a standard-reference temperature or to determine the temperature at which the measurement is made, and then, by means of correction tables or a correction dial on the bridge, to convert the measurement to a standard-reference temperature.

Whitney and Briggs (1897) measured the resistance of 9 soils at 13 temperatures and calculated the average relation of resistance to temperature. Whitney and Means (1897) used these temperature data to construct a table used in converting resistance measurements of saturated soil to the standard temperature of 60° F. Data from this table, which has been widely used since its publication 50 years ago, are given in table 16 in chapter 6, along with instructions for its use.

More recently a study was made by Campbell, Bower, and Richards (1949) to determine the effect of temperature on the electrical conductivity of soil extracts. Saturation extracts from 21 soils were measured at 5 temperatures, ranging from 0° to 50° C. The temperature coefficient of the electrical conductivity for these representative soil extracts varied somewhat with temperature, but in the range from 15° to 35° it was verified that for each degree centigrade increase in temperature the conductivity increased very nearly 2 percent of the value at 25°. The details of the procedures for measuring electrical conductivity and making temperature corrections are given in Method 4.

Comparison of Percent Salt in Soil and Extract Measurements

The diagram shown in figure 7 facilitates the interpretation of salinity in relation to crop response. It is based on the following assumptions: $P_{sw} = $ p. p. m./$10,000 = 0.064 \times EC \times 10^3$; $P_{ss} = (P_{sw} \times P_w)/100$; OP

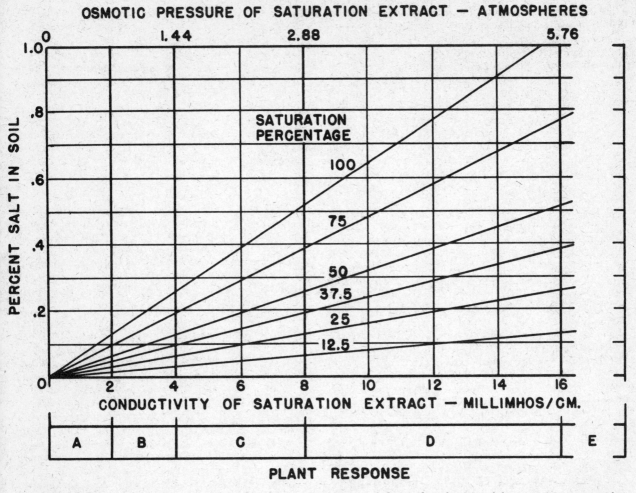

FIGURE 7.—Relation of the percent salt in the soil to the osmotic pressure and electrical conductivity of the saturation extract and to crop response in the conductivity ranges designated by letters. These ranges are related to crop response by the salinity scale on page 9.

$= 0.36 \times EC \times 10^3$. $P_{sw} =$ percent salt in water; $P_{ss} =$ percent salt in soil; $P_w =$ percent water in soil; and $OP =$ osmotic pressure in atmospheres. The lower scale gives values for the conductivity of the saturation extract. The top scale shows the osmotic pressure of the saturation extract. The osmotic pressure of the soil solution at the upper limit of the field-moisture range will be approximately double these values.

The diagonal lines help correlate the conductivity of the saturation extract with the percent salt content for various soil textures. For example, at $EC_e \times 10^3 = 4$, nearly all crops make good growth and for a soil with a saturation percentage of 75, as seen in the diagram, this corresponds to a salt content of about 0.2 percent. On the other hand, 0.2 percent salt in a sandy soil for which the saturation percentage is 25 would correspond to $EC_e \times 10^3 = 12$, which is too saline for good growth of most crop plants. Partial lists of crop plants in their order of tolerance to soil salinity are given in chapter 4.

The diagram indicates the growth conditions of crops to be expected for various degrees of salinity in the active root zone of the soil, i. e., the soil volume that is permeated by roots and in which moisture absorption is appreciable. Obviously, the diagram does not apply for soil in which salt has been deposited after the roots have been established and have become nonabsorbing, or to soil adjacent to the plant, either high or low in salt, that has not been permeated by roots. With mature row crops, for example, salt may have accumulated in the ridge to such an extent that the roots no longer function as moisture absorbers and, therefore, the ridge cannot be considered as characteristic of the active plant-root environment.

Chemical Determinations

Soil Reaction—pH

The pH value of an aqueous solution is the negative logarithm of the hydrogen-ion activity. The value may be determined potentiometrically, using various electrodes (Method 21), or colorimetrically, by indicators whose colors vary with the hydrogen-ion activity. There is some question as to the exact property being measured when methods for determining the pH values of solutions are applied to soil-water systems. Apparent pH values are obtained, however, that depend on the characteristics of the soil, the concentration of dissolved carbon dioxide, and the moisture content at which the reading is made. Soil characteristics that are known to influence pH readings include: the composition of the exchangeable cations, the nature of the cation-exchange materials, the composition and concentration of soluble salts, and the presence or absence of gypsum and alkaline-earth carbonates.

A statistical study of the relation of pH readings to the exchangeable-sodium-percentages of soils of arid regions has been made by Fireman and Wadleigh (1951). The effect of various factors such as moisture content, salinity level, and presence or absence of alkaline-earth carbonates and gypsum upon this relationship was also studied. Some of the more pertinent statistical data obtained are presented in table 4. While all the coefficients of correlation given in the table are highly significant, the coefficients of determination show that at best no more than 54 percent of the variance in exchangeable-sodium-percentage is associated with the variance in pH reading. The data on the effect of moisture content indicate that the reliability of prediction of the exchangeable-sodium-percentage from pH readings decreases as the moisture content is increased. Similarly, the data on the effect of salinity indicate that the reliability of prediction is lowest when the salt level is either low or very high. An increase in pH reading of 1.0 or more, as the moisture content is changed from a low to a high value, has been found useful in some areas for detecting saline-alkali soils. However, the reliability of this procedure should be tested before use on any given group of soil samples.

Experience and the statistical study of Fireman and Wadleigh permit the following general statements regarding the interpretation of pH readings of saturated soil paste: (1) pH values of 8.5 or greater almost invariably indicate an exchangeable-sodium-percentage of 15 or more and the presence of alkaline-earth carbonates; (2) the exchangeable-sodium-percentage of soils having pH values of less than 8.5 may or may not exceed 15; (3) soils having pH values of less than 7.5 almost always contain no alkaline-earth carbonates and those having values of less than 7.0 contain significant amounts of exchangeable hydrogen.

Soluble Cations and Anions

Analyses of saline and alkali soils for soluble cations and anions are usually made to determine the composition of the salts present. Complete analyses for soluble ions provide an accurate determination of total salt content. Determinations of soluble cations are used to obtain the relations between total cation concentration and other properties of saline solutions, such as electrical conductivity and osmotic pressure. The relative concentrations of the various cations in soil-water extracts also give information on the composition of the exchangeable cations in the soil.

The soluble cations and anions commonly determined in saline and alkali soils are calcium, magnesium, sodium, potassium, carbonate, bicarbonate, sulfate, and chloride. Occasionally nitrate and soluble silicate also are determined. In making complete analyses, a determination of nitrate is indicated if the sum of cations expressed on an equivalent basis significantly exceeds that of the commonly determined anions. Appreciable amounts of soluble silicate occur only in alkali soils having high pH values. In analyses made by the usual methods, including those recommended in this hand-

TABLE 4.—*Coefficient of correlation* (r)[1] *and coefficient of determination* (r^2) *for the relation of pH reading to exchangeable-sodium-percentage as influenced by moisture content, salinity level, and presence or absence of alkaline-earth carbonates and gypsum*

Moisture content (percent)	Salinity as $EC_e \times 10^3$ at 25° C.	Alkaline-earth carbonates	Gypsum	Samples	r	r^2
				Number		*Percent*
Saturation..........	Variable...........	Variable...........	Variable...........	868	0. 66	44
500..................	....do.............	....do.............	....do.............	271	.65	43
1,000................	....do.............	....do.............	....do.............	289	.53	28
6,000................	....do.............	....do.............	....do.............	346	.48	24
Saturation..........	0–4................	....do.............	....do.............	349	.56	31
Do.............	4–8................	....do.............	....do.............	91	.72	52
Do.............	8–15...............	....do.............	....do.............	115	.70	49
Do.............	15–30..............	....do.............	....do.............	87	.74	54
Do.............	> 30...............	....do.............	....do.............	69	.49	24
Do.............	Variable...........	Present............	Present............	237	.72	52
Do.............	....do.............	....do.............	Absent............	452	.56	32
Do.............	....do.............	Absent............	....do.............	154	.41	17

[1] All values are significant at the 1-percent level.

book, any soluble silicate present is determined as carbonate.

As shown by Reitemeier (1946) and others, values obtained from determinations of the soluble-cation and soluble-anion contents of saline and alkali soils are markedly influenced by the moisture content at which the extraction is made. The total dissolved quantities of some ions increase with increasing moisture content, while concurrently those of others may decrease; almost invariably values obtained for total salt content increase with increasing moisture content at extraction. Processes that are responsible for the changes in the relative and total amounts of soluble ions which occur with increasing moisture content include cation-exchange reactions, negative adsorption of ions, hydrolysis, and the increased solution of silicate minerals, alkaline-earth carbonates, and gypsum. Ideally, the determination of soluble ions should be made on extracts obtained at a moisture content in the field-moisture range. However, the preparation of such extracts is time-consuming and requires the use of special extraction equipment (Method 3d). Saturation percentage is the lowest practical moisture content for obtaining extracts on a routine basis. Use of the saturation extract is, therefore, recommended for the determination of soluble ions. Methods are available that permit determination of the electrical conductivity and the common soluble constituents on 10 to 50 ml. of saturation extract. As a rule, about one-fourth of the moisture in a saturated soil paste can be removed by ordinary pressure or vacuum filtration.

The choice of methods for the determination of the various cations and anions depends upon the equipment available and the personal preference of the analyst. No attempt is made here to present all of the methods that are suitable. The methods given were chosen on the basis of their convenience and reliability. Owing to the fact that the amount of extract available for analysis is usually limited, most of the methods selected are of the semimicro type. They generally involve the use of a centrifuge, a flame photometer, and a photoelectric colorimeter. Where the amount of extract is not limited, the macromethods employed for water analysis given in chapter 8 may be used. Most of these methods do not require the use of a centrifuge or photoelectric colorimeter.

Soluble Boron

The importance of soluble boron from the standpoint of soil salinity lies in its marked toxicity to plants when present in relatively small amounts. Toxic concentrations of boron have been found in the saturation extracts of a number of saline soils. It is necessary, therefore, to consider this constituent as a factor in the diagnosis and reclamation of saline and alkali soils. High levels of boron in soils can usually be reduced by leaching. During the leaching process, boron may not be removed in the same proportion as other salts. If the concentration of boron is high at the outset, a considerable depth of leaching water may be necessary to reduce

the boron content to a safe value for good plant growth. This is illustrated by a recent leaching test. At the beginning of the test, the conductivity of the saturation extract of the top 12 inches of soil was 64.0 mmhos/cm. After 4 feet of irrigation water had passed through the soil, the conductivity was reduced to 4.2 mmhos/cm.; after 8 feet, the conductivity was 3.4 mmhos/cm.; and after 12 feet, it was 3.3 mmhos/cm. The concentration of boron in the saturation extract at the start of the test was 54 p. p. m. After the passage of 4 feet of water, the concentration was 6.9 p. p. m.; after 8 feet, it was 2.4 p. p. m.; and after 12 feet, it was 1.8 p. p. m. Thus, leaching with 4 feet of water reduced the salinity to a safe level, but the boron content was still too high for good growth of plants sensitive to boron.

Permissible limits for boron in the saturation extract of soils can at present be given only on a tentative basis. Concentrations below 0.7 p. p. m. boron probably are safe for sensitive plants (ch. 4); from 0.7 to 1.5 p. p. m. boron is marginal; and more than 1.5 p. p. m. boron appears to be unsafe. The more tolerant plants can withstand higher concentrations, but limits cannot be set on the basis of present information. For land on which crops are being grown, a better appraisal of boron conditions often can be made by an analysis of plant samples (ch. 4) than can be obtained from an analysis of soil samples.

Exchangeable Cations

When a sample of soil is placed in a solution of a salt, such as ammonium acetate, ammonium ions are adsorbed by the soil and an equivalent amount of cations is displaced from the soil into the solution. This reaction is termed "cation exchange," and the cations displaced from the soil are referred to as "exchangeable." The surface-active constituents of soils that have cation-exchange properties are collectively termed the "exchange complex" and consist for the most part of various clay minerals and organic matter. The total amount of exchangeable cations that a soil can retain is designated the "cation-exchange-capacity," and is usually expressed in milliequivalents per 100 gm. of soil. It is often convenient to express the relative amounts of various exchangeable cations present in a soil as a percentage of the cation-exchange-capacity. For example, the exchangeable-sodium-percentage (ESP) is equal to 100 times the exchangeable-sodium content divided by the cation-exchange-capacity, both expressed in the same units.

Determinations of the amounts and proportions of the various exchangeable cations present in soils are useful, because exchangeable cations markedly influence the physical and chemical properties of soils. The exchangeable-cation analysis of saline and alkali soils is subject to difficulties not ordinarily encountered with other soils, such as those from humid regions. Saline and alkali soils commonly contain alkaline-earth carbonates and a relatively high concentration of soluble salts. They may have low permeability to aqueous solutions and to alcohol. Solutions capable of displacing exchangeable cations from soils dissolve most or all of the soluble salts and significant amounts of the carbonates of calcium and magnesium if they are present. The soluble salts should not be washed out of the soil prior to extracting the exchangeable cations, because of significant changes that take place as a result of dilution and hydrolysis. The dissolving of salts, therefore, necessitates independent determinations of soluble-cation contents and correction of the exchangeable-cation analysis for their presence, while the occurrence of calcium and magnesium carbonates prevents accurate determination of exchangeable calcium and magnesium. Furthermore, the low permeability of many alkali soils renders the conventional leaching techniques for displacement of cations time-consuming and inconvenient.

Neutral normal ammonium acetate is the salt solution most commonly used for the extraction of exchangeable cations and for the saturation of the exchange complex in the determination of cation-exchange-capacity. Although this solution has many advantages for exchangeable-cation analysis, some saline and alkali soils fix appreciable amounts of ammonium as well as potassium ions under moist conditions. The fixation of ammonium does not interfere with the extraction of exchangeable cations, but values obtained for cation-exchange-capacity by ammonium saturation are low by amounts equal to the quantity of ammonium fixed. The desirability of using a cation not subject to fixation for the determination of cation-exchange-capacity is, therefore, evident.

As discussed in a previous section, the determined values for the soluble-ion contents of soils vary with the moisture content at which the extraction is made. Because equilibria exist between the soluble and exchangeable cations in soils, the changes in relative and total concentrations of soluble cations with variations in moisture content are accompanied by changes in the relative composition of the exchangeable cations. In a strict sense, therefore, values for exchangeable-cation contents apply only at the moisture content used for the extraction of soluble cations. Owing to difficulties involved in the determination of soluble cations at moisture contents in the field range, it is convenient to determine exchangeable-cation contents at the saturation percentage.

Consideration of the various factors involved in the determination of the exchangeable cations and the cation-exchange-capacity of saline and alkali soils has led to the adoption of the following scheme of analysis:

(a) Extract a sample of the soil with an excess of neutral normal ammonium acetate solution and determine the milliequivalents of the various cations removed per 100 gm. of soil.[4]

(b) Prepare a saturation extract of the soil and determine the milliequivalents of the various soluble cations per 100 gm. of soil.[4]

(c) Calculate the exchangeable-cation contents of the soil by subtracting the amounts of the various cations dissolved in the saturation extract from the

amounts extracted by the ammonium acetate solution.

(d) Determine the cation-exchange-capacity by measuring the milliequivalents of sodium adsorbed per 100 gm. of soil upon treating a sample with an excess of normal sodium acetate solution of pH 8.2.

The difficulties encountered in leaching soil samples of low permeability are overcome by shaking and centrifuging samples in centrifuge tubes with successive portions of the extraction and wash liquids. Neutral normal ammonium acetate solution is used for the extraction of exchangeable plus soluble cations, because its interference in analytical procedures is easily eliminated. Of the common cations, sodium appears to be the most suitable for determining cation-exchange-capacity. As mentioned previously, ammonium and potassium are subject to fixation in difficultly exchangeable form and the usual presence of calcium and magnesium carbonates in saline and alkali soils precludes the use of extractants containing calcium or magnesium. The fact that sodium is a prominent cation in most saline and alkali soils also favors its use in the determination of cation-exchange-capacity (Method 19).

Gypsum

Gypsum is found in many soils of arid regions, in amounts ranging from traces to several percent. In some soils, gypsum was present in the sedimentary deposits from which the soil was derived; whereas, in other soils the gypsum was formed by the precipitation of calcium and sulfate during salinization. Owing to leaching, gypsum commonly occurs at some depth in the former instance, while in the latter its content is usually greatest in the surface layers of the soil.

Information regarding the gypsum content of alkali soils is important, because it usually determines whether the application of chemical amendments will be required for reclamation. Also, the presence of considerable amounts of gypsum in the soil might permit the use of an irrigation water having an unfavorably high sodium content.

The precise determination of gypsum in soils is difficult, because of inherent errors involved in the extraction of this mineral by water. Studies by Reitemeier (1946) and others show that at least three factors other than the solution of gypsum may influence the amounts of calcium and sulfate extracted from gypsiferous soils. They are: (1) The solution of calcium from sources other than gypsum; (2) exchange reactions in which soluble calcium replaces other cations, such as sodium and magnesium; and (3) the solution of sulfate from sources other than gypsum.

---

[4] If the soil is known to contain carbonates of calcium and magnesium, determination of these cations is omitted. Likewise, if the soil is known to contain gypsum not completely soluble in the saturation extract, the determination of calcium is omitted. In the absence of prior knowledge regarding the calcium and magnesium carbonate and gypsum contents of the soil, the calcium and magnesium determinations are disregarded if upon completion of the exchangeable-cation analysis the sum of the values obtained for exchangeable-cation contents is found to exceed the cation-exchange-capacity value.

Three methods are given in chapter 6 for the estimation of gypsum in soils. Methods 22a and 22b are based on the low solubility of the salt in an aqueous solution of acetone. Method 22a is essentially qualitative, although a rough estimate of gypsum content may be obtained by visual observation of the amount of precipitate obtained. This method can be successfully employed under field conditions. In Method 22b the separated and washed gypsum precipitate is determined quantitatively. The use of Method 22c is advantageous when characterization of the soil includes the determination of calcium plus magnesium in the saturation extract. It is based on the increase in soluble-divalent-cation content as the moisture content of the soil is increased from the saturation percentage to a moisture content sufficient to dissolve the gypsum present. It should be noted that this method can give negative values for gypsum content as a result of the replacement of exchangeable sodium and potassium by calcium as the moisture content of the soil is increased. This is likely to occur only in alkali soils containing little or no gypsum.

Alkaline-Earth Carbonates (Lime)

The alkaline-earth carbonates that occur in significant amounts in soils consist of calcite, dolomite, and possibly magnesite. Owing to low rainfall and limited leaching, alkaline-earth carbonates are usually a constituent of soils of arid regions. The amounts present vary from traces to more than 50 percent of the soil mass. Alkaline-earth carbonates influence the texture of the soil when present in appreciable amounts, for the particles commonly occur in the silt-size fraction. The presence of fine alkaline-earth carbonate particles is thought to improve the physical condition of soils. Conversely, when alkaline-earth carbonates occur as caliche or as cementing agents in indurated layers, the movement of water and the development of root systems is impeded. Alkaline-earth carbonates are important constituents of alkali soils, for they constitute a potential source of soluble calcium and magnesium for the replacement of exchangeable sodium. As discussed in another section, the choice of chemical amendments for the replacement of exchangeable sodium is directly related to the presence or absence of alkaline-earth carbonates.

Effervescence upon application of acid (Method 23a) can be used to detect as little as 0.5 percent of alkaline-earth carbonates in soils. This test suffices for most purposes. When a better estimate of the alkaline-earth-carbonate content of soils is desired, Methods 23b or 23c may be used. A quantitative determination of small amounts of alkaline-earth carbonates in soils is sometimes desirable in connection with proposed applications of acid-forming amendments. For precise determinations, the reader is referred to the methods of Williams (1949) and Schollenberger (1945).

Physical Determinations

The problem of evaluating soil physical conditions has recently been separated into components by the American Society of Agronomy (1952); and they are discussed under the headings of mechanical impedance, aeration, soil water, and soil temperature. These are logical ultimate aspects; but, for practical work on alkali soils, measuring methods are needed that yield immediate results having more or less direct diagnostic significance. Some progress is being made toward evaluating the physical status of soil in terms of physical properties, i. e., intrinsic qualities of soil that can be expressed in standard units and that have values which are substantially independent of the method of measurement. Infiltration rate, permeability, bulk density, pore-size distribution, aggregation, and modulus of rupture appear to be such properties. Experience indicates that the physical status of any given soil is not static. There is a range of variation of physical status that is related to productivity, and this is reflected in corresponding ranges in the values of pertinent physical properties.

Information on the existing physical status of a problem soil is useful for purposes of diagnosis or improvement, but it might also be useful to know how much better or worse the status can be made by chemical and physical treatments simulating those applicable under field conditions. Soils can be treated to increase the exchangeable-sodium-percentage and then puddled to indicate how unfavorable the physical status can be made. It should also be possible by use of soil amendments and chemical aggregants to get some indication of how favorable the physical status can be made. Practical use of the concept that there is a range of physical states for any given soil may have to wait for refinements in measuring methods, but the idea seems to be pertinent to the improvement of alkali soils.

Infiltration Rate

Water-movement rates attainable in soil under field conditions relate directly to irrigation, leaching, and drainage of saline and alkali soils. Infiltration refers to the downward entry of water into soils and the term "infiltration rate" has special technical significance in soils work. Definitions of soil-water terms adopted by the Soil Science Society of America (1952) are followed, and are included in the Glossary.

The infiltration rate of soil is influenced by such factors as the condition of the soil surface, the chemical and physical status and nature of the soil profile, and the distribution of water in the profile. All of these factors change more or less with time during infiltration.

The infiltration rate is measured under field conditions. The principal methods used have involved flooding or impounding water on the soil surface, sprinkling to simulate rain, and measuring water entry from rills or furrows. In addition to the multitude of local physical conditions that are encountered in the field, the availability of equipment, materials, and services will largely decide what method to use in measuring infiltration. Although many measurements have been made, as evidenced by the extensive bibliography of Davidson (1940), there does not seem to be a generally accepted procedure applicable to all situations. Many of the infiltration measurements made by this Laboratory have been in connection with basin irrigation on test plots ranging from 10 to 20 feet square. The water-subsidence rate in a large plot is probably the best indication of the infiltration rate as related to leaching operations, but this method is usually not feasible for exploratory or diagnostic measurements in new areas. The cylinder method of Musgrave (1935) is probably the most versatile of the various methods available. A guard ring is needed if lateral spreading is excessive. Procedures for making infiltration measurements are given in Method 28.

Water having the same quality as that which will be used for irrigation or leaching must be used for infiltration tests in the field, otherwise the results may be misleading. The length of time the tests should be conducted and the depth of water to be applied depend upon the purpose of the test and the kind of information that is sought. If it is a matter of appraising an irrigation problem, the depth corresponding to one irrigation may be sufficient; but, if information on infiltration for planning a leaching operation is needed, it may be desirable to apply the full depth of leaching water to a test plot. It often happens that subsurface drainage is sufficiently restricted to cause the infiltration rate to decrease considerably with time. It should be kept in mind, therefore, that although small area tests will give useful information on soil changes during leaching, the infiltration values thus obtained will apply to large areas only if underdrainage is not limiting.

Experience indicates that the infiltration rate of a given soil can be high or low, depending on physical status and management history. Infiltration rate is often critically influenced by surface soil conditions, but subsurface layers also are sometimes limiting. Water distribution in the profile and depth of water applied are modifying factors. The infiltration rate can be undesirably high or undesirably low. It is the low end of the range that may be a critical limiting factor in the agricultural use of alkali soils. It is difficult to specify a boundary limit between satisfactory and unsatisfactory infiltration rates at the low end of the range, because so many factors are involved, including the patience and skill of the farmer. However, if the infiltration rate is less than 0.25 cm./hr. (0.1 in./hr.) special water-management problems are involved that may make an irrigation enterprise unprofitable for average operators.

Permeability and Hydraulic Conductivity

The permeability of soil, in a qualitative sense, refers to the readiness with which the soil conducts or transmits fluids. In a quantitative sense, when permeability is expressed with numbers, it seems desirable that permeability be defined as a property of the porous medium alone and independent of the fluid used in its measurement. The term "hydraulic conductivity," on the other hand, is used to refer to the proportionality factor in the Darcy flow equation. These distinctions represent increased specialization in the use of these terms as approved by the Soil Science Society of America (1952). No change in the qualitative use of the word "permeability" is involved. In the quantitative sense, involving numerical values, the term "intrinsic permeability" will mostly be used and will refer to a length-squared measurement that may be identified in a general way to the cross-sectional area of some equivalent or effective size of pore.

An immediate consequence of this clarification of nomenclature is a new method for evaluating pore-space stability or structural stability of soil. For porous media with fixed structure, such as sandstone or fired ceramic, measurements of intrinsic permeability with air, water, or organic liquids all give very nearly the same numerical value. Gravity, density, and the viscosity of the liquid are taken into account in the flow equation. However, if the intrinsic permeability for a soil as measured with air is markedly greater than the permeability of the same sample as subsequently measured using water, then it may be concluded that the action of water in the soil brings about a change in structure indicated by the change in permeability. The ratio of air to water permeability, therefore, is a measure of the structural stability of soils, a high ratio indicating low stability.

Intrinsic-permeability measurements are based on the equation $v = k'dgi/\eta$, where v is the flow velocity, k' is the intrinsic permeability, d is the density of the fluid, g is the acceleration of gravity, i the hydraulic gradient, and η is the viscosity. Procedures for measuring intrinsic permeability with gases and liquids are given as Methods 37a and 37b. The air-water permeability ratio increases greatly as the exchangeable-sodium content of the soil increases, indicating that exchangeable sodium decreased the water stability of the soil structure.

It is seen from the Darcy equation, $v = ki$, that k, the hydraulic conductivity, is the effective flow velocity or discharge velocity of water in soil at unit hydraulic gradient, i. e., when the driving force is equal to 1 gravity. Methods 34a and 34b give procedures for measuring hydraulic conductivity on undisturbed and disturbed soil samples.

Under some circumstances, especially when the soil surface has been subject to submergence by water for a considerable period and when the hydraulic conductivity is nearly uniform with depth, the hydraulic gradient beneath the soil surface may approach unity, i. e., the downward driving force is composed entirely of the gravity force with no pressure gradient. Under this condition the infiltration rate is equal to the hydraulic conductivity, but this is probably the exception rather than the rule under field conditions. Consequently, the relation between infiltration rate and hydraulic conductivity is not a simple one. For example, at the Malheur Experimental Area in Oregon, very low hydraulic-conductivity values were obtained and yet infiltration was adequate to support good crops with sprinkler irrigation. It was found by use of tensiometers that values for the hydraulic gradient during infiltration ranged up to 10 in some cases. This soil was deep and silty and the suction gradient in the soil added significantly to the rate of downward movement of water. If the downward flow is interrupted by a layer of very low conductivity, then the hydraulic gradient may approach zero as the soil pores become filled and the condition of static equilibrium under gravity is approached.

It is to be expected that if the hydraulic conductivity of surface soil is as low as 0.1 cm./hr. (0.04 in./hr.) leaching and irrigation may present serious difficulties. Irrigation agriculture under average conditions of management skill, water quality, and drainage conditions would have doubtful success unless the hydraulic conductivity could be increased appreciably by soil-improvement measures.

Moisture Retention by Soil

The effect of soil salinity on crops is related to the range over which the moisture content of the soil varies, because the concentration of the soil solution depends both on the amount of soluble salt and the amount of water present. The permanent-wilting percentage, as indicated in the review by Veihmeyer and Hendrickson (1948), is generally accepted as being the lower limit of water available for plant growth in nonsaline soil. For all practical purposes, the 15-atmosphere percentage (Method 31) can be used as an index of the permanent-wilting percentage and, therefore, also as an acceptable index of the lower limit of the available range of soil moisture. This lower limit appears to be an intrinsic property of the soil that is largely determined by soil texture and appears to be substantially independent of the kind of plant grown on the soil.

It is much more difficult to set an upper limit for the range of water content available to plants in the field. In addition to dependence upon soil texture at the point in question, the upper limit depends also on the variation throughout the profile of such factors as pore-size distribution and water conductivity. The distribution of water with depth influences the hydraulic gradient, and, therefore, also the rate of downward movement of water. For example, with or without active roots, the moisture content in the surface layers of a deep permeable soil will decrease more slowly if the profile is deeply wetted than if only a shallow depth is wetted and the underlying soil is dry. Also, the total amount of water actually available from any given layer of surface soil depends on the rooting depth and transpiration rate of the crop. The hydraulic boundary conditions that characterize the field situation would be extremely difficult to reproduce for a soil sample removed from the profile, and it is not surprising that no generally satisfactory laboratory method has been found for estimating the upper limit of water available

for crop growth under field conditions. A field determination under representative field conditions is the best method for obtaining the upper limit of the field-moisture range.

For most medium- to fine-textured soils, the upper limit of available water is approximately twice the moisture percentage of the lower limit. This does not hold true for the coarse-textured soils. It has been found by the United States Bureau of Reclamation (1948) that for the sandy soils occurring on the Yuma Mesa, Arizona, the water retained in a sample of soil at the $\frac{1}{10}$-atmosphere percentage (Method 29) satisfactorily approximates the upper limit of available water under field conditions.

Density and Porosity

The bulk density (apparent density) of soil is the mass of soil per unit volume, and the porosity of soil is the fraction of the soil volume not occupied by soil particles. Bodman (1942) has discussed soil density in connection with water content and porosity relationships and has prepared useful nomograms (fig. 8).

The bulk density of soil can be measured by several methods. For a certain range of moisture contents with soils that are comparatively free of gravel and stones, it is possible to press into the soil a thin-walled tube having a suitable cutting edge. The soil is then smoothed at each end of the tube and oven-dried at 105° C. The bulk density is the mass of soil contained in the tube divided by the volume of the tube, as indicated in Method 38.

The porosity of soil (n) may be obtained directly from air-pycnometer measurements or can be calculated from the relation $n = (d_p - d_b)/d_p$, where d_p is the average density of the soil particles and d_b is the bulk density.

The particle density of many soils averages around 2.65 gm. cm.$^{-3}$. The average particle density for peat soils or for pumice soils is much lower. Direct measurements of particle density can be made with pycnometer bottles (Method 39).

The bulk density of most soils ranges from 1.0 gm. cm.$^{-3}$ for clays, to 1.8 gm. cm.$^{-3}$ for sands. This corresponds to the range of 62.4 to 112 lb. ft.$^{-3}$. The corresponding porosity range will be from about 0.60 to 0.30. Bulk density may become a critical factor in the productivity of soil. Veihmeyer and Hendrickson (1946) found that plant roots were unable to penetrate a gravelly loam soil when the bulk density exceeded a value of around 1.8 gm. cm.$^{-3}$. Also, when the bulk density of medium- to fine-textured subsoils exceeds about 1.7 gm. cm.$^{-3}$, hydraulic conductivity values will be so low that drainage difficulties can be anticipated.

Aggregation and Stability of Structure

The arrangement of soil particles into crumbs or aggregates that are more or less water stable is an important aspect of soil structure. Alkali soils often have a dense, blocky, single-grain structure, are hard to till when dry, and have low hydraulic conductivity when

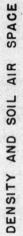

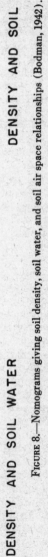

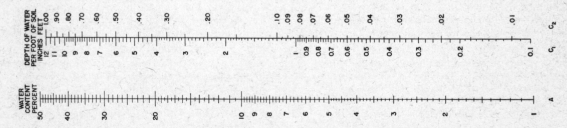

DENSITY AND SOIL AIR SPACE

DENSITY AND SOIL WATER

FIGURE 8.—Nomograms giving soil density, soil water, and soil air space relationships (Bodman, 1942).

wet. This is generally because the aggregates and also the pores of such soils are not stable. The aggregates slake down in water, and the pores become filled with fine particles.

Several methods have been proposed for measuring the water stability of soil aggregates, the most common being the wet-sieving method proposed by Yoder (1936). A modification of the Yoder procedure is given as Method 42a. Soils that are low in organic matter and contain appreciable amounts of exchangeable sodium seldom contain aggregates of larger sizes and for that reason measuring procedures adapted for the smaller aggregates are included as Method 42b. This determination is related to Middleton's (1930) "dispersion-ratio," but Method 42a gives the percentage by weight of particles smaller than 50μ that are bound into water-stable aggregates greater than 50μ. Insufficient data are available at the present time to specify limits that will help to distinguish between problem and nonproblem soils as far as aggregate-size distribution is concerned.

Childs (1940) followed the change in moisture-retension curves with successive wettings to get an index of the stability of structure, or, more precisely, the stability of the pore-space arrangement. Reeve and coworkers (fig. 1) have shown that the ratio of the air permeability to the water permeability for soils is also a useful index of the stability of soil structure (Method 37).

Recent studies by Allison (1952) and by Martin and associates (1952) indicate that dispersed soils may be rapidly and effectively improved by application of aggregating agents of the polyelectrolyte type. Applied at the rate of 0.1 percent on the dry-soil basis, this material has effectively improved the physical condition of alkali soils on which it has been tried. Salinity appears to have little or no effect on the process. A higher degree of aggregation was obtained where the aggregating agent in solution was sprayed on dry soil and mixed in than when it was applied dry to a moist soil followed by mixing. Regardless of the manner of application, large increases in infiltration rate and hydraulic conductivity resulted from its use.

Although not yet economically feasible for general agricultural use, aggregating agents can be an effective research tool for investigational work with saline and alkali soils. By their use, for instance, plant response to different levels of exchangeable sodium or different Ca : Na ratios may be studied on "conditioned" soils in the absence of poor structure and accompanying conditions of deficient aeration and low water-movement rates ordinarily present in alkali soils.

It seems likely, also, that soil-aggregating chemicals may provide a rapid method for appraising the structural improvement potentially attainable from organic-matter additions. Organic-matter additions, while slower to give results, have long been used in agriculture. There may be soils, such as those high in silt and low in clay, in which coarse organic matter may give improvements in physical condition that are unattainable with chemical aggregants.

Crust Formation

Soils that have low stability of structure disperse and slake when they are wetted by rain or irrigation water and may develop a hard crust as the soil surface dries. This crust presents a serious barrier for emerging seedlings, and with some crops often is the main cause of a poor stand. Alkali soils are a special problem in this regard, but the phenomenon is by no means limited to these soils.

Factors influencing development of hard surface crusts appear to be high exchangeable sodium, low organic matter, puddling, and wetting the soil to zero tension, which occurs in the field with rain or irrigation. Crust prevention would, therefore, involve removal of exchangeable sodium, addition of organic matter, and care to avoid puddling during tillage and other operations. Where possible, the placement of the seed line somewhat above the water level in a furrow is desirable so that the soil above the seed will be wetted with water at appreciable tensions, thus lessening the tendency for soil aggregates at the surface to disintegrate.

The procedure for measuring the modulus of rupture of soil (Method 43) was developed for appraising the hardness of soil crusts, since a satisfactory measuring method is essential in developing and testing soil treatments for lessening soil crusting.

Choice of Determinations and Interpretation of Data

Equilibrium Relations Between Soluble and Exchangeable Cations

Cation exchange can be represented by equations similar to those employed for chemical reactions in solutions. For example, the reaction between calcium-saturated soil and sodium chloride solution may be written: $CaX_2 + 2NaCl \rightleftharpoons 2NaX + CaCl_2$, where X designates the soil exchange complex. As shown by the equation, the reaction does not go to completion, because as long as soluble calcium exists in the solution phase there will be adsorbed calcium on the exchange complex and vice versa. Equations have been proposed by various workers for expressing the equilibrium distribution of pairs of cations between the exchangeable and soluble forms. For metallic cation pairs of equal valence, many of the equations assume the same form and give satisfactory equilibrium constants, but variable results are obtained with the different equations when cations of unequal valence are involved. According to the work of Krishnamoorthy and Overstreet (1950), an equation based on the statistical thermodynamics of Guggenheim (1945) is most satisfactory for cation pairs of unequal valence. All of the equations become less satisfactory when applied to mixtures of cation-exchange materials having different equilibrium constants.

The use of cation-exchange equations for expressing the relationship between soluble and exchangeable cations in soils of arid regions involves inherent difficulties. The difficulties arise from the presence of mixtures of different kinds of cation-exchange materials in soils and from the fact that usually four cation species must be dealt with. Moreover, there are no accurate methods available for determining exchangeable calcium and magnesium in soils containing alkaline-earth carbonates and gypsum. Despite these difficulties, some degree of success has been attained in relating the relative and total concentrations of soluble cations in the saturation extract of soils to the exchangeable-cation composition, using a somewhat empirical approach. Direct determinations show that, when soils are leached with salt solutions containing a mixture of a monovalent cation and a divalent cation until equilibrium between the soil and solution is established, the proportions of exchangeable monovalent and divalent cations present on the soil-exchange complex vary with the total-cation concentration as well as with the monovalent : divalent cation ratio of the salt solutions. Gapon (1933), Mattson and Wiklander (1940), Davis (1945), and Schofield (1947) have proposed, in effect, that the influence of total-cation concentration is taken into account and a linear relation with the exchangeable monovalent: divalent cation ratio is obtained when the molar concentration of the soluble monovalent cation is divided by the square root of the molar concentration of the soluble divalent cation.

Two ratios of the latter type, designated as the sodium-adsorption-ratio (SAR) and potassium-adsorption-ratio (PAR), are employed for discussing the equilibrium relation between soluble and exchangeable cations. The sodium-adsorption-ratio and potassium-adsorption-ratio are defined as $Na^+/\sqrt{(Ca^{++}+Mg^{++})/2}$ and $K^+/\sqrt{(Ca^{++}+Mg^{++})/2}$, respectively, where Na^+, K^+, Ca^{++}, and Mg^{++} refer to the concentrations of the designated soluble cations expressed in milliequivalents per liter.

The relationship between the sodium-adsorption-ratio and the ratio exchangeable sodium : (exchange capacity minus exchangeable sodium) at the saturation moisture percentage for 59 soil samples representing 12 sections in 9 Western States is shown in figure 9. A similar relationship involving the potassium-adsorption-ratio, exchange capacity, and exchangeable potassium is given in figure 10. The correlation coefficients for the two sets of values are sufficiently good to permit practical use of the relations. Data for soils having exchangeable sodium/(exchange capacity minus exchangeable sodium) and exchangeable potassium/(exchange capacity minus exchangeable potassium) ratios greater than 1, which correspond to exchangeable-cation-percentages of more than 50, are not included in the graphs. Limited data indicate that for these soils the relations shown in the graphs are somewhat less precise. Using the data presented in figure 9, the relation between the exchangeable-sodium-percentage (ESP), and the sodium-adsorption-ratio (SAR) is given by the equation:

$$ESP = \frac{100\,(-0.0126+0.01475\,SAR)}{1+(-0.0126+0.01475\,SAR)}$$

Similarly, the relation between the exchangeable-potassium-percentage (EPP) and the potassium-adsorption-ratio (PAR) is given by the equation:

$$EPP = \frac{100\,(0.0360+0.1051\,PAR)}{1+(0.0360+0.1051\,PAR)}$$

The former equation was employed to obtain the average relation between exchangeable-sodium-percentage and the sodium-adsorption-ratio, which is shown by the nomogram given in figure 27, chapter 6.

Chemical Analyses of Representative Soil Samples

Data of typical chemical analyses of saline, non-saline-alkali, and saline-alkali soil samples are given in table 5. Similar analyses of samples of normal soils from arid regions are also given for comparative purposes. These analyses are presented to show the differences in the chemical characteristics of the four classes of soils and to illustrate how the analyses may be interpreted and cross-checked for reliability.

Nonsaline-Nonalkali Soils

Samples numbered 2741, 2744, and R–2867 are classed as normal with respect to salinity and alkali, because the electrical conductivity of their saturation extracts is less than 4 mmhos/cm. and their exchangeable-sodium-percentage is less than 15. The reaction of the samples ranges from slightly acid to slightly alkaline. While the composition of the soluble ions varies somewhat, the amounts present are small, and all of the saturation extracts have low sodium-adsorption-ratios. Alkaline-earth carbonates may or may not be present. Also, gypsum may or may not be present, although none of the samples selected contains this constituent.

Saline Soils

The electrical conductivity of the saturation extracts of these samples is in excess of 4 mmhos/cm., but the exchangeable-sodium-percentage is less than 15. In no case does the pH reading exceed 8.5. Chloride and sulfate are the principal soluble anions present in these samples, the bicarbonate content is relatively low, and carbonate is absent. The soluble-sodium contents exceed those of calcium plus magnesium somewhat, but the sodium-adsorption-ratios are not high. Gypsum and alkaline-earth carbonates are common constituents of saline soils. As shown by the values for the electrical conductivity of the saturation extracts, the salinity levels are sufficiently high to affect adversely the growth of most plants. Reclamation of the soils will require leaching only, providing drainage is adequate.

Nonsaline-Alkali Soils

The exchangeable-sodium-percentages of these soil samples exceed 15, but the soluble-salt contents are low.

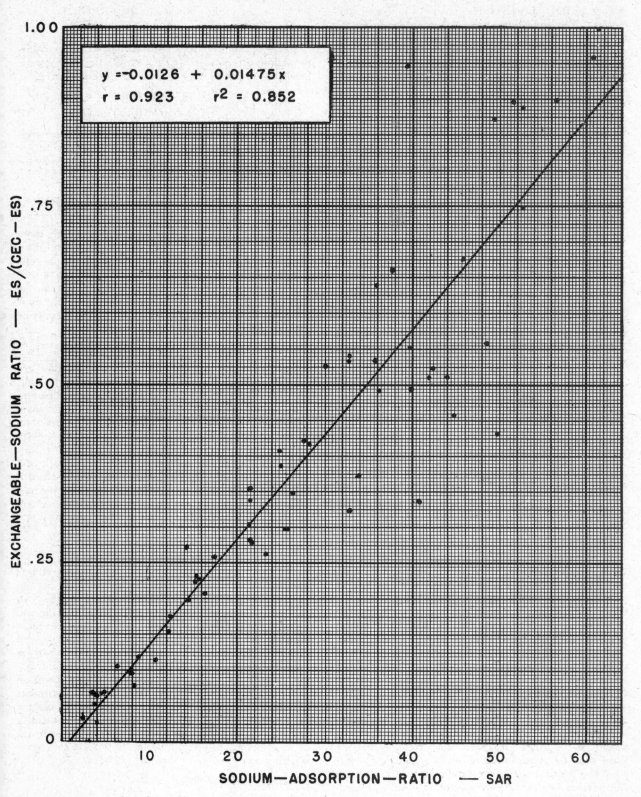

FIGURE 9.—Exchangeable-sodium ratio ($ES/[CEC—ES]$) as related to the sodium-adsorption-ratio (SAR) of the saturation extract. ES, exchangeable sodium; CEC, cation-exchange-capacity.

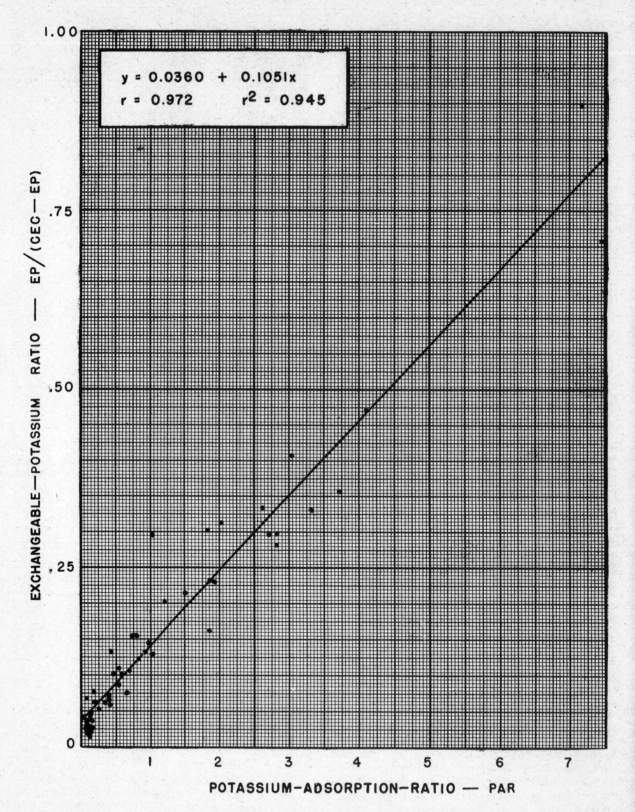

FIGURE 10.—Exchangeable-potassium ratio $(EP/[CEC—EP])$ as related to the potassium-adsorption-ratio (PAR) of the saturation extract. EP, exchangeable potassium; CEC, cation-exchange-capacity.

TABLE 5.—*Chemical analyses of soil samples from arid regions*

SOIL DETERMINATIONS

Soil and sample No.	Saturation percentage	pH of saturated soil	Cation-exchange-capacity	Exchangeable-cation-percentages					Gypsum	Alkaline-earth carbonates [1]
				Na	K	Ca	Mg	H		
			Meq./100 gm.						Meq./100 gm.	
Normal soils:										
2741	35.6	6.4	20.3	2	8	54	29	7	0	—
2744	32.4	7.8	29.4	10	1	.....	.....	.....	0	+
R–2867	40.4	7.9	17.4	3	1	.....	.....	0	0	+
Saline soils:										
574	52.0	7.9	14.4	13	3	.....	.....	0	7.1	+
756	46.5	8.0	17.0	8	2	.....	.....	0	0	+
575	40.0	8.0	18.6	10	17	.....	.....	0	0	+
Nonsaline-alkali soils:										
2747	58.8	8.3	33.4	18	3	.....	.....	0	0	+
2738	61.2	7.3	34.2	24	2	31	30	13	0	—
535	38.7	9.6	21.9	46	32	.....	.....	0	0	+
Saline-alkali soils:										
2739	61.5	7.3	35.7	26	2	27	35	10	0	—
2740	59.7	7.8	40.3	26	2	.....	.....	0	42.2	+
536	35.8	9.3	26.2	63	8	.....	.....	0	0	+

SATURATION EXTRACT DETERMINATIONS

Soil and sample No.	Electrical conductivity	Cations					Anions					Sodium-adsorption-ratio (SAR)
		Ca^{++}	Mg^{++}	Na^+	K^+	Total	CO_3^-	HCO_3^-	SO_4^-	Cl^-	Total	
	Mmhos/cm.	Meq./l.	Meq./l.	Meq./l.	Meq./l.	Meq./l.	Meq./l.	Meq./l.	Meq./l	Meq./l.	Meq./l.	
Normal soils:												
2741	0.60	2.71	2.26	1.20	0.91	7.08	0	2.60	2.09	0.87	5.56	0.8
2744	1.68	3.33	1.94	12.2	.70	18.17	0	6.14	4.28	4.93	15.35	7.5
R–2867	.84	2.76	1.69	5.22	.18	9.85	0	6.63	2.67	.44	9.74	3.5
Saline soils:												
574	13.9	31.5	37.2	102.0	.21	170.91	0	4.50	90.0	78.0	172.50	17.4
756	12.0	37.0	34.0	79.0	.40	150.40	0	7.20	62.2	47.0	[2]148.40	13.3
575	8.8	28.4	22.8	53.0	1.10	105.30	0	5.20	74.0	29.0	108.20	10.5
Nonsaline-alkali soils:												
2747	1.74	1.10	1.42	15.6	.42	18.54	0	6.51	8.48	2.86	17.85	13.9
2738	2.53	1.41	1.01	21.5	.28	24.20	0	3.29	3.80	16.7	23.79	19.6
535	3.16	1.10	.30	29.2	4.10	34.70	8.40	18.70	4.60	7.50	39.20	35.0
Saline-alkali soils:												
2739	9.19	6.73	9.85	79.5	.48	96.56	0	2.35	20.1	72.0	94.45	27.6
2740	16.7	32.4	38.3	145.0	.51	216.21	0	3.29	105.0	105.0	213.29	24.4
536	5.6	.60	.90	58.5	1.6	61.60	5.00	19.9	21.5	16.3	62.70	67.6

[1] +, Present; −, absent.　　　　[2] Includes 32.0 meq./l. of NO_3.

Usually the pH readings are greater than 8.5, but they may be lower if the exchangeable-sodium-percentage does not greatly exceed 15 (sample No. 2747) or if alkaline-earth carbonates are absent (sample No. 2738). Gypsum seldom occurs in these soils. The chief soluble cation is sodium, and appreciable amounts of this cation may be present as the bicarbonate and carbonate salts. The sodium-adsorption-ratio of the saturation extract may be quite high. Sample No. 2738 is an example of a nonsaline-alkali soil that is free of alkaline-earth carbonates and contains some exchangeable hydrogen. Replacement of exchangeable sodium will be required for its reclamation. Gypsum is a suitable amendment, but the application of acid or acid-forming amendments may cause excessive soil acidity unless limestone is also applied. The application of limestone alone will tend to replace the exchangeable sodium. Sample Nos. 2747 and 535 will also require replacement of exchangeable sodium for reclamation; but, owing to the presence of alkaline-earth carbonates, acid, any acid-forming amendment, or gypsum may be applied. The application of limestone alone will obviously be of no value.

Saline-Alkali Soils

Soils of this class are characterized by their appreciable contents of soluble salts and exchangeable sodium. The electrical conductivity of the saturation extract is greater than 4 mmhos/cm., and the exchangeable-sodium-percentage exceeds 15. The pH reading may vary considerably but is commonly less than 8.5. Except that a higher proportion of the soluble cations consists of sodium, the composition of the soluble salts usually is similar to that of saline soils. Although only the most salt-sensitive plants will be affected by the salinity level of sample No. 536, the exchangeable-sodium-percentage is too high to permit the growth of most crops. Both replacement of exchangeable sodium and leaching are required for reclamation of these soils. With respect to the suitability of various amendments for the replacement of exchangeable sodium, sample No. 2739, like No. 2738, will require the application of soluble calcium, whereas sample No. 536, like samples 2747 and 535, can be treated with soluble calcium, acid, or acid-forming amendments. Owing to its high content of gypsum, sample No. 2740 will not require the application of amendments for the replacement of exchangeable sodium.

Cross-Checking Chemical Analyses for Consistency and Reliability

A means of locating gross errors in the chemical analyses of soils is provided by the considerable number of interrelations that exist among the values obtained for various determinations. An understanding of the principles involved in these interrelations aids in the interpretation of the analyses.

ELECTRICAL CONDUCTIVITY AND TOTAL CATION CONCENTRATION.—The EC of soil solutions and saturation extracts when expressed in millimhos per centimeter at 25° C. and multiplied by 10 is approximately equal to the total soluble-cation concentration in milliequivalents per liter.

CATION AND ANION CONCENTRATION.—The total soluble-anion concentration or content and the total soluble-cation concentration or content, expressed on an equivalent basis, are nearly equal.

pH AND CARBONATE AND BICARBONATE CONCENTRATIONS.—If carbonate ions are present in a soil extract in titratable quantities, the pH reading of the extract must exceed 9. The bicarbonate concentration seldom exceeds 10 meq./l. in the absence of carbonate ions, and at pH readings of about 7 or less seldom exceeds 3 or 4 meq./l.

pH AND CALCIUM AND MAGNESIUM CONCENTRATIONS.—The concentration of calcium and magnesium in a saturation extract seldom exceeds 2 meq./l. at pH readings above 9. Therefore, calcium plus magnesium is low if carbonate ions are present in titratable amounts, and calcium plus magnesium is never high in the presence of a high concentration of bicarbonate ions.

CALCIUM AND SULFATE IN A SOIL-WATER EXTRACT AND GYPSUM CONTENT OF THE SOIL.—The solubility of gypsum at ordinary temperatures is approximately 30 meq./l. in distilled water and 50 meq./l. or more in highly saline solutions. However, owing to the common ion effect, an excess of either calcium or sulfate may depress the solubility of gypsum to a value as low as 20 meq./l. Hence, the saturation extract of a nongypsiferous soil may contain more than 30 meq./l. of both calcium and sulfate (i. e. saline soil No. 756), and that of a gypsiferous soil may have a calcium concentration as low as 20 meq./l. As a general rule, soils with saturation extracts that have a calcium concentration of more than 20 meq./l. should be checked for the presence of gypsum.

pH AND ALKALINE-EARTH CARBONATES.—The pH reading of a calcareous soil at the saturation percentage is invariably in excess of 7.0 and generally in excess of 7.5; a noncalcareous soil may have a pH reading as high as 7.3 or 7.4.

pH AND GYPSUM.—The pH reading of gypsiferous soils at the saturation percentage is seldom in excess of 8.2 regardless of the ESP.

pH AND ESP.—A pH reading at the saturation percentage in excess of 8.5 almost invariably indicates an ESP of 15 or more.

ESP AND SAR.—In general, ESP increases with SAR. There are occasional deviations, but generally low SAR values of the saturation extract are associated with low ESP values in the soil, and high SAR values denote high ESP values.

CEC AND SP.—Because both cation-exchange-capacity and moisture-retention properties are related to the texture of soils, there generally exists a fair correlation among these properties, particularly in soils with similar parent materials and mode of origin.

Factors That Modify the Effect of Exchangeable Sodium on Soils

As might be expected, alkali soils having similar exchangeable-sodium-percentages may vary considerably with respect to their physical properties, their ability to produce crops, and their response to management practices, including the application of amendments. Although the reasons for the variable behavior of alkali soils are imperfectly understood, experience and limited data indicate that the effect of exchangeable sodium may be modified by several soil characteristics. Determinations of some or all of these characteristics are often of value in the investigation of alkali soils.

Texture

It is well known that the distribution of particle sizes influences the moisture retention and transmission properties of soils. Particle-size analysis may be made, using Method 41. As a rule, coarse-textured soils have low-moisture retention and high permeability, whereas fine-textured soils have high-moisture retention and generally have lower permeability. However, owing to a high degree of aggregation of the particles, there are notable examples of fine-textured soils that are moderately permeable. The presence of a high percentage (50 or more) of silt-size particles (effective diameter 2μ to 50μ) often causes soils to have relatively low permeability. There is also evidence that some silt-size particles, presumably those having a platy shape, are more effective in reducing permeability than others. In general, the physical properties of fine-textured soils are affected more adversely at a given exchangeable-sodium-percentage than coarse-textured soils. For example, the hydraulic conductivity of a coarse-textured soil having an exchangeable-sodium-percentage of 50 may be as great as that of a fine-textured soil having an exchangeable-sodium-percentage of only 15 or 20. Inasmuch as fine-textured soils generally have higher cation-exchange-capacities than coarse-textured soils, expressing the critical levels of sodium in milliequivalents per 100 gm. tends to eliminate the texture factor in evaluating the effect of exchangeable sodium.

Surface Area and Type of Clay Mineral

Soil particles may be considered to have two types of surfaces: external and internal. Primary minerals such as quartz and feldspars and the clay minerals kaolinite and illite have external surfaces only. Clay minerals of the expanding lattice type such as montmorillonite, which exhibits interlayer swelling, have internal as well as external surfaces. The external surface area of soils is directly related to texture, whereas internal surface area is related to the content of minerals that exhibit interlayer swelling. Determinations of the amounts of ethylene glycol retained as a monomolecular layer by heated and unheated samples of soil (Method 25) permit estimation of the external and the internal surface areas, provided appreciable amounts of vermiculite and endellite minerals are not present. In any case, the ethylene glycol retained by unheated soil in excess of that retained by a corresponding heated sample is an index of interlayer swelling.

As determined by Method 25, the external surface areas of most soils lie in the range 10 to 50 m.²/gm. (square meters per gram), whereas the internal surface area varies to a greater extent, being nil in soils that contain no interlayer swelling minerals and as high as 150 m.²/gm. or more in soils with a high content of expanding lattice-type minerals. X-ray diffraction patterns indicate that the clay fraction (particles $<2\mu$ effective diam.) of many soils of arid regions are predominantly interstratified mixtures of various proportions of montmorillonite and illite, although sometimes individual crystals of these minerals occur. The amount of kaolinite present is usually small.

It is generally recognized that soils containing clay of the expanding lattice (montmorillonitic) type exhibit such properties as swelling, plasticity, and dispersion to a greater extent than soils containing equivalent amounts of nonexpanding lattice (illitic and kaolinitic) clays, especially when appreciable amounts of exchangeable sodium are present. Whether the more adverse physical properties imparted by the former type of clays are caused by their greater total surface area or to the fact that they exhibit interlayer swelling is not definitely known. Further studies may show that the susceptibility of soil to injury by exchangeable sodium is related to total surface area as measured by ethylene glycol retention.

Potassium Status and Soluble Silicate

Several medium- to fine-textured alkali soils have been examined at the Laboratory and have been found to be much more permeable than would ordinarily be expected on the basis of their high exchangeable-sodium-percentages. In some cases, the permeability is such that the soils can be leached readily with large quantities of irrigation water and the excess exchangeable sodium removed without the use of chemical amendments. The soils have several characteristics in common, which include a high pH value (9.0 or higher), a high exchangeable-potassium-percentage (25 to 40), and an appreciable content of soluble silicate. The silicate concentration of the saturation extracts of these soils has been found to vary from 5 to 40 meq./l., and additional quantities of this anion as well as sodium are removed upon leaching. As shown by ethylene glycol retention, Dyal and Hendricks (1952) and Bower and Gschwend (1952), saturation of montmorillonite clays and soils with potassium followed by drying decreases interlayer swelling. Moreover, Mortland and Gieseking (1951) have shown by means of X-ray diffraction studies that montmorillonite clays, when dried in the presence of potassium silicate, are changed to micalike clays that would have less tendency to swell and disperse under the influence of exchangeable sodium. Ethylene glycol retention determinations made on some of the alkali soils having high exchangeable-potassium-percentages and containing appreciable soluble silicate give relatively low values for interlayer swelling. While further research is needed to clarify the role of exchangeable potassium and soluble silicate, there is a distinct indication that alkali soils containing unusually high amounts of these constituents are less susceptible to the development of adverse physical conditions.

Organic Matter

While the organic-matter content of soils of arid regions is usually low under virgin conditions, it commonly increases with the application of irrigation water and cultivation, especially when crop management is good. Aside from its value as a source of plant nutrients, organic matter has a favorable effect upon soil physical properties.

There is considerable evidence that organic matter tends to counteract the unfavorable effects of exchangeable sodium on soils. Campbell and Richards (1950)

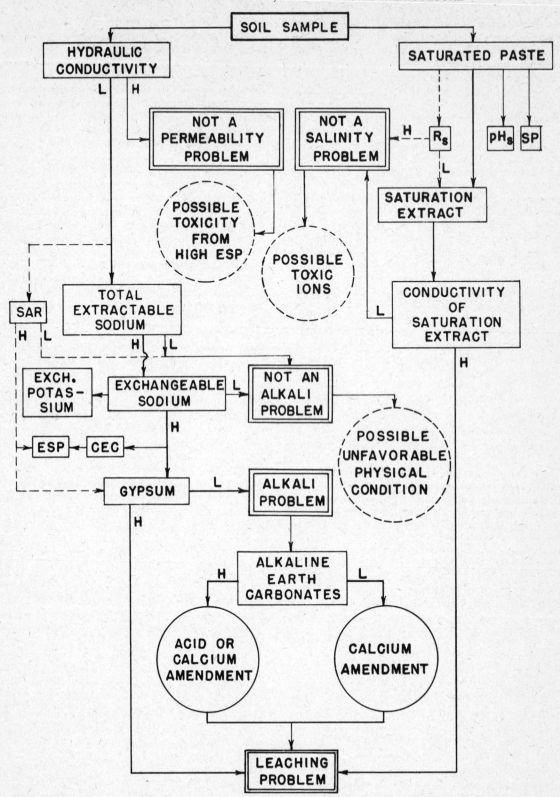

FIGURE 11.—Sequence of determinations for the diagnosis and treatment of saline and alkali soils: *H*, High; *L*, low; *R*s, electrical resistance of soil paste; *SAR*, sodium-adsorption-ratio; *ESP*, exchangeable-sodium-percentage; *CEC*, cation-exchange-capacity.

and Fireman and Blair [5] found that peat and muck soils containing appreciable quantities of exchangeable sodium had good physical properties, and numerous investigators have demonstrated a beneficial effect of organic matter additions upon alkali soils. For example, Bower and associates (1951) found that the application of manure at the rate of 50 tons per acre to an alkali soil of the "slick spot" type increased the degree of aggregation of the surface soil significantly and the infiltration rate approximately threefold. The available data indicate that organic matter improves and prevents deterioration of the physical condition of the soil by its interaction with the inorganic cation-exchange material, by serving as energy material for micro-organisms which promote the stable aggregation of soil particles, and by decreasing the bulk density of soils.

The organic-matter content of soils is ordinarily obtained by multiplying the organic-carbon content by 1.72. The dry-combustion method is most accurate for the determination of organic carbon, but it is time-consuming and cannot be applied to soils containing carbonates. Wet-combustion methods such as the one given in Method 24 are suitable for use on soil containing carbonates, but the application of a correction factor is required to compensate for the incomplete oxidation of the organic matter.

Sequence of Determinations for Soil Diagnosis

The salinity status and the hydraulic conductivity are measured for all samples. The sequence of further determinations depends on whether the result obtained from a previous determination (fig. 11) is considered to be high or low. Criteria for distinguishing high and low values are discussed in chapter 6.

The determinations are ordinarily discontinued when the guide lines of the two main branches of the diagram lead to a heavy-walled box, except in the case of an

[5] FIREMAN, M., and BLAIR, G. Y. CHEMICAL AND PHYSICAL ANALYSES OF SOILS FROM THE HUMBOLDT PROJECT, NEVADA. [Unpublished.] January 1949.

alkali problem where alkaline-earth carbonates should also be determined if the use of acid or acid-forming amendments is contemplated. At two places in the diagram, dotted lines indicate where optional alternate determinations can be made. The alternate determinations cost somewhat less but have lower reliability.

Hydraulic-conductivity measurements on disturbed samples provide an indication of the moisture-transmission rate of the soil. It has been found for most soils that exchangeable sodium is not excessive if this rate is high. However, coarse soils such as sands and peats may contain sufficient amounts of exchangeable sodium to be toxic to plants and yet have high permeability. If the hydraulic conductivity is low, the total extractable sodium or the sodium-adsorption-ratio (SAR) should be determined. If either of these is low, the low hydraulic-conductivity value previously obtained may be the result of an inherently unfavorable physical condition related to texture, low content of organic matter, or high-swelling type clay rather than the presence of exchangeable sodium. For these samples, organic matter, ethylene glycol retention, and particle-size analyses may yield useful information.

If the total extractable-sodium content or the SAR value is high, the exchangeable sodium should be determined or, alternatively, the exchangeable-sodium-percentage can be estimated from the SAR value. If the exchangeable-sodium content or exchangeable-sodium-percentage is high, a gypsum determination should be made. A high-gypsum value indicates that leaching only is required, while a low-gypsum value indicates need for amendments. When there is a low-gypsum value, the presence or absence of alkaline-earth carbonates is ascertained to indicate the type of chemical amendment that can be used for the replacement of exchangeable sodium. The addition of amendments should be followed by leaching. Other determinations, such as pH, saturation percentage, cation-exchange-capacity, exchangeable potassium, toxic ions, and texture, provide additional information and are made if circumstances warrant.

Chapter 3

Improvement and Management of Soils in Arid and Semiarid Regions in Relation to Salinity and Alkali

The development and maintenance of successful irrigation projects involve not only the supplying of irrigation water to the land but also the control of salinity and alkali. The quality of irrigation water, irrigation practices, and drainage conditions are involved in salinity and alkali control. In establishing an irrigation project, soils that are initially saline require the removal of the excess salts and may require chemical amendments in addition to an adequate supply of irrigation water. On the other hand, soils that initially are nonsaline may become unproductive if excess soluble salts or exchangeable sodium are allowed to accumulate because of improper irrigation and soil management practices or inadequate drainage.

Basic Principles

Although farming practices may vary from one irrigated area to another, the following general principles related to salinity and alkali have universal application.

Plant growth is a function of the total soil-moisture stress, which is the sum of the soil-moisture tension and the osmotic pressure of the soil solution. Through controlled leaching, the osmotic pressure of the soil solution should be maintained at the lowest feasible level; and, by a practical system of irrigation, the soil-moisture tension in the root zone should be maintained in a range that will give the greatest net return for the crop being grown.

Water flows in both saturated and unsaturated soil in accordance with Darcy's law, which states that the flow velocity is proportional to the hydraulic gradient and the direction of flow is in the direction of the greatest rate of decrease of hydraulic head. This principle makes it possible to determine the direction of flow of ground water by simple methods. A knowledge of the source and direction of flow of ground water is especially useful in solving drainage problems.

Soluble salts in soil are transported by water. This is an obvious but basic principle pertaining to the control of salinity. Salinity, therefore, can be controlled if the quality of the irrigation water is satisfactory and if the flow of water through the soil can be controlled.

The concentration of soluble salts in the soil solution is increased as water is removed from the soil by evaporation and transpiration. Desiccation of surface soil by transpiration and by evaporation creates a suction gradient that will produce an appreciable upward movement of water and salt. This upward flow, especially if the water table is near the soil surface, is a process by which many soils become salinized.

Soluble salts increase or decrease in the root zone, depending on whether the net downward movement of salt is less or greater than the net salt input from irrigation water and other sources. The salt balance in soil, as affected by the quantity and quality of irrigation water and the effectiveness of leaching and drainage, is of paramount importance. If irrigation agriculture is to remain successful, soil salinity must be controlled (Scofield, 1940).

Equilibrium reactions occur between the cations in the soil solution and those adsorbed on the exchange complex of the soil. The use of amendments for changing the exchangeable-cation status of soil depends upon these equilibrium reactions. Adsorption of excessive amounts of sodium is detrimental to the physical status of the soil and may be toxic to plants. When the exchangeable-sodium content of soil is excessive or tends to become so, special amendment, leaching, and management practices are required to improve and maintain favorable soil conditions for plant growth.

Whether soil particles are flocculated or dispersed depends to some extent upon the exchangeable-cation status of the soil and, also, upon the ionic concentration of the soil solution. Soils that are flocculated and permeable when saline may become deflocculated when leached.

Irrigation and Leaching in Relation to Salinity Control

Irrigation is the application of water to soil for the purpose of providing a favorable environment for plants. Leaching, in agriculture, is the process of dissolving and transporting soluble salts by the downward movement of water through the soil. Because salts move with water, salinity depends directly on water management, i. e., irrigation, leaching, and drainage. These three aspects of water management should be considered collectively in the over-all plan for an irrigated area if maximum efficiency is to be obtained.

Irrigation

In subhumid regions, when irrigation is provided on a standby or supplemental basis, salinity is usually of little concern, because rainfall is sufficient to leach out any accumulated salts. But in semiarid or arid regions salinity is usually an ever-present hazard and must be taken into account at all stages of planning and operation.

The subject of water quality in relation to irrigation is discussed at length in chapter 5 and is mentioned here only to emphasize the fact that water quality must be considered in determining the suitability of soils for irrigation. In general, waters with high salt contents should not be used for irrigation on soils having low infiltration and drainage rates. The higher the salt content of the water, the greater the amount of water that must be passed through the soil to keep the soluble-salt content at or below a critical level. Experience indicates that there are soils in which low water-movement rates make the cost of drainage so high that irrigation agriculture is not feasible under present economic conditions.

Pumping from ground water for irrigation has several advantages. It often affords direct local control of the water table when water is pumped from unconfined or partially confined aquifers. This has been demonstrated in the Salt River Valley, Arizona, the San Joaquin Valley, California, and elsewhere. Wells can often be located on the farm, thereby eliminating the need for elaborate distribution systems. Water is available for use at all times, which provides maximum flexibility in irrigation. If it is possible to obtain irrigation water from both ground-water and surface supplies, a balance between the two sources can often be established to insure favorable drainage of the irrigated soils. Another indirect advantage of pumping water for irrigation comes from the fact that the direct visible cost of operating pumps causes the farmer to avoid the wasteful overuse of water which often is the cause of the need for drainage improvement.

Excessive losses from water conveyance and distribution systems must be prevented, otherwise drainage problems will be aggravated with attendant salinity hazards. Distribution systems and irrigation schedules should be designed so that water is available at times and in amounts needed to replenish the soil moisture without unnecessary use on irrigated fields and without regulatory waste of water which may directly or indirectly contribute to unfavorable drainage conditions. In some cases, water is used under continuous free-flow systems to maintain water rights rather than on a basis of consumptive use. Salinity and drainage problems could undoubtedly be alleviated in some areas by changing to a system of direct charge for the volume of water used.

The quantity of water available for irrigation may have a marked effect upon the control of salinity. In areas where water is cheap and large volumes are used, irrigation practices are often inefficient. Overuse and waste of irrigation water contribute to drainage difficulties and salinity problems. Efficient irrigation practices can be developed more readily in the planning of irrigation systems than by applying corrective measures on the farm. Limited quantities of water should be supplied, based upon consumptive use and leaching requirements, for the area in question. Where an abundant supply of water is available for irrigation, restrictions may become necessary if drainage problems arise. Water requirements for leaching are discussed in a following section.

Lining canals to reduce seepage losses and the distribution of water by underground pipe systems should receive careful consideration. Much can be done in the layout of distribution systems to reduce seepage losses by locating canals and laterals properly. In some areas, earth and asphalt linings for irrigation canals have been used successfully. The buried asphalt membrane lining used by the United States Bureau of Reclamation on a number of projects has been shown to be effective in reducing seepage losses. In the Coachella Valley, California, an underground concrete-pipe distribution system, and a concrete-lined main canal, serve approximately 70,000 acres of land. Reduction of seepage losses and improvement in drainage conditions were major factors in the selection of these facilities.

Automatic control of distribution systems, combined with lined canals and laterals, is being used successfully in Algeria and elsewhere to eliminate regulatory waste and to reduce the cost of operation. Automatic control makes water available at the farm at all times and allows water to be taken out or shut off from the main distribution system at laterals or at farm outlets at any time. All regulatory changes to maintain proper flow from the point of diversion to the farm are performed automatically. This eliminates waste on the farm and throughout the system. Older irrigation districts with drainage and salinity problems might well consider some of the advantages of the newly developed automatic distribution systems. A modernization of the distribution system in some cases may be the most economical way to solve a drainage problem.

The selection of an irrigation method for applying water to the soil is related to salinity. The method that is best adapted in any particular case depends upon a number of conditions: The crop to be grown, topography, soil characteristics, availability of water, soluble-salt content of the water, and salinity status of the soil. The primary objective of any irrigation method is to supply water to the soil so that moisture will be readily available at all times for crop growth, but soil salinity is definitely an influencing factor.

It is desirable, both for plant use and for leaching, to apply the water uniformly over the irrigated area.

The four principal methods used for the application of water are flooding, furrow, sprinkling, and sub-irrigation.

The flooding method should be favored if salinity is a serious problem. Wild flooding, border-strip or border-check flooding, and basin flooding are used. Wild flooding is not practiced extensively, except for pastures, alfalfa, and small grains. This method can be used only in relatively level areas where water can be flooded over the surface without the use of levees or borders for control. The border-strip or border-check method of irrigation utilizes levees or borders for control of the water. The water is not impounded by this method, except perhaps at the lower end of the strip, but is flooded over the surface and down the slope in the direction of the borders. It is adapted for use with alfalfa and grains and in orchards; but excessive water penetration near the head ditch and at the ends of the strips usually results. There is a tendency for insufficient penetration to occur midway or two-thirds of the way down the strip which generally causes salt to accumulate in this location.

The basin method of flooding is often used for orchards and various other crops in areas where water can be impounded in a rectangular basin. A variation of this method is the contour-basin method. Borders are constructed along the contours at intervals of about 0.1 to 0.2 foot. This allows larger basins to be made where there is appreciable slope. The basin methods of irrigation provide better control of the depths of water applied and greater uniformity in application than border or furrow methods.

Furrow irrigation is well adapted to row crops and is suitable for use where the topography is too rough or steep for other methods. With this method there is a tendency for salts to accumulate in the ridges, because the leaching occurs only in the furrows. Wide-bottomed furrows that resemble narrow border strips have certain advantages for wetting the soil surface uniformly and thereby controlling salt accumulation in a larger fraction of the root zone. Where the area is plowed and the surface soil is mixed occasionally, the increase in salt over a period of time may not be serious. If excess salt does accumulate, rotation of crops accompanied by a change in method of irrigation to flooding or ponding is often possible as a salinity-control measure. In the furrow and border-check methods the length of run, size of stream, slope of the land, and time of application are factors that govern the depth and uniformity of application. Proper balance among these factors, therefore, is directly related to leaching and salinity control.

Irrigation by sprinkling is generally more costly than by other methods and has not been used extensively until recent years. Originally this method was used primarily for orchards, truck crops, and nurseries; but its use has been extended to include sugar beets, peas, beans, and many other crops. This method allows a close control of the depth of water applied and when properly used results in uniform distribution. It is often used in areas where the slope is too great for other

methods. There is a tendency to apply too little water by this method; and, unless a special effort is made, leaching to maintain the proper salt balance will not be accomplished.

Subirrigation is the least common of the various methods of irrigation and is not suitable for use where salinity is a problem. Even under the most favorable circumstances, this method does not appear to be suitable for long-time use unless periodic leaching is accomplished by rainfall or surface irrigations.

Leaching

The leaching of soluble salts from the root zone is essential in irrigated soils. The need for leaching can be illustrated by considering the effect that salts in irrigation water have upon the salinity of soil if no leaching occurs. Without leaching, salts accumulate in direct proportion to the salt content of the irrigation water and the depth of water applied. The concentration of the salts in the soil solution results principally from the extraction of moisture from the soil by the processes of evaporation and transpiration. Assuming no precipitation of soluble constituents during the salinization process, the depth of irrigation water (D_{iw}) of known electrical conductivity (EC_{iw}) that will contain sufficient salt to increase the electrical conductivity of the saturation extract of a depth of soil (D_s) by an amount $(\triangle EC_e)$ can be calculated from the equation:

$$D_{iw}/D_s = (d_s/d_w)\ (SP/100)\ (\triangle EC_e/EC_{iw}) \quad (1)$$

where d_s/d_w is the ratio of the densities of the soil and the water, and SP is the saturation percentage.[6]

As an example, let: $EC_{iw} \times 10^6 = 1,000$, $d_s = 1.2$ gm. cm.$^{-3}$, $d_w = 1$ gm. cm.$^{-3}$, and $SP = 40$. Make the calculation for a change in electrical conductivity of the saturation extract of 4 mmhos/cm., or $\triangle EC_e \times 10^6 = 4,000$. Substituting these values in the equation we find $D_{iw}/D_s = 1.9$. Thus less than 2 feet of reasonably

----

[6] For the purposes of this problem, electrical conductivity of water is a satisfactory measure of salt concentration. If D_{iw} represents the depth of irrigation water applied and D_{sw} represents the equivalent free depth of this water after entering the soil and being concentrated by transpiration and evaporation, then $D_{iw}/D_{sw} = EC_{sw}/EC_{iw}$, where the right-hand side of the equation is the ratio of the electrical conductivities of the soil water and the irrigation water. The conductivity of the saturation extract EC_e provides a convenient scale for appraising soil salinity; therefore, consider the condition where the content of moisture in the soil is the saturation percentage and $\triangle EC_e$ is the increase in soil salinity produced by the water application under consideration. For this case, the depth of soil water (D_{sw}) contained in a depth of soil (D_s) is given by the relation

$$D_{sw} = \frac{d_s}{d_w} \cdot \frac{SP}{100}\, D_s$$

Substituting these values in the above equation and rearranging gives:

$$\frac{D_{iw}}{D_s} = \frac{d_s}{d_w} \cdot \frac{SP}{100} \cdot \frac{\triangle EC_e}{EC_{iw}} \quad (1)$$

The equation makes it possible to calculate the depth of irrigation water per unit depth of soil required to produce any specified increase in soil salinity expressed in terms of $\triangle EC_e$, for any given conductivity of the irrigation water (EC_{iw}).

good quality irrigation water contains sufficient salt to change a 1-foot depth of a salt-free loam soil to a saline condition, if there is no leaching or precipitation of salt in the soil.

Hundreds of thousands of acres of land in western United States have been profitably irrigated for many years with water having an electrical conductivity value approximating 1,000 micromhos/cm. It is apparent that considerable leaching has been provided, since almost enough salt is added to the soil each season to make the soil saline. With this quality of water, salinity troubles have occurred if the water table has approached to within 3 or 4 feet of the surface of the soil. In such cases extensive drainage and leaching operations have been necessary. Some areas have been abandoned, because it was not economically feasible to provide soil drainage sufficient to take care of required leaching.

Leaching Requirement

The leaching requirement may be defined as the fraction of the irrigation water that must be leached through the root zone to control soil salinity at any specified level.[7] This concept has greatest usefulness when applied to steady-state water-flow rates or to total depths of water used for irrigation and leaching over a long period of time. Obtaining calculated or experimentally determined values of the leaching requirement is complicated by many factors, but it is profitable to consider some simplified theoretical cases. The leaching requirement will depend upon the salt concentration of the irrigation water and upon the maximum concentration permissible in the soil solution. The maximum concentration, except for salt crusts formed by surface evaporation, will occur at the bottom of the root zone and will be the same as the concentration of the drainage water from a soil where irrigation water is applied with areal uniformity and with no excess leaching. Increase of the concentration of salts from the value existing in the irrigation water to the value occurring in the drainage water is related directly to consumptive use. On cropped areas this will consist mostly of water extracted from the soil by roots and so will depend on the salt tolerance of the crop. Ex-

[7] In the report of the U. S. National Resources Committee (1938), C. S. Scofield with the cooperation of R. A. Hill, proposed a formula for what was called "service equivalence," in which the concentration of the drainage water and the concentration of the irrigation water are taken into account. In addition to the salt removed through drainage, it is inherent with this formula that soluble salt is removed from the soil at a rate equal to the consumptive use of water times half the concentration of the irrigation water.

A further contribution to this subject was made at the Irrigation Conference sponsored by the Texas Agricultural Experiment Station at Ysleta, Texas, in July 1951. At this conference, F. M. Eaton proposed what he called a "drainage formula" for calculating the fraction of the irrigation water to be used for leaching. A private communication to the Laboratory from F. M. Eaton, under date of August 1952, contained a mimeographed paper entitled "Formulas for estimating drainage and gypsum requirements for irrigation waters," in which the bases for the Ysleta formula are presented.

pressed in terms of electrical conductivity, the maximum concentration of the soil solution should probably be kept below 4 mmhos/cm. for sensitive crops. Tolerant crops like beets, alfalfa, and cotton may give good yields at values up to 8 mmhos/cm., while a very tolerant crop like barley may give good yields at values of 12 mmhos/cm. or higher.

To illustrate the significance of the leaching requirement, consider first the simplest possible case with the following assumed conditions: Uniform areal application of irrigation water; no rainfall; no removal of salt in the harvested crop; and no precipitation of soluble constituents in the soil. Also, the calculation will be based on steady-state water-flow rates or the total equivalent depths of irrigation and drainage waters used over a period of time. With these assumptions, moisture and salt storage in the soil, depth of root zone, cation-exchange reactions, and drainage conditions of the soil do not need to be considered, providing that drainage will permit the specified leaching. The leaching requirement (LR) as defined above, is simply the ratio of the equivalent depth of the drainage water to the depth of irrigation water (D_{dw}/D_{iw}) and may be expressed as a fraction or as percent. Under the foregoing assumed conditions, this ratio is equal to the inverse ratio of the corresponding electrical conductivities, that is:

$$LR = \frac{D_{dw}}{D_{iw}} = \frac{EC_{iw}}{EC_{dw}} \qquad (2)$$

For field crops where a value of $EC_{dw} = 8$ mmhos/cm. can be tolerated, the formula would be $D_{dw}/D_{iw} = EC_{iw}/8$. For irrigation waters with conductivities of 1, 2, and 3 mmhos/cm., respectively, the leaching requirements will be 13, 25, and 38 percent. These are maximum values, since rainfall, removal of salt by the crop, and precipitation of salts such as calcium carbonate or gypsum in the soil are seldom zero; and, if properly taken into account, these factors all would enter in such a way as to reduce the predicted value of the leaching requirement.

Some care must be exercised in using equation 2, to make sure that the condition of steady-state or longtime average is understood. The equation does not apply if leaching is automatically taken care of by rainfall. Depending on soil texture and depth to water table, this may be the case even in semiarid regions, if the precipitation is confined to a small fraction of the year. Under these conditions, equation 1, which gives the buildup of salinity with depth of irrigation water applied, is useful for predicting salinity increases during an irrigation season or over a period of several seasons when rainfall may be abnormally low.

As an average over a long time, the conductivity of the irrigation water used in equation 2 should be a weighted average for the conductivities of the rainwater (EC_{rw}), and the irrigation water (EC_{iw}), i. e.:

$$EC_{(rw+iw)} = \frac{D_{rw}EC_{rw} + D_{iw}EC_{iw}}{D_{rw} + D_{iw}} \qquad (3)$$

where D_{rw} and D_{iw} are the depths, respectively, of the rainwater and irrigation water entering the soil. Long-time averages may deviate markedly from actual conditions at any one time, as, for example, if the entire root zone is leached through during a short period of extra high rainfall.

Information on the consumptive use of water by the crop is necessary if the leaching-requirement concept is to be used for determining either the depth of irrigation water that must be applied or the minimum depth of water to be drained, in order to keep the soil salinity from exceeding a specified value. The depth of irrigation water (D_{iw}) is related to consumptive use, (D_{cw}) and the equivalent depth of drainage water (D_{dw}) by the equation:

$$D_{iw} = D_{cw} + D_{dw} \qquad (4)$$

Using equation 2 to eliminate D_{dw} from equation 4 gives:

$$D_{iw} = D_{cw}/(1-LR) \qquad (5)$$

Expressing the leaching requirement (LR) in this equation in terms of the conductivity ratio in equation 2 gives:

$$D_{iw} = \left(\frac{EC_{dw}}{EC_{dw} - EC_{iw}}\right) D_{cw} \qquad (6)$$

The depth of irrigation water (D_{iw}) is thus expressed in terms of the electrical conductivity of the irrigation water and other conditions determined by crop and climate; namely, consumptive use and salt tolerance of the crop. The salt tolerance of the crop is taken into account in the selection of permissible values of EC_{dw}. Equations 5 and 6 are subject to the assumptions made in deriving equation 2.

Under actual farming conditions, the depth of water applied per irrigation and the areal uniformity of application are certainly not precisely controlled. Measured water application efficiencies often run as low as 25 percent and seldom exceed 80 percent. Under these conditions, high precision in the determination of the leaching requirement has little significance. A formula like equation 2 would appear to have greatest usefulness in connection with the more saline irrigation waters, and for this case it appears to be justifiable to disregard the salt removed from the soil in the harvested crops. Consider alfalfa growing in the Imperial Valley, California, where 6 tons per acre of sun-cured hay is a common annual yield. The salt added to the soil in the irrigation water consumed by this crop would be about 4 tons. Of this salt, not more than 0.4 ton would be removed in the harvested crop. Under these conditions, therefore, neglecting the salt removed in the crop overrates the salt input to the soil by a factor of about one-tenth. Taking $EC_{dw}=8$ and $EC_{iw}=1$, the calculated steady-state leaching requirement for salt-tolerant crops of the Imperial Valley is 13 percent. A fractional error of one-tenth in this value would not be serious, in view of other uncertainties involved in the practical use of the figure.

The relative significance of the salt removed in the harvested crop will increase as the salt input from irrigation water decreases, but for soils with normal drainage the practical usefulness of a calculated value of the leaching requirement decreases as the salinity of the irrigation water decreases. A special case exists where leaching is severely restricted by low soil permeability and the salt content of the water is also very low. Under these conditions, salt removed from the soil in the harvested crop might conceivably become an important factor determining the permanence of irrigation agriculture.

The steady-state leaching requirement (equation 2), expressed in terms of electrical conductivity, is convenient where soil moisture availability to plants and osmotic pressure relations are the principal concern. Cation exchange is known to effect a change in the relative composition of irrigation and drainage waters, but this process is stoichiometric and does not enter explicitly in the equation. It may happen, however, that with a particular irrigation water and a particular crop, some specific toxic constituent as, for example, the chloride ion or boron, might comprise the most critical problem. A leaching requirement for this constituent could then be calculated, provided some maximum permissible concentration of the toxic ion C_{dw} in the water draining from the soil can be specified and provided also that the other assumptions previously made are tenable. The leaching requirement equation then becomes:

$$\frac{D_{dw}}{D_{iw}} = \frac{C_{iw}}{C_{dw}} \qquad (7)$$

where C_{iw} is the concentration of the toxic ion in the irrigation water.

There will be instances, of course, where precipitation of soluble constituents in the soil cannot be neglected when calculating the leaching requirement. Gypsum is deposited in soils from some irrigation waters. Data are being accumulated on the precipitation of calcium and magnesium with bicarbonate in the irrigation water. This latter reaction is considered in chapter 5 on irrigation water quality. Taking precipitation effects into account complicates a leaching requirement equation and will not be included in the present discussion. It should be recalled again that the foregoing equations are based on the assumptions: uniform water application to the soil, no precipitation of soluble salt in the soil, negligible salt removal in the harvested crop, and soil permeability and drainage adequate to permit the required leaching.

Quantitative consideration of the leaching requirement is important when drainage is restricted or when the available irrigation water is efficiently used. If a large fraction of the water diverted for irrigation is wasted in various conveyance, regulatory, and, especially, application losses, then estimates of leaching requirement have little practical significance.

Leaching Methods

Leaching can be accomplished by ponding an appreciable depth of water on the soil surface by means of dikes or ridges and thus establishing downward water movement through the soil. This is the most effective procedure that can be used for removing excess soluble salts from soil. Contour checks can be used for ponding water on the soil where there is considerable slope. Contour borders ranging from 1.5 to 4 ft. or more high are constructed at elevation intervals ranging from 0.2 to 0.5 ft. Overflow gates, placed in the borders connecting adjacent plots, facilitate the control of water and allow a number of contour checks to be kept full simultaneously. Frequent applications of excess irrigation water applied by flooding between border strips while a crop is being grown are sometimes used for leaching. The effectiveness depends upon how uniformly the water is applied and how much water passes through the soil. Either continuous flooding or periodic water applications may be used for leaching. If the soil transmits water slowly, periodic drying may improve infiltration rates.

In cold climates, leaching operations can often be conducted in the fall after the crops mature and before the soil freezes. In warmer climates, leaching operations can be conducted during winter when the land would otherwise be idle. At this time, also, water may be more plentiful and the water table and drainage conditions more favorable than during the regular irrigation season. Unless drainage is adequate, attempts at leaching may not be successful, because leaching requires the free passage of water through and away from the root zone. Where drainage is inadequate, water applied for leaching may cause the water table to rise so that soluble salts can quickly return to the root zone.

Visible crusts of salt on the surface of saline soils have sometimes led to the use of surface flushing for salt removal, i. e., the passing of water over the soil surface and the wasting of the runoff water at the bottom of the field. This method does not appear to be sufficiently effective to be worth while for most field situations. All known tests of the flushing method under controlled conditions confirm this conclusion. Turbulence in the flowing water causes some mixing, but mostly the water at the soil surface that contacts and dissolves the salt moves directly into the dry soil during the initial wetting process when the infiltration rate is highest. In one test the salt added to the soil in the water used for flushing exceeded the amount of salt removed in the waste water.

The depth of water required for irrigation and leaching and the effect of leaching on the depth to water table can be estimated with the aid of the nomograms given in figure 8, chapter 2. The following examples will serve to illustrate the use of the nomograms in connection with irrigation, leaching, and drainage.

(a) For a uniform soil with an initial moisture percentage of 10, an upper limit of field moisture of 20 percent, and a bulk density of 1.6 gm. cm.$^{-3}$, how deeply will a 6-in. irrigation wet the soil? In the left nomogram of figure 8, place a straightedge on 1.6 of the scale B_1 and on 10 of scale A. Scale C_1 then indicates that 1.94 in. of water are required to raise the moisture content of 1 foot of this soil by 10 percent.

Therefore, $6/1.94 = 3.09$ ft. $= 37$ in. is the depth of wetting.

(b) For a uniform soil with an initial moisture content of 12.5 percent, an upper limit of field moisture of 25 percent, and a bulk density of 1.3 gm. cm.$^{-3}$, what depth of water must be applied to make 3 in. of water pass through the soil at the 4-ft. depth? Evidently the moisture content of the surface 4 ft. of soil must be increased by 12.5 percent before leaching will occur. Place a straightedge on 1.3 of the left nomogram of scale B_1 (fig. 8), and on 12.5 of scale A. Scale C_1 then indicates that 2 in. of water per foot of soil are required to change the moisture percentage of this soil from 12.5 to 25. Eight inches of water would be required to bring the top 4 ft. of soil to the upper limit of moisture retention, and therefore 11 in. of irrigation water should be applied in order to cause 3 in. of water to pass below the 4-ft. depth.

(c) For a uniform soil with a bulk density of 1.5 gm. cm.$^{-3}$ and an average moisture content of 20 percent over a depth interval of 1 foot above the water table, what depth of water in surface inches, when added to the ground water, will make the water table rise 1 foot? Assume the particle density (real density) of the soil is 2.65 gm. cm.$^{-3}$. In the right-hand nomogram of figure 8, place a straightedge on 1.5 of scale A_1 and on 2.65 of scale B_1. Scale C_1 then indicates a porosity of 0.44. Consequently, this soil when completely saturated will hold 0.44 ft. of water per foot of soil. In the left nomogram place a straightedge on 20 of scale A_1 and 1.5 of scale B_1. Scale C_2 then indicates that a moisture content of 20 percent corresponds to 0.3 ft. of water per foot of soil. Subtracting this from 0.44 indicates that 0.14 ft. of water per foot of soil, or (from scales C_1 and C_2) 1.7 surface inches of water is sufficient to bring 1-ft. depth of this soil to saturation and hence to cause a rise of approximately 1 foot in the ground-water level.

Field Leaching Trials

Numerous field trials have demonstrated the effectiveness of leaching for salt removal. For example, Reeve and coworkers (1948) found that gypsiferous, saline-alkali soils in the Delta Area, Utah, are reclaimable by leaching with 4 ft. of water. The right-hand curve in figure 12 shows the salt distribution with depth at the beginning of leaching tests. This soil had been idle for many years, with the water table fluctuating between 2 and 5 feet below the soil surface. Leaching treatments of 0, 1, 2, and 4 ft. of water were applied to test plots. The curves in the figure show the resulting change in salt content with depth. Wheat was planted and subsequently irrigated with 18 to 24 in. of water in 3 applications of 6 to 8 in. each. In addition, approximately 12 in. of rain fell during the winter months, making a total of 30 to 36 in. of water applied in addition to the initial differential leaching treatments. The increase in yield of wheat was approximately linear in relation to the depth of water used for leaching (fig. 13).

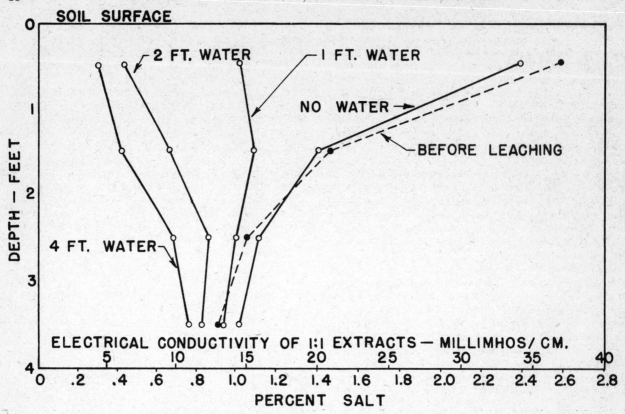

FIGURE 12.—Distribution of salt content with depth as related to depth of water applied for leaching in the Delta Area, Utah (Reeve and others, 1948).

Leaching practices, although basically the same, may vary from one region to another. In the Delta Area tests, the ponding method was used, and water was added in successive increments until the total amount for leaching had been applied. About 10 days were required to leach the plots with 4 ft. of water. In some parts of the Imperial and Central Valleys of California, where infiltration rates are low, water is ponded on the surface by the contour-check method for periods up to 120 days. In such instances, rice is sometimes grown to aid in the reclamation process and also to provide income during leaching. In other areas, rice is included regularly in the crop rotation as an aid in salinity control.

In addition to the removal of excess salts and exchangeable sodium, other practices are usually required for complete reclamation. Plant nutrients that are leached from the soil must be replaced, and fertilizer practices following leaching should compensate for plant nutrient losses. Nitrogen is the principal nutrient subject to leaching loss. Soil structure that may have deteriorated during the salinization or alkalization process must be restored. Unfavorable soil structure after leaching is sometimes a special problem and may be improved by adding manure or other forms of organic matter, by growing crops that are beneficial to structure, or by alternate wetting and drying, as indicated by the field tests of Reitemeier and associates (1948) and Bower and coworkers (1951).

Special Practices for Salinity Control

The failure to recognize that saline and alkali soils require special management practices can result in low production or in complete crop failure. These special practices can be followed over a period of time to improve lands that are partially affected or to prevent reclaimed lands from again becoming unproductive. Where only irrigation water of poor quality is available or where drainage and full-scale reclamation are not economically feasible, it may be possible to carry on successfully what might be referred to as "saline agriculture." Irrigation, leaching, and tillage practices can all be directed toward salinity control. Salt-tolerant crops can be selected and chemical amendments used when necessary.

Many crop failures result from growing crops that have low salt tolerance. Alfalfa, barley, sugar beets, and cotton are tolerant crops that can often be grown where salinity is a problem. Lists of salt-tolerant fruits, vegetables, field, and forage crops are given in chapter 4.

In general, irrigation methods and practices that provide uniformity of application and downward movement of water through soils favor salinity control. Methods that pond or flood water over the soil surface, such as border, check, and basin methods of irrigation, give greater uniformity of application than furrow or corrugation methods. Only part of the surface is covered by water with the furrow and corrugation methods so that movement of water is downward and outward from the furrow and is upward into the ridges. Wadleigh and Fireman (1949) have shown that by furrow irrigation excessive amounts of salts concentrate in the ridges. Salt distribution resulting from furrow irrigation in a test plot that was salinized initially to 0.2 percent is shown in figure 14. They further showed that cotton plants in the ridges extracted moisture mainly from beneath the furrows where leaching occurred and that there was little root activity in the ridges.

Germination and emergence of plants is often a critical factor in over-all production. Ayers (1951) has shown that the germination of seeds is greatly retarded and that the number of seeds germinating may be materially decreased by salinity. If favorable conditions can be maintained during the germination and seedling stages, certain crops may make fair growth even under moderately high salinity conditions. Heald and others (1950) conducted experiments in Washington on the preemergence irrigation of beets. They showed that irrigation next to the seed row caused movement of salts away from the seeds and into the ridges. This allowed the seeds to germinate and to become established in essentially nonsaline conditions, thereby increasing yield by increasing stand (fig. 15). Further over-all leaching increased sugar beet yields.

Careful leveling of land makes possible more uniform application of water and better salinity control. Barren spots that appear in otherwise productive fields are often the result of high spots that do not get sufficient water for good crop growth and likewise do not get sufficient water for leaching purposes. Lands that have been irrigated 1 or 2 years after leveling can often be improved by replaning. This removes the surface unevenness caused by the settling of fill material. Annual crops should be grown following land leveling, so that replaning after 1 or 2 years of irrigation can be accomplished without crop disturbance.

Crusting of the soil and failure of seedlings to emerge may indicate an alkali condition that might be corrected by amendments. Irrigating more frequently, especially during the germination and seedling stage, will tend to soften hard crusts and help to get a better stand.

Drainage of Irrigated Lands in Relation to Salinity Control

Drainage in agriculture is the process of removal of excess water from soil. Excess water discharged by flow over the soil surface is referred to as surface drainage, and flow through the soil is termed internal or subsurface drainage. The terms "artificial drain-

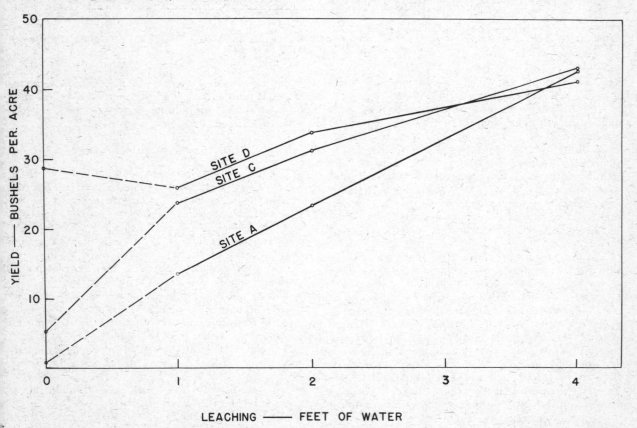

FIGURE 13.—Grain yields as related to the depth of water used for leaching in the Delta Area, Utah (Reeve and coworkers, 1948).

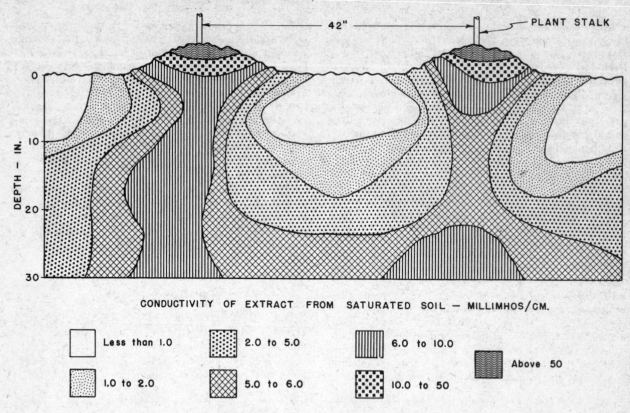

CONDUCTIVITY OF EXTRACT FROM SATURATED SOIL — MILLIMHOS/CM.

Less than 1.0   2.0 to 5.0   6.0 to 10.0   Above 50

1.0 to 2.0   5.0 to 6.0   10.0 to 50

FIGURE 14.—Salt distribution under furrow-irrigated cotton for soil initially salinized to 0.2 percent salt and irrigated with water of medium salinity (Wadleigh and Fireman, 1949).

age" and "natural drainage" indicate whether or not man has changed or influenced the drainage process.

Irrigated land is drained primarily to increase agricultural productivity, but there are other beneficial effects. Areas that are poorly drained require the expenditure of large sums of money annually for construction of highway subgrades and for safeguarding public health, since mosquito control and other disease problems are related to drainage conditions. Drainage improvements serve many public and private interests, and the justification for drainage improvements should be based upon all benefits that may be derived therefrom.

The drainage program for irrigated land should be initiated and continuously integrated with the development of the irrigation system in order to attain an efficient over-all water and salinity control program. The removal of excess water and salts must be considered in every irrigation enterprise. Excess water may be partially discharged or removed from the soil by natural means, but often supplementary drainage facilities are required. Irrigation practices, together with methods of distributing water, are related to drainage, and sometimes the need for artificial drainage facilities may be lessened or avoided altogether by efficient management of irrigation water.

The design of drainage systems is influenced by many factors, and there are no simple rules or formulas by which all of these factors can be taken into consideration. However, the principal factors can be grouped under drainage requirements, water-transmission properties of soil, and boundary conditions.

Drainage Requirements

The permissible depth and mode of variation of the water table with respect to the soil surface and the quantity of water that a drainage system must convey, both surface and subsurface, relate to drainage design and may be referred to as the drainage requirements. The climate, the quality of the irrigation water, the characteristics of the soil, the crops, and the cropping system must all be considered in the determination of drainage requirements for any given locality.

The adequacy of drainage for agricultural purposes depends upon whether or not there is an excess of water on or in the soil for periods of time that are detrimental to crops. Inadequate aeration of the soil may be a direct consequence of inadequate drainage and may result in a limitation of growth of plants or severe damage to root systems through pathological, physiological, or nutritional disturbances, or through limitation of the effective depth of the root zone. The optimum moisture content of the soil for tillage and other farming practices is also involved because farm operations can be seriously delayed by wet soil.

In irrigated regions the adequacy of drainage is related to salinity. Salts in the irrigation water, in the soil, or in shallow ground waters increase the drainage requirements. In addition to aeration effects and soil-moisture requirements for tillage, a minimum allowable water-table depth that will permit adequate leaching and that will prevent concentration of salts in the root zone by upward flow must be established. The depth to the water table must be such that upward flow of saline ground water into the root zone is reduced or eliminated. Thus, irrigation, leaching, and soil-management practices that are involved in the control of salinity are important in establishing drainage requirements.

As a minimum requirement, a drainage system must be adequate to remove from the soil the equivalent depth of water that must be passed through the root zone in order to maintain a favorable salt balance. With a knowledge of the consumptive use, the minimum amount of water required to be drained can be estimated by the use of equations 2 and 4:

$$LR = \frac{D_{dw}}{D_{iw}} = \frac{EC_{iw}}{EC_{dw}} \qquad (2)$$

$$D_{iw} = D_{cw} + D_{dw} \qquad (4)$$

Equation 2 gives the fraction of the water applied as irrigation that must pass through and beyond the root zone to maintain the electrical conductivity of the drainage water below a specified value (EC_{dw}) for the steady-state or long-time average salt-balance conditions. Equation 4 gives the depth of irrigation water (D_{iw}) as a function of consumptive use (D_{cw}) and the equivalent depth of drainage water (D_{dw}). Solving equation 2 for D_{iw}, substituting in equation 4, and rearranging gives:

$$D_{dw} = \frac{D_{cw}}{1 - LR} LR \qquad (8)$$

Expressing LR in this equation in terms of the conductivity ratio of equation 2 gives:

$$D_{dw} = \frac{EC_{iw}}{EC_{dw} - EC_{iw}} D_{cw} \qquad (9)$$

The depth of the water to be drained (D_{dw}) is thus expressed in terms of the electrical conductivity of the irrigation water and other conditions determined by the crop and climate; namely, consumptive use and salt tolerance of the crop. The salt tolerance of the crop is taken into account in the selection of permissible values of EC_{dw}. Equations 8 and 9 are subject to the assumptions made in deriving equation 2.

AT THINNING TIME FOLLOWING PRE-EMERGENCE IRRIGATION

AT MATURITY FOLLOWING NORMAL IRRIGATION

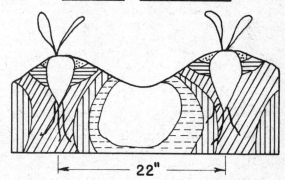

RELATIVE SALT CONCENTRATIONS

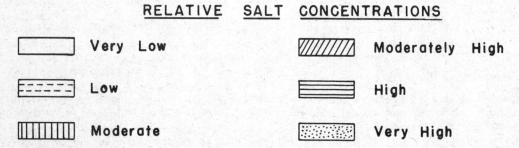

FIGURE 15.—Salt concentration in the vicinity of growing beets as related to position in the furrow (redrawn from Heald and others, 1950).

The term D_{dw} in the equation does not include drainage water that moves in laterally from adjacent areas and that must pass into and through the drainage system, but represents only the depth by which irrigation water, assumed to be applied uniformly at the soil surface, exceeds the consumptive use. For any specified EC_{dw}, which depends upon the salt tolerance of the crop, the depth of drainage water (D_{dw}) is the minimum depth of water that is required to be drained. This condition is satisfied when the previously defined leaching requirement is just met. For a value of $EC_{dw}=8$, which applies for moderately tolerant crops, and for irrigation waters of $EC_{iw}=0.5$, 1, 2, and 4 mmhos/cm., the depths of drainage water that must pass through the soil are 7, 14, 33, and 100 percent of the consumptive use (D_{cw}), respectively.

The passage of excess water through the root zone is accompanied by a decrease in the electrical conductivity of the drainage water. The equivalent depth of drainage water that is required to be drained (D_{dw}) from soil where irrigation water is applied inefficiently but uniformly may be estimated by substituting in equation 9 the electrical conductivity of the drainage water (EC_{dw}) as sampled and measured from the bottom of the root zone.

The depth of water that is drained beyond the root zone may also be expressed in terms of the water-application efficiency and the total depth of water applied or the consumptive use. The equation $E = D_{cw}/D_{iw}$ is based on the definition of water-application efficiency (Israelson, 1950), where E represents water-application efficiency and the other symbols are as previously defined. Solving this equation for D_{cw} in one case and for D_{dw} in the other, substituting in equation 4 and solving for D_{dw}, we obtain:

$$D_{dw} = D_{iw}(1-E) \qquad (10)$$

and

$$D_{dw} = D_{cw}\left(\frac{1}{E} - 1\right) \qquad (11)$$

Measured application efficiencies often run as low as 25 percent and seldom exceed 80 percent. Correspondingly, the water to be drained that comes directly from irrigation will range from 20 to 75 percent of the irrigation water applied and from 25 to 300 percent of the consumptive use. The total quantity or equivalent depth of water to be drained will be equal to that given by these equations plus that from other sources, such as seepage from canals and artesian aquifers. Seepage from canals is a major source of excess ground water in many areas, and seepage losses of 30 to 50 percent of the water diverted often occur.

Water-Transmission Properties of Soils

The principles and background theory for fluid flow in porous media are well known and are adequately treated in the literature. A discussion of the forces and properties determining the flow and distribution of water in soil, both saturated and unsaturated, and a description of measuring methods are given by Richards (1952). An important part of this background theory is embodied in the well-known Darcy equation, which in its generalized form states that for isotropic media the flow velocity, or specific discharge, is proportional to the hydraulic gradient and is in the direction of the greatest rate of decrease of hydraulic head.

The water-transmission properties of subsoils that cannot be controlled or changed appreciably have a direct bearing upon the design and layout of drainage systems. Soils, generally, are highly variable with respect to water-transmission properties, and it is necessary to assess the nonhomogeneity and to appraise the influence of soil variations on the direction and rate of flow of ground water.

Boundary Conditions

This concept is commonly used in the solution of flow problems and involves a geometric surface defining the boundaries of the problem along with hydraulic conditions over this surface, i. e., hydraulic head, hydraulic gradient, and flow. In other words, the external influences and constraints characterizing any given flow problem are included in the boundary conditions. While the root zone is the region of primary concern for agricultural drainage, a drainage problem may involve a considerably larger and deeper region. The upper and lateral bounding surfaces may be reasonably definite, but the lower boundary will depend on stratigraphy and hydraulic conditions. Many irrigated areas of the West are in alluvial valleys where topography and stratigraphy vary widely and where there may be diverse sources of ground water. The identification and delineation of these sources is especially important in establishing and defining boundary conditions.

Surface drains function mostly to eliminate water from the soil surface that may otherwise contribute to underground flow. Deep gravity drains, tile, and open ditches provide outflow points below the ground surface for controlling water-table depths and hence are a part of the boundary conditions. They are mostly less than 15 ft. deep because of construction limitations. Where conditions are favorable for pumping, water tables can usually be maintained at greater depths and thereby be controlled more effectively by pumping than by any other method. Most wells are installed to obtain water for irrigation, but often they also function to improve drainage conditions.

Layout and Placement of Drains

Drainage systems may consist of intercepting drains or relief-type drains, depending upon their location and function. Intercepting drains collect and divert water before it reaches the land under consideration, and relief drains are placed to remove water from the land being drained. Pumped wells, tile, or open drains may serve either of these purposes. Relief-type drains are used in broad valleys where the land has little slope, whereas intercepting drains more often are used in areas where topography is irregular. In areas of rolling or irregular topography, where lands of appreciable slope are irrigated, water that percolates downward through the surface soil often flows laterally through subsoil materials in the direction of the land slope. In these areas, seeps may be caused by a decrease in grade, a decrease in soil permeability, a thinning out of permeable underlying layers, the occurrence of dikes or water barriers, or the outcropping of relatively impermeable layers or hardpans. If the seepage water cannot be eliminated at its source, the placement of tile or open drains immediately above the seep to intercept such flows is usually the most effective procedure for solving this type of drainage problem.

Proper placement of drains is of considerable importance in the design of a drainage system. In nonuniform soils drainage systems may best be designed by considering the nature and extent of subsoil layers and by locating the drains with respect to these subsoil materials. Generally drains should be oriented perpendicular to the direction of ground-water flow and, where possible, should connect with sand and gravel layers or deposits. In soils of alluvial origin, the orientation of both permeable and impermeable deposits may be such that a few well-placed drains may control ground water over a much larger area than the same length of drain installed with uniform spacing in accordance with some arbitrary pattern. This has been demonstrated in a number of irrigated areas. For example, in the Grand Valley, Colorado, open drains that cut across and intercept sand and gravel deposits provide much more effective drainage than drains dug parallel to these deposits.

In areas where artesian conditions occur, drainage by tile and open drains is often impractical. Although the quantity of upward flow from an artesian source may be small, it usually exerts an important controlling effect on the height of the water table between drains. Artesian aquifers in many cases may be highly permeable and ideally located for drainage purposes, but they may be unavailable for receiving and discharging excess water applied at the soil surface because of the artesian pressure condition. Reduction of the water pressure in these aquifers by pumping or other means should be a first consideration.

The problem of flow into drains under falling water-table conditions has not been solved analytically. However, solutions have been developed for the ponded condition where drains are installed in saturated isotropic soil with a layer of water covering the surface. The falling water-table case typifies the drainage conditions in irrigated soils where it is desired to maintain adequate depth of water table between drains, whereas the ponded area more nearly represents conditions in humid regions where it is desired to remove excess water in short time periods following precipitation. Although the falling water-table condition differs appreciably from the ponded case, some of the important findings with the ponded area may have useful application for the falling water-table condition. For the ponded case, assuming isotropic soil, Kirkham (1949) concluded that "The most important single geometrical factor governing rate of seepage of water from soil into drains is the drain depth. Doubling the depth of drains will nearly double the rate of flow." For the falling water-table case, which is the usual condition in arid regions, the depth to the water table midway between drains is directly dependent upon the depth of the drains. For a given spacing, assuming soil conditions do not change with depth and other conditions remain constant, the depth to water table midway between drains increases directly with drain depth.

Proximity of drains to relatively impermeable layers is also an important consideration. Kirkham (1948, p. 59) states: "Drains should not be placed too near, on, or in an impervious layer. . . . It is found that lowering the drain onto or into an impervious layer, although increasing the hydraulic head, decreases the flow rate. . . ." He further states that "Drain shape (as well as size) appears to be unimportant in governing seepage rate into drains." From this, it is apparent that drain size should be determined primarily upon the basis of flow-velocity requirements. A gravel pack around tile drains is commonly used as a filter to allow free flow of water and at the same time to prevent sediment from entering the tile line.

Techniques for Drainage Investigations

A drainage investigation should provide information regarding the occurrence, flow, and disposition of excess water within a given basin or area. Information regarding hydrology, geology, meteorology, topography, and soils is needed and for some areas is already published and available. Reports of earlier drainage surveys should not be overlooked.

Measurements of Hydraulic Head

Inadequate drainage may be manifest by the presence of ponded water, marshy lands, and the growth of hydrophytic plants; but, in the absence of these obvious signs, depth to ground water is the most common index of the adequacy of drainage. Uncased observation wells are commonly used for determining the depth of the water table. Sometimes ground-water observation wells are lined with perforated casing. If there is a vertical component of flow, the true elevation of the water table is difficult to determine unless piezometers are used.

The water table is the elevation in the profile at which the soil water is at atmospheric pressure. This elevation corresponds to the bottom of the shallowest hole in which free water will collect. In a deeper hole or an observation well with perforated casing, the equilibrium elevation at which the water stands represents a balance between inflow and outflow for all the soil layers penetrated by the hole and may not be a useful hydraulic-head value.

The hydraulic head of ground water at each point in the soil is the elevation at which water stands in a riser connected to the point in question. There should be no leakage externally along such a riser or piezometer in order to insure that the elevation at which water stands in the piezometer is determined by the pressure in the ground water at the bottom end of the tube. This condition of external sealing is readily met under most field conditions for piezometers installed in accordance with Methods 35a and 35b. Measurements of hydraulic head and hydraulic gradient provide basic information on drainage conditions and the source and flow of ground water.

The number and arrangement of sites at which ground-water measurements should be made will depend upon the nature of the area in question and the purpose for which the measurements are made. In typical irrigated valleys information on both the adequacy of drainage and direction of ground-water flow is usually desired. Wells may be located to serve both purposes. Observation wells are often placed in a grid pattern for which spacing is selected to coincide with the land-survey system. In gently sloping areas, points of measurement can be farther apart than in areas of irregular topography. For determining the direction of the horizontal component of flow, water-table readings may be made at any desired spacing. More measurement sites are required in localities where there are abrupt changes in the slope of the water table.

Water-table contour maps and water-table isobath maps are useful in interpreting water-table data (Methods 36a and 36b). Profile flow patterns (Method 36c) may be used to show the nature of flow in cases where vertical as well as horizontal components of flow occur, such as sidehill seeps, seepage from canals, flow into drains, and upward flow from artesian aquifers. Water-table isopleths, which are described in Method 36d, can be used to show time fluctuations of the water table on a profile section.

Convenient methods for installing small-diameter piezometers have been described by Christiansen (1943), Pillsbury and Christiansen (1947), and Reger and others (1950). Piezometers may be installed by either driving or jetting as outlined in Methods 35a and 35b. The jetting technique provides a log of the nature and arrangement of subsoil materials in addition to the installation of a pipe for hydraulic-head readings. Piezometers 150 feet deep have been installed by this method.

Water levels in irrigation and domestic wells are often used for ground-water study. Water levels in such wells may or may not represent the water-table level. Deep-well readings should not be used as a measure of water table unless it can be definitely established by independent water-table measurements that the well reflects the true water-table level. Information regarding wells, such as total depth of well and depth of screens or perforations, is necessary in order to interpret well readings correctly.

Determination of Subsoil Stratigraphy

Hand augers, power augers, driven tubes, standard well-drilling equipment, and jetted piezometers can be used for studying subsoil materials and for locating and characterizing subsurface layers. The development of the jetting method of installing piezometers has made it possible to make subsoil investigations at only a fraction of the cost of augering or the use of well-drilling methods. Piezometers may be jetted for the sole purpose of determining subsoil stratigraphy, or the pipe may be left in place after the soil log is obtained as a permanent installation for hydraulic-head measurements.

Subsoil logs from jetted piezometers are usually made on the basis of texture, since information on texture provides an indication of the water-transmission properties of soils. Depths of strata changes may sometimes be obtained to within ±0.1 ft. by this method, and soil layers can be distinguished that are too thin to be logged by well-drilling methods. An estimate of the texture and consolidation of the material is made from the vibration or feel of the pipe to the hands during the downward motion, from the rate of downward progress, from the examination of sediments carried by the effluent, and from the observation of color changes that occur in the effluent. (See Method 35b.)

Standard well-drilling equipment may be used for obtaining samples of subsurface materials and for logging underground strata. Logs of irrigation, domestic, or municipal water-supply wells that have been drilled in an area may usually be found in either county or State governmental offices. Some States require well drillers to file with the State engineer a log of each well drilled. Such logs provide useful information regarding the major clay layers and principal water-bearing aquifers. They are often deficient in pertinent details, however, especially concerning subsoil changes at shallow depths. In interpreting well logs the method of drilling should be taken into consideration. Logs of wells drilled by bailing methods, where sediments are actually obtained and examined from within a limited depth range, are usually more reliable than logs obtained by other drilling methods.

Hand augers and driven tubes are generally limited to depths less than 20 ft. They are used mainly for appraising stratigraphy near the surface. Power augers of various types are commercially available that can be used to depths of 60 ft. or more. In sandy soils it is sometimes necessary to case the hole with pipe or tubing as augering progresses in order to get a hole drilled to the desired depth and to obtain samples.

Undisturbed cores, 4 in. in diameter and from depths up to 10 ft., can be obtained by use of the power-driven core-sampling machine, an earlier model of which has been described by Kelley and coworkers (1948). This machine is trailer mounted and is usable over terrain passable to trucks. Soil cores are useful for the observation of structure and for making various physical measurements on undisturbed subsoil materials. Cracks, root holes, and fine sand lenticles may be overlooked with augering and other sampling methods, but these are preserved for examination in an undisturbed core.

Determination of Water-Transmitting Properties of Soils

In addition to determining the position and extent of subsoil materials as outlined above, information on the rates at which soils transmit water is required in planning and designing drainage systems. *Soils are extremely variable with regard to water transmission.* The heterogeneous nature in which most alluvial soils are deposited adds materially to the problem of assessing their water-transmitting properties. Soils formed both in place and by alluvial deposition may be extremely variable not only in a lateral direction but with depth as well. The problem of appraising the water-transmitting properties of soils involves measurements by suitable methods at representative sites or on representative samples.

The ratio of the waterflow velocity to the hydraulic gradient is called the hydraulic conductivity. This is the proportionality factor in the Darcy equation. This quantity varies over a range, as much as 100,000 to 1, in earth materials in which drainage operations are conducted. Hydraulic conductivity is often related to texture, coarse soils having high conductivity. Particle-size distribution may also be an important factor. Porous media with uniform particle sizes tend to be more permeable than materials having a more or less continuous range of sizes.

The hydraulic conductivity of soils, although related in a general way to texture, depends also upon soil structure. Soils near the surface that may be dry much of the time and are subject to alternate wetting and drying, freezing and thawing, plant root action, and alteration by other biological processes may exhibit entirely different water-transmitting properties than soils of similar texture below a water table. From the standpoint of drainage the latter are of greater importance, since subsurface drainage is concerned largely with water movement below the water table.

Hydraulic conductivity can be measured for disturbed samples or undisturbed cores in the laboratory or for undisturbed soil in the field. Measurements on disturbed samples of aquifer materials may be satisfactory for drainage investigation purposes, if the samples are packed to field density. Methods for making such measurements are summarized by Wenzel (1942).

Several methods have been developed for measuring the hydraulic conductivity of soil in place in the field below a water table. A procedure developed by Diserens (1934) and Hooghoudt (1936) in Holland makes use of the rate of water seepage into an auger hole below the water table and is described in Method 34d. The mathematical treatment developed by Kirkham and Van Bavel (1949) for this method assumes homogeneous isotropic soil, but hydraulic-conductivity determinations by this method in nonuniform soils may be taken as average or effective values. The auger-hole method is limited to soils below a water table in which the walls of the auger hole are stable. With the use of suitable screens it may also be used in sands or other noncohesive soils.

The piezometer method, based on the analysis by Kirkham (1946), has been adapted for large diameter tubes by Frevert and Kirkham (1949) and for small diameter pipes by Luthin and Kirkham (1949). The latter procedure is particularly suitable for determining the hydraulic conductivity of individual layers of soil. It is essentially a cased auger hole in which an opening or cavity is placed at any desired depth in the soil, following the procedure outlined in Method 34c.

Drainage design may be influenced by the fact that both uniform and nonuniform soils may be anisotropic with respect to hydraulic conductivity, i. e., the conductivity may vary with direction in the soil. Alternate lenses of coarse and fine sediments are commonly found in alluvial soils and usually conduct water more readily in a horizontal than a vertical direction. The above field methods may be useful in obtaining information on the degree to which soils are anisotropic. Reeve and Kirkham (1951) point out that field methods in which long cavities with respect to the diameter are used, such as is usually the case with both the auger-hole and the small-pipe piezometer methods, measure essentially the hydraulic conductivity in a horizontal direction, whereas the large-diameter tube method, which has a horizontal inflow surface, essentially measures conductivity for vertical flow. Hydraulic conductivity in any desired direction can be measured with undisturbed cores.

Since most soils are not uniform, the problem of appraising the water-transmitting properties, as related to depth and spacing of drains, involves not only the method of measurement but also a statistical problem of sampling as well. The number of samples required for soil appraisal is increased if the soil is highly variable or if the samples are small in size. Reeve and Kirkham (1951) showed that the effective sizes of sample associated with a small core (2-in. diam. × 2 in. long), a piezometer (1-in. diam. × 4-in. cavity), a tube (8-in. diam. with a cavity length equal to zero), and an auger hole (4-in. diam. × 30 in. deep), are in the ratio of 1, 35, 270, and 1,400, respectively; the latter three values being based on the region in which 80 percent of the hydraulic-head difference is dissipated. It is apparent that field methods for appraising conductivity on large undisturbed volumes of soil have distinct advantages over laboratory methods.

Information on the water conductance of subsurface aquifers often has application to drainage appraisal and can be obtained from well tests. High specific yield, i. e., high rate of flow per unit drawdown, indicates high aquifer permeability and vice versa. Data from existing wells can be used or new wells can be drilled. Wenzel (1942) has summarized and discussed the equations and methods used by a number of investigators of pumped wells. Theis (1935) presented equations for flow into wells for nonequilibrium conditions, and Jacob (1940, 1947) reviewed the principles of flow in artesian aquifers. Peterson and coworkers (1952) have developed equations and procedures for study of ground-water flow to wells for the steady-state or equilibrium condition.

Chemical Amendments for Replacement of Exchangeable Sodium

The kind and amount of chemical amendment to be used for the replacement of exchangeable sodium in soils depend upon the soil characteristics, the desired rate of replacement, and economic considerations.

Suitability of Various Amendments Under Different Soil Conditions

Chemical amendments that are applied to alkali soils are of three types:

Amendments for alkali soils:	Chemicals
Soluble calcium salts_____	Calcium chloride
	Gypsum
Acids or acid-formers_____	Sulfur
	Sulfuric acid
	Iron sulfate
	Aluminum sulfate
	Lime-sulfur
Calcium salts of low solubility____	Ground limestone
(May also contain magnesium)	Byproduct lime from sugar factories

While each type of amendment has a place in reclamation, effectiveness under different soil conditions is governed by several factors, the principal ones being the alkaline-earth carbonate content and the pH reading. From the standpoint of their response to the various types of amendments, alkali soils may be divided into three classes: (1) Soils containing alkaline-earth carbonates, (2) soils having a pH reading greater than 7.5 but practically free of alkaline-earth carbonates, and (3) soils having a pH reading of less than 7.5 and containing no alkaline-earth carbonates.

Any of the soluble calcium salts, acids, or acid-formers may be used on soils in class 1, but limestone will be of no value. The addition of acid or acid-forming amendments to soils in classes 2 and 3 tends to make them acid in reaction. When the amount of acid or acid-forming amendment needed for reclamation is sufficient to make the soil excessively acid, the choice of amendment is limited to soluble calcium salts, unless limestone also is applied. In general the acidification of soils of arid regions to a pH reading as low as 6 to 6.5 is usually beneficial to plant growth. To determine if the amount of acid or acid-former needed for reclamation is sufficient to cause excess acidity, the amendment can be applied at the desired rate to a sample of the soil and a pH reading can be obtained after the reaction is complete. If the addition of sulfur, which reacts slowly in the soil, is contemplated, the addition of a chemically equivalent amount of sulfuric acid may be useful to predict the pH reading that may eventually be obtained upon complete oxidation of the sulfur. While the application of limestone alone to soils of classes 2 and 3 will tend to be beneficial, the effectiveness of lime on different soils varies markedly, inasmuch as the solubility of $CaCO_3$ decreases with increasing pH reading. Data on $CaCO_3$ solubility in

relation to pH reading are given by De Sigmond (1938) as follows:

pH value of $CaCO_3$ saturated solution:	Solubility of $CaCO_3$ (Meq./l.)
6.21_____	19.3
6.50_____	14.4
7.12_____	7.1
7.85_____	2.7
8.60_____	1.1
9.20_____	.82
10.12_____	.36

Sodium carbonate or carbon dioxide was used to obtain pH readings above or below 7. On the basis of these data it is apparent that the effectiveness of limestone as an amendment is markedly decreased at pH readings above 7.5, whereas it may be quite effective at pH readings below 7. Hence, limestone may be used to advantage on class 3 soils, but its value on class 2 soils is questionable. Some soils that contain excess exchangeable sodium also contain appreciable exchangeable hydrogen and, therefore, have an acid reaction. In Hungary large areas of such soils have been quickly and effectively reclaimed by the addition of chalk ($CaCO_3$).

Chemical Reactions of Various Amendments in Alkali Soils

The following chemical equations illustrate the manner in which various amendments react in the different classes of alkali soils. In these equations the letter X represents the soil exchange complex.

Class 1. Soils Containing Alkaline-Earth Carbonates

GYPSUM.—$2NaX + CaSO_4 \rightleftharpoons CaX_2 + Na_2SO_4$

SULFUR.—

(1) $2S + 3O_2 \rightleftharpoons 2SO_3$ (microbiological oxidation)
(2) $SO_3 + H_2O \rightleftharpoons H_2SO_4$
(3) $H_2SO_4 + CaCO_3 \rightleftharpoons CaSO_4 + CO_2 + H_2O$ [8]
(4) $2NaX + CaSO_4 \rightleftharpoons CaX_2 + Na_2SO_4$

LIME-SULFUR (CALCIUM POLYSULFIDE).—

(1) $CaS_5 + 8O_2 + 4H_2O \rightleftharpoons CaSO_4 + 4H_2SO_4$
(2) $H_2SO_4 + CaCO_3 \rightleftharpoons CaSO_4 + CO_2 + H_2O$ [8]
(3) $2NaX + CaSO_4 \rightleftharpoons CaX_2Na_2SO_4$

IRON SULFATE.—

(1) $FeSO_4 + H_2O \rightleftharpoons H_2SO_4 + FeO$
(2) $H_2SO_4 + CaCO_3 \rightleftharpoons CaSO_4 + CO_2 + H_2O$ [8]
(3) $2NaX + CaSO_4 \rightleftharpoons CaX_2 + Na_2SO_4$

---

[8] The reaction of H_2SO_4 and $CaCO_3$ may also be written as follows: $H_2SO_4 + 2CaCO_3 \rightleftharpoons CaSO_4 + Ca(HCO_3)_2$. Under these conditions the $Ca(HCO_3)_2$ as well as the $CaSO_4$ would be available for reaction with exchangeable sodium and 1 atom of sulfur when oxidized to H_2SO_4 could theoretically result in the replacement of 4 sodium ions by calcium. Kelley (1951, p. 135) found under field conditions that approximately 3 exchangeable sodium ions per atom of sulfur were replaced, whereas a greenhouse-pot experiment conducted at this Laboratory indicated that the reaction takes place without the formation of appre-

Class 2. Soils Containing No Alkaline-Earth Carbonates; pH 7.5 or Higher

GYPSUM.—Same as in class 1.

SULFUR.—Steps (1) and (2) as in class 1.

$$(3)\ 2NaX + H_2SO_4 \rightleftharpoons 2HX + Na_2SO_4$$

LIME-SULFUR.—Step (1) as in class 1.

$$(2)\ 10NaX + 4H_2SO_4 + CaSO_4 \rightleftharpoons 8HX + CaX_2 + 5Na_2SO_4$$

IRON SULFATE.—Step (1) as in class 1.

$$(2)\ 2NaX + H_2SO_4 \rightleftharpoons 2HX + Na_2SO_4$$

LIMESTONE.—Two possibilities suggested by Kelley and Brown (1934) are:

$$(1)\ 2NaX + CaCO_3 \rightleftharpoons CaX_2 + Na_2CO_3$$
$$(1)\ NaX + HOH \rightleftharpoons NaOH + HX$$
$$(2)\ 2HX + CaCO_3 \rightleftharpoons CaX + CO_2 + H_2O$$

Class 3. Soils Containing No Alkaline-Earth Carbonates; pH Less Than 7.5

GYPSUM.—Same as in class 1 and 2.

SULFUR.—Same as in class 2.

LIME-SULFUR.—Same as in class 2.

IRON SULFATE.—Same as in class 2.

LIMESTONE.—Same as in class 2, and if exchangeable hydrogen is present:

$$(1)\ 2HX + CaCO_3 \rightleftharpoons CaX_2 + CO_2 + H_2O$$

Estimation of Amounts of Various Amendments Needed for Exchangeable-Sodium Replacement

Exchangeable sodium and cation-exchange-capacity determinations serve as valuable guides for estimating the amounts of chemical amendments needed to reduce the exchangeable-sodium-percentages of alkali soils to given levels. The procedure for estimating the amount of amendment needed for a given set of conditions can be illustrated by an example. Suppose the 0 to 12-in. layer of an alkali soil contains 4 meq. of exchangeable sodium per 100 gm. and has a cation-exchange-capacity of 10 meq. per 100 gm. The exchangeable-sodium-percentage is therefore 40. It is desired to reduce the exchangeable-sodium-percentage to about 10. This will necessitate the replacement of 3 meq. of exchangeable sodium per 100 gm. Assuming quantitative replacement, it will be necessary to apply the amendment at the rate of 3 meq. per 100 gm. of soil. By referring to table 6, which relates tons of gypsum and sulfur per acre-foot of soil to milliequivalents of sodium per 100 gm. of soil, it is found that 5.2 tons of gypsum or 0.96 ton of sulfur are required. If it is desired to use amendments other than gypsum or sulfur, the supple-

ciable amounts of Ca (HCO₃)₂. A high soil-moisture level, low soil temperatures, and the release of CO₂ by plant roots would favor the formation of Ca (HCO₃)₂ as a product of the reaction.

mentary data given below will be helpful in converting the tons of sulfur found to be needed in table 6 to tons of other amendments.

Amendment:	Tons equivalent to 1 ton of sulfur
Sulfur	1.00
Lime-sulfur solution, 24 percent sulfur	4.17
Sulfuric acid	3.06
Gypsum $(CaSO_4 \cdot 2H_2O)$	5.38
Iron sulfate $(FeSO_4 \cdot 7H_2O)$	8.69
Aluminum sulfate $(Al_2(SO_4)_3 \cdot 18H_2O)$	6.94
Limestone $(CaCO_3)$	3.13

TABLE 6.—Amounts of gypsum and sulfur required to replace indicated amounts of exchangeable sodium

Exchangeable sodium (Meq. per 100 gm. of soil)	Gypsum [1] $(CaSO_4 \cdot 2H_2O)$	Gypsum [1] $(CaSO_4 \cdot 2H_2O)$	Sulfur (S)	Sulfur (S)
	Tons/acre-foot [2]	Tons/acre-6 inches [3]	Tons/acre-foot [2]	Tons/acre-6 inches [3]
1	1.7	0.9	0.32	0.16
2	3.4	1.7	.64	.32
3	5.2	2.6	.96	.48
4	6.9	3.4	1.28	.64
5	8.6	4.3	1.60	.80
6	10.3	5.2	1.92	.96
7	12.0	6.0	2.24	1.12
8	13.7	6.9	2.56	1.28
9	15.5	7.7	2.88	1.44
10	17.2	8.6	3.20	1.60

[1] The amounts of gypsum are given to the nearest 0.1 ton.
[2] 1 acre-foot of soil weighs approximately 4,000,000 pounds.
[3] 1 acre-6 inches of soil weighs approximately 2,000,000 pounds.

The reaction between an amendment such as gypsum and exchangeable sodium is an equilibrium reaction and, therefore, does not go entirely to completion. The extent to which the reaction goes to completion is determined by the interaction of several factors, among which are the differences in the replacement energies of calcium and sodium, the exchangeable-sodium-percentage, and the total cation concentration of the soil solution. For the usual case where a quantity of gypsum equivalent to the amount of exchangeable sodium present in the surface 6- or 12-in. layer of soil is applied, some progress has been made in determining the percentage of the applied calcium that reacts with exchangeable sodium. The available data indicate that when the exchangeable-sodium-percentage of the soil exceeds 25, 90 percent or more of the calcium supplied by the amendment replaces exchangeable sodium as the soil is leached. The percentage of added calcium that replaces exchangeable sodium does not become less than 50 until the exchangeable-sodium-percentage becomes less than 10. It should be pointed out that under the above conditions not all of the replacement of exchangeable sodium takes place in the depth of soil upon which the application is based, although the greater part of it does. As a general rule, it is suggested that the rates of gypsum and sulfur application indicated by table 6 be multiplied by the factor 1.25 to compensate for the lack of quantitative replacement.

A simple test based on the work of McGeorge and Breazeale (1951) has been proposed by Schoonover for determining the gypsum requirement[9] of alkali soils. The test, which is given as Method 22d, involves an arbitrary procedure and does not measure a distinct chemical property of the soil. The relation between the exchangeable-sodium content and the gypsum requirement, as determined by Method 22d, of 29 non-gypsiferous soil samples has been studied at the Laboratory. The ranges in various characteristics of the samples were as follows: electrical conductivity of the saturation extract, 0.2 to 30 mmhos/cm.; exchangeable-sodium-percentage, 6.3 to 65.5; and exchangeable-potassium-percentage, 2.1 to 27.3. As indicated by a correlation coefficient of 0.96, a good relation was found between exchangeable-sodium content and gypsum requirement. For soil samples having exchangeable-sodium contents ranging from 0.1 to 12 meq./100 gm., the relation between the two variables is expressed by the equation: Exchangeable sodium, milliequivalents/100 gm. $= 0.96 + 0.99 \times$ gypsum requirement, milliequivalents/100 gm.[9] Inasmuch as Method 22d gives a good estimate of the exchangeable-sodium content of these alkali soils, it would appear to be useful for estimating the amount of gypsum needed when information on the exchangeable-sodium content and the cation-exchange-capacity is not otherwise available. Amounts of gypsum can be converted to quantities of other chemical amendments by the use of table 6 and data on page 49.

Speed of Reaction of Amendments and Economic Considerations

The choice of a chemical amendment may be influenced by the time required for its reaction in the soil. In general, the cheaper amendments are slower to react. Consequently, if immediate replacement of exchangeable sodium is desired, one of the quicker acting but more expensive amendments will be needed.

Owing to its high solubility in water, calcium chloride is probably the most readily available source of soluble calcium, but it is seldom used because of its cost. Sulfuric acid and iron and aluminum sulfates that hydrolyze readily in the soil to form sulfuric acid

are also quick-acting amendments. Sulfuric acid is often cheap enough for field application, but the use of iron and aluminum sulfates usually is not economically feasible. Because of their relatively low cost, gypsum and sulfur are the most common amendments used for reclamation. The rate of reaction of gypsum in replacing sodium is limited only by its solubility in water; its solubility is about 0.25 percent at ordinary temperatures. The presence of sodium and chloride ions in the water increases the solubility of gypsum, whereas calcium and sulfate ions tend to decrease its solubility. Limited data indicate that the application of 3 to 4 ft. of irrigation water is sufficient to dissolve 4 or 5 tons/acre of agricultural gypsum having a degree of fineness such that 85 percent will pass a 100-mesh sieve.

As sulfur must first be oxidized by microbial action to the sulfate form to be available for reaction, it is usually classed as a slow-acting amendment. McGeorge and Greene (1935) have shown in laboratory studies of Arizona soils that sulfur applications of about 1 ton/acre are rapidly and usually completely oxidized in 2 or 3 weeks under favorable moisture and temperature conditions. Larger applications required more time for complete oxidation. They also found that within the usual particle-size limits of agricultural sulfur, the coarse-grade material was practically as effective as the finer and more expensive grades. In spite of these findings, various agriculturists frequently report incomplete oxidation of sulfur in soils a year or more after application. Often this appears to be caused by the presence of lumps of the sulfur and insufficient mixing of the amendment with the soil following application.

As previously mentioned, the solubility of limestone when applied to alkali soils is markedly influenced by the pH reading and by the presence of exchangeable hydrogen. Unless the soil is decidedly acid, the chemical reaction of limestone is slow. Particle size is also an important factor affecting the rate at which limestone, gypsum, and sulfur react in soils. The finer the particle size the more rapid the reaction.

There is considerable interest at present in the use of lime-sulfur as an amendment. Lime-sulfur is a brown, highly alkaline liquid containing calcium polysulfides and some calcium thiosulfate. The calcium content is ordinarily about one-fourth that of the sulfur content, and its action depends mostly on the sulfur content. Usually the material is applied in irrigation water. Like elemental sulfur, it must first be oxidized to sulfuric acid and then react with alkaline-earth carbonates to produce a soluble form of calcium.

Application of Amendments

From the standpoint of efficiency in replacing exchangeable sodium, it is advantageous to leach most of the soluble salts out of the soil before applying chemical amendments. As a result of the removal of soluble salts, a higher proportion of the calcium supplied by the addition of amendments is adsorbed by the soil-

---

[9] SCHOONOVER, W. R. EXAMINATION OF SOILS FOR ALKALI. University of California Extension Service, Berkeley, California. 1952. [Mimeographed.]

In a private communication, C. D. Moodie of the Washington Agricultural Experiment Station has reported a study of the relation between the gypsum requirement and the exchangeable-sodium contents of soils from the Yakima Valley, Washington. A relation similar to that obtained by Schoonover was obtained for soils containing low amounts of exchangeable potassium, but for soils containing high amounts of exchangeable potassium the slope of the regression line was considerably lower. Thus, estimates of the exchangeable-sodium content based on the gypsum requirement and the equation given in this handbook may be high if the soil contains large amounts of exchangeable potassium.

exchange complex. The advantage gained through increased efficiency in exchangeable-sodium replacement by leaching prior to the application of amendments may be more than offset by the decrease in soil permeability that usually accompanies the leaching of saline-alkali soil. Whether amendments should be applied before or after removal of soluble salts, therefore, will depend upon permeability relationships.

Such chemical amendments as gypsum, sulfur, and limestone are normally applied broadcast and then incorporated with the soil by means of a disk or plow. Thorough incorporation is especially important when sulfur is used to insure rapid oxidation to the sulfate form. Because of hazards in handling, the application of sulfuric acid is difficult under ordinary field conditions. However, special equipment is now available that sprays the concentrated acid on the soil surface. Although chemical amendments are ordinarily applied to the surface, deeper placement may be advantageous if the exchangeable-sodium accumulation occurs uniformly in the subsoil, or B horizon. While there appears to be no information on the subject, it is possible to obtain deep placement by distributing the amendment behind a plow or subsoiler.

Amendments are sometimes applied in the irrigation water. Special equipment for treating irrigation waters with gypsum has been described by Fullmer (1950). A simple method of treatment consists in placing a bag of gypsum with the side slit open in the irrigation ditch, preferably at a weir where the water has considerable turbulence.

Except where sulfur is used, saline-alkali soils should be leached immediately following the application of amendments. Leaching dissolves and carries the amendment downward, and it also removes the soluble sodium salts that form as a result of cation exchange. Soils receiving sulfur ordinarily should not be leached until sufficient time has been allowed for most of the sulfur to oxidize and form gypsum, but the soils should be kept moist, as moisture is essential to the process of microbial oxidation.

Improvement of the physical condition of alkali soils involves the rearrangement and aggregation of soil particles as well as the replacement of exchangeable sodium. This has been demonstrated and emphasized by Gardner (1945). The rearrangement of soil particles so as to improve physical condition is facilitated by alternate wetting and drying, by alternate freezing and thawing, and by the action of plant roots.

Laboratory and Greenhouse Tests as Aids to Diagnosis

While physical and chemical analyses made on saline and alkali soil samples provide basic data that may be needed to ascertain the cause of low productivity and the treatments required for reclamation, supplementary tests conducted on soil columns or in greenhouse pots are often helpful in obtaining satisfactory answers to soil problems. Such tests may be used to verify conclusions reached on the basis of physical and chemical tests or to check on how the soil responds to indicated treatments for improvement. It should be recognized, however, that plant growth on saline and alkali soils contained in small pots may be at variance with growth obtained under field conditions. Laboratory and greenhouse tests are less costly, less laborious, and less time-consuming than field tests and often provide valuable clues as to the behavior of the soil in the field. Generally, all but the more promising procedures for improving saline and alkali soils can be eliminated by laboratory and greenhouse studies.

Laboratory tests on soil columns may be used to estimate the amount of leaching needed for removal of excess soluble salts; to determine the response of soils to the addition of various kinds and amounts of amendments; and to determine the changes in such soil properties as permeability, pH reading, and exchangeable-sodium-percentage that take place upon leaching. Determinations on soil columns are especially useful in the diagnosis of saline-alkali soils, as the characteristics of these soils usually change markedly upon being leached.

It would be best to conduct tests on undisturbed soil cores. A power-driven soil sampler capable of taking 4-inch diameter cores to a depth of 10 feet has been developed by Kelley and associates (1948). In the absence of a core sampler, disturbed samples representing the various soil layers may be packed in tubes of convenient diameter and length. A technique similar to that used for making hydraulic-conductivity measurements on disturbed soil samples can be used in setting up these soil columns. Leaching and amendment treatments may then be applied to the soil columns, and the effects upon water-movement rates noted. Changes in soluble-salt content, pH reading, and exchangeable-sodium status obtained by various treatments may be determined by removing the treated soil from the tube and making the appropriate analyses.

Greenhouse tests are useful when it is desired to obtain information on plant-growth responses. They may be used for various purposes such as to determine whether the soil contains sufficient soluble salt or exchangeable sodium to affect plant growth adversely, to determine plant response to leaching and the addition of chemical amendments, and to estimate the fertilizer needs of saline and alkali soils (Bower and Turk, 1946).

Greenhouse pot tests may be conducted under various conditions. The procedure to be followed will depend upon the facilities available, the kind of plant to be grown, and the purpose of the tests. A few suggestions for conducting greenhouse tests are:

(a) If possible, use the crop or crops to be grown in the field.

(b) Use containers of soil as large as feasible. If leaching treatments are to be employed, provision should be made for measuring the volume and salt content of the leachate.

(c) An attempt should be made to grow the crop during its normal season and to avoid excessive temperatures that are often obtained under greenhouse conditions.

(d) Replicate each treatment at least twice and arrange each set of treatments in randomized blocks.

(e) If possible, irrigate with water having the same composition as that to be used in the field.

(f) If the soil has been leached or amendments applied, it may be desirable to analyze the soil at the conclusion of the test to determine the changes in the soil properties that have taken place.

Although this handbook is not primarily concerned with soil fertility, it should be recognized that saline and alkali soils, like other soils of arid regions, usually respond markedly to nitrogen and phosphorus fertilization. Adequate fertilization after the removal of excess soluble salts and exchangeable sodium is usually required to obtain maximum productivity. The greenhouse technique devised by Jenny and coworkers (1950) for determining nutrient level and fertilizer response is suggested as a possible method for determining the fertilizer requirements of saline and alkali soils.

Reclamation Tests in the Field

Leaching operations and the application of amendments in the field usually entail considerable expense. Therefore, before attempting the improvement of saline and alkali soils on a large scale, it is frequently desirable to determine whether a proposed treatment will be successful. Often this can be ascertained on an experimental basis by the use of field plots. It is not the purpose of this section to give methods for conducting field-plot experiments of the research type. However, procedures are given that are considered adequate for testing treatments involving leaching, cultural practices, and the application of amendments. Tests in which drainage is a treatment are difficult to conduct on a plot basis and, hence, will not be considered.

Saline and alkali soils usually are extremely variable in nature, their characteristics often changing markedly over relatively short distances. Therefore, considerable care should be taken to select a test area that is as uniform as possible and yet representative of the soils to be considered. Examination and tests of soil samples from various locations over the proposed test area are valuable in determining soil uniformity. Sometimes it is difficult to locate a single area of sufficient size and uniformity to conduct the test. Then it is advisable to place individual replications on separate areas within the field.

Selection of the size and shape of plots is influenced by the kinds of treatments to be used, the crop to be grown, the method of applying water, and the amount of space needed for the operation of equipment. Ordinarily, the plots should be as small as possible, as this tends to reduce soil variability within the test area. If at all feasible, a border or dike should be constructed around each plot to control the application of water. This permits the impounding of water for leaching and the estimation of infiltration rates. Tests that involve only the application of amendments such as gypsum or manure may be conducted on plots as small as 15 ft. by 15 ft. On such plots, the amendments can be applied by hand. When leaching is a differential treatment, plots of somewhat larger size are needed, as border effects may be of considerable magnitude in small plots. Leaching tests have been satisfactorily conducted on $\frac{1}{50}$-acre plots. Cultural treatments, such as subsoiling and deep plowing, may require the use of fairly large plots to permit operation of the machinery. From the standpoint of minimizing border effects, plots should be as nearly square as possible. Square plots are usually convenient to handle when the land is flood-irrigated, but when the slope of the land is such that water must be applied in furrows or corrugations a long narrow plot must be used. Cropping procedure and tillage operations must also be considered in selecting the shape of the plot.

The design of field-plot tests is governed primarily by the treatments to be used (fig. 16). The simplest design is that in which the various treatments are arranged in blocks and located at random, each treatment occurring only once in each block. Individual blocks serve as replications. This design is satisfactory for comparing various amendments or cultural practices or for testing the effect of leaching. If the test involves a combination of amendments and leaching or cultural treatments, it is advantageous to employ a split-plot design in which leaching or cultural treatments constitute main plots and the amendment treatments consist of subplots. Owing to the marked variability of saline and alkali soils, it is recommended that treatments be replicated at least four times. All treatments within each replicate block should be located at random.

The improvement of saline and alkali soils may be evaluated by means of plant-growth responses, soil analyses, and determinations such as infiltration rate. When the problem is one of excess salinity only, determinations of crop yields on the various plots often will suffice for the evaluation of the treatments. If facilities are available, it is also advisable to determine by analysis the soluble-salt content of the soil before and after treatment. In alkali soils where poor physical condition is a problem, the effect of the treatments upon the soil as well as upon plant growth should be determined. Changes in the exchangeable-sodium content of the soil upon treatment may be determined by soil analyses, whereas improvement in water-transmission properties may be estimated by means of infiltration measurements. Estimates of infiltration rates are readily obtained when individual plots are flood-irrigated. Infiltration rates on furrow-irrigated plots may be estimated by measuring the amount of water applied to the plot and the amount that runs off.

Applications of chemical amendments influence both the physical and chemical properties of alkali soils. In studying the response of plants on alkali soils to the application of chemical amendments, it may be desir-

LEACHING OR CULTURAL TREATMENTS
(BASIN IRRIGATION)

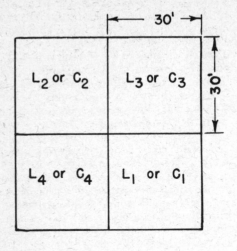

AMENDMENT TREATMENTS
(BASIN IRRIGATION)

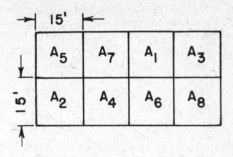

COMBINATION OF AMENDMENT AND LEACHING OR CULTURAL TREATMENTS
(BASIN IRRIGATION)

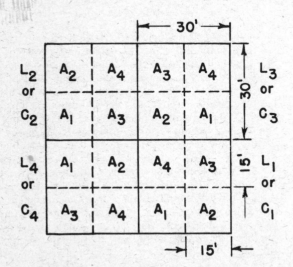

CULTURAL OR AMENDMENT TREATMENTS
(FURROW IRRIGATION)

FIGURE 16.—Example showing individual replicates of plot layouts for conducting field tests: C, Cultural treatments; L, leaching treatments; A, amendment treatments; ——— main plot boundary; ------ subplot boundary. The subscripts refer to treatment levels, for example: L_1, control; L_2, 12 surface inches; L_3, 36 surface inches.

able to separate the strictly chemical aspects of the response from the physical aspects. Preliminary tests indicate that treatment of alkali soils with the recently developed commercial aggregating agents will largely eliminate poor physical condition without altering the chemical characteristics appreciably. Therefore, reclamation tests that include applications of chemical amendments and commercial aggregating agents singly as well as in combination are suggested as a means for determining the nature of the response.

Reclamation of Saline and Alkali Soils in Humid Regions

This chapter deals primarily with the improvement and management of saline and alkali soils as they occur in the arid and semiarid regions of western United States. Any treatment of the subject would be incomplete, however, without reference to the pioneer research work and the extensive practical experience with the reclamation of saline and alkali soils in the Netherlands and other low countries in humid regions. Underlying principles relating to soil properties and plant responses apply equally well to both cases. The main difference is that in humid climates precipitation exceeds consumptive use, so that if drainage is adequate, i. e., if the water table is maintained at a sufficient depth, excess soluble salts are leached out of the soil by rain water.

It often happens that the rainfall pattern in humid climates during the crop growing season is not ideal and it is profitable to maintain the water table at some elevation that is in or near the root zone. Subirrigation is hazardous in arid regions, but it is a relatively common practice in humid climates. In any climate this practice requires close attention to the concentration of soluble salts in the root zone, and careful coordination between subirrigation, leaching, and drainage requirements. Hooghoudt (1952) has recently reviewed the methods and practices used in the Netherlands for tile drainage and subirrigation.

A special case of salinity in humid as well as arid climates occurs in greenhouse soils. This type of agriculture has considerable economic importance in many countries. Since crop production is directly dependent on irrigation and the leaching action of rainfall is absent, water management to control salinity and exchangeable sodium in the soil is the same as for irrigation agriculture in an arid climate.

Economically, in humid climates the most important consideration of soil salinity and exchangeable sodium has been in connection with the drainage and reclamation of soils underlying salty lakes and shallow coastal waters. In the Netherlands, experience with this process extends over many centuries, and the large areas of fertile agricultural land that have been gained by this means have become a major factor in the national economy. Zuur (1952) has sketched historical and technical aspects and has given an introduction to the extensive literature of the Netherlands on this subject. He states that, to start with, soils reclaimed from the sea contain about 2 percent sodium chloride. In 2 years after ditching, this content is reduced "in the wet Dutch climate" to 0.1 percent or less in the surface 80 cm. of sandy soils. Clay soils require a longer time to leach to this depth, but crops can be grown fairly soon after artificial drainage is established.

Most of the polder soils of the Netherlands, coming both from recent marine deposits and from old sea clays, contain sufficient sulfur and calcium carbonate so that with the oxidation processes which accompany drainage, the soil solution is kept saturated with gypsum for several years. This is a most fortunate circumstance because the removal of exchangeable sodium takes place simultaneously with the reduction of salinity, without the need for the addition of chemical amendments. Zuur (1952) has given the data in table 7 as being typical of changes in the exchangeable-cation status of a polder soil following drainage.

TABLE 7.—*Exchangeable cations in the topsoil of a polder reclaimed from salt water (Zuur, 1952)*

Time	Ca	Mg	K	Na
	Percent	Percent	Percent	Percent
Just after drainage	17	35	9	39
4 years after ditching	73	17	5	5
7 years after ditching	82	10	6	2
Final situation	87	8	4	1

The reclamation of soils that have been subjected to sea-water inundation is an agricultural problem that has assumed considerable economic importance and has been given a great deal of attention by soil and plant scientists. This is particularly serious when it occurs on older cultivated soils in humid regions, because of the lack of soluble calcium for replacing exchangeable sodium concurrently with the leaching out of the soluble salts. Leaching by rain water changes the soil from the saline-alkali to the nonsaline-alkali condition, with the attendant deterioration of structure. Reclamation then requires soluble calcium for replacing exchangeable sodium and careful management and cultural practices for some time to reestablish a favorable physical status of the soil. Van den Berg (1952) provides an introduction to the literature on this subject.

Chapter 4

Plant Response and Crop Selection for Saline and Alkali Soils

Significance of Indicator Plants for Saline Soils

Hilgard (1906) was among the first to recognize the significance of certain native plants as indicators of the characteristics of soils, and to make use of them in determining the availability of saline and alkali soils to agriculture. More recently, Sampson (1939, *p. 200*) has stated:

> In the future a broader use of indicator communities and species is likely, but such use is sure to be backed by sounder evidences than it has at this time. Preceding this possible broadened use there must first be more critical study of the growth requirements of both the indicator plant and the economic species; only then will the indicator concept reach its maximum reliance.

Some progress has been made in developing quantitative methods for the study of the indicator plant concept; and, in some areas, data have been obtained that relate the growth performance of indicator plants and their ability to survive to the physical and chemical measurements of the soils in which they grow. Kearney and associates (1914) made a quantitative study of plant communities as indicators of salinity and soil moisture in the Tooele Valley, Utah, and determined the moisture equivalent, wilting coefficient, and salt content for six characteristic plant communities. For example, they concluded that land characterized by a sagebrush association is capable of crop production with irrigation, and that a greasewood-shadscale type of vegetation indicates land that is suitable for crop production under irrigation only after the excess salts are removed by leaching. Harris and coworkers (1924, *p. 922*), working in the same valley, found "a close parallelism between physiochemical properties of tissue fluids of native species on the one hand and the characteristics of the soil and the capacity of the land for crop production on the other."

In connection with investigations of grazing in western Utah, Stewart, Cottam, and Hutchings (1940) investigated the root penetration of several desert plants as influenced by soil salinity and the nature of the root system of the plant. They found that roots of shadscale readily penetrated soil having 1,000 to 10,000 p. p. m. salt, but those of sagebrush did not. Billings (1945) studied the soil characteristics of several plant communities in western Nevada, including greasewood and greasewood-shadscale associations, and reported data on soil type, texture, pH, and electrical conductivity of the soil solution. He found rather high alkalinity (pH 8.5 to 9.5) throughout the profile in the greasewood association, and conductances of 1:5 soil:water extracts ranging from 1.6 to 8.4 mmhos/cm. in the 2- to 50-cm. depths.

Roberts (1950) has investigated the chemical effects of salt-tolerant shrubs on soils in the semiarid regions of western United States, and found that such shrubs as greasewood and shadscale were responsible for significant changes in some of the chemical characteristics of the soil profile. Data from several hundred field pH tests and some laboratory analyses showed striking differences among the pH, exchangeable sodium, and total salt content of soils under some species of shrubs as compared to those under other species and to the soils in intervening barren areas. Soils in a mixed shadscale-greasewood association in the Antelope Springs silty clay loam in southwestern Utah had a higher pH value under greasewood than under shadscale, and both values were higher than the pH of barren soil. A similar relationship was found with respect to EC_e and sodium status.

Fireman and Hayward (1952) made a quantitative study of several indicator plants growing in mixed and pure associations in the Escalante Desert, Utah, to determine the relation of vigor, age, and distribution of indicator plants to the physical and chemical characteristics of the soils of their habitats, and to compare soils occupied by the root systems of indicator plants and the soils in the adjacent interspaces. The pH values of saturated soil pastes and 1:10 soil:water suspensions, particularly of the surface soil, generally were higher under shadscale and invariably higher under greasewood than under sagebrush or in the adjacent bare areas. The *ESP* of the soil was somewhat higher under shadscale and very much higher under greasewood than under sagebrush or in the barren areas, and the soluble-salt content was appreciably higher under shadscale and greasewood than in adjacent bare soil or under other shrubs.

These and other studies by Flowers (1934), Harris

(1920), and Shantz and Piemeisal (1924) indicate that a vegetational survey can be useful in appraising an area if quantitative data are available regarding the soils and the ecology and physiology of the indicator plants. However, certain precautions should be taken in the use of indicator plants as a basis for the diagnosis of saline and alkali soils. In the first place, it would be unwise to appraise land on the basis of a single species unless it is a reliable indicator. Some species of plants growing in semiarid regions are poor indicators, even though they may tolerate large quantities of salt, because they will also grow very well in the absence of salinity or alkali. Tussockgrass, saltgrass, and shadscale, especially, tolerate an appreciable degree of salinity but will grow well in the absence of salt. Even greasewood is not an infallible indicator, since it has been found making thrifty growth on nonsaline sand dunes.

A second point to emphasize is the need for very careful sampling. The studies by Roberts and by Fireman and Hayward, cited above, indicate that large differences may occur in soil samples from sites only a few feet apart, especially when the plant association is a mixed one. If a vegetational survey and related soil sampling are to serve as a basis for determining the suitability of soils for irrigated agriculture, the analysis of the plant population and the collection of soil samples must take into account the possible effects of the indicator plants on the chemical and physical characteristics of the soil.

A third consideration relates to the purity and density of stand and the vegetative vigor of the various species present in the area to be evaluated. In the following paragraphs, the statements regarding the significance of various indicator plants are based on the assumption that they occur in a relatively pure stand and that they are growing in a normal manner. In the case of mixed associations, the appraisal should take into account the indications of all of the dominant species in the plant community.

Several species of plants native to western United States are regarded as good indicator plants if the precautions noted above are observed. Some of the best known indicator plants are listed below, and pertinent available data are given regarding their ranges, characteristics of the soils on which they grow (texture, soil moisture, salinity, etc.), and the conditions which they may indicate with respect to reclamation or soil-management practices needed for irrigation agriculture. The order in which the indicator plants are listed is based on the approximate level of soil salinity associated with the occurrence of the species in pure stand or as one of the dominant species. The information given was compiled from the data and field observations of the authors cited in this chapter.

Indicator Plants [10]

MESQUITE (*Prosopis juliflora*).—Range: Southern Kansas to southeastern California, Baja California and Sonora, Mexico, to eastern Texas. Occurs on a variety of textural soil classes that are very permeable and well-drained, with a low water table and an intermediate moisture-holding capacity (*SP* 25 to 50).[11] The soils are usually nonsaline throughout the 4-foot profile, but salt may accumulate at the surface under some conditions. Indications: Suitable for agriculture if water is available.

CREOSOTEBUSH (*Larrea tridentata*).—Range: Southern Colorado and southern Utah to west Texas, west to California and Mexico. On dry plains and slopes. Occurs on soils of coarse and moderately coarse texture that are very permeable and well-drained, with low water table and low to intermediate moisture-holding capacity (*SP* 15 to 40). The soils are nonsaline to a depth of 4 feet (<0.03 percent) [12] and nonalkali. Indications: Where stands are good, the soils are nonsaline and of sufficient depth to support a specialized agriculture provided water is available. If stands are poor, the soils may be shallow, underlain with layers of rock or hardpan, and unsuitable for crop production.

SAGEBRUSH (*Artemisia tridentata*).—Range: South Dakota to British Columbia, south to northern New Mexico and northern Arizona; rare in southern California. Occurs on loamy soils (loamy sand, gravelly loam, sandy loam, loams, silt loam, and clay loam) that are more or less permeable and well-drained, and the soil moisture may vary from low to high (*SP* 15 to 70). The soils are nonsaline (<0.05 percent) and nonalkali in the zone occupied by the roots. Indications: The soils are suited for irrigation agriculture or dryland farming, provided they are in an area where precipitation is adequate and the growing season is favorable. No reclamation practices are required. Sagebrush is not a good indicator of soil texture, because it occurs on a wide range of textural classes. It may grow well on soils that are too stony for farming.

WINTERFAT, or WHITESAGE (*Eurotia lanata*).—Range: Saskatchewan, Canada, to Washington, south to Texas, Arizona, and California. May be in pure stands, but frequently occurs in mixed associations with shadscale, rabbitbrush, and greasewood. Occurs on loamy soils that are permeable and well-drained, with a low water table and low to intermediate moisture-holding capacity (*SP* 20 to 45). Soils usually nonsaline in the first foot or two (<0.03 percent), but roots may penetrate soil layers having salt in excess of 1,000 p. p. m. (0.1 to 0.6 percent). Indications: Where winterfat is dominant, the soils are usually nonsaline, but this plant can tolerate some salt; therefore, leaching may be required.

DESERT SALTBUSH (*Atriplex polycarpa*).—Range: Arizona, Nevada, Utah, central California to northwestern Mexico. Occurs on moderately coarse-textured soils (sandy loam, fine sandy loam) that are moist in winter and dry in summer and fall. The water table

[10] The authors acknowledge the assistance of W. G. Harper, Division of Soil Survey, in the preparation of this section.
[11] See Method 3b for estimating saturation percentage (*SP*) in coarse-textured soils.
[12] Values for salinity in this and following statements are given as percent salt (dry-weight basis).

is usually low, and the moisture-holding capacity is intermediate (*SP* 25 to 50). The soils may be non-saline in the first foot, but they usually contain some salt in the subsoil (0.04 to 0.5 percent). Indications: Where stands are pure and growth is good, the soils are nonsaline or slightly saline and are suitable for irrigation agriculture. Where growth is poor, there may be a limy hardpan or salt in the subsoil. Leaching and drainage may be necessary.

ARROWWEED (*Pluchea sericea*).—Range: Texas, southern Utah, southern California, and northern Mexico. Occurs on loamy soils which are usually permeable, with an intermediate moisture-holding capacity (*SP* 30 to 50). There is usually a high water table or available moisture below the first foot throughout the year. It frequently occurs with the saltbush (*Atriplex lentiformis*), but it is less salt tolerant than that plant. The soils may be strongly saline in the surface foot (0.6 to 2.0 percent), the salinity decreasing with depth (0.1 to 0.5 percent in the fourth foot). Indications: The soils are usually saline or strongly saline; but, where the subsoil is permeable, the land is suitable for agriculture after drainage and leaching.

SHADSCALE (*Atriplex confertifolia*).—Range: North Dakota to Oregon, south to New Mexico, northern Arizona, and California. Plains and valleys in mountainous areas. Usually occurs on medium to moderately fine-textured soils. The soils have an intermediate to high moisture-holding capacity (*SP* 25 to 60), may have restricted permeability, and a high water table may develop, depending upon subsoil conditions. The soils are nonsaline to slightly saline in the first foot (0.02 to 0.1 percent), the salinity increasing with depth (0.3 to 1.0 percent). The soils may contain exchangeable sodium, and the pH of the surface soil may exceed a value of 9.0. Indications: Shadscale is salt and alkali tolerant, but it has a wide range of tolerance and may grow well on soils that are nonsaline or slightly saline. It usually indicates a soil with harmful amounts of salt or exchangeable sodium in the subsoil. The soils may be farmed after leaching, but drainage may be required.

GREENMOLLY (*Kochia americana*).—Range: Wyoming to northeastern California, south to northern Arizona and New Mexico. Occurs on medium- to fine-textured soils that are usually homogeneous to a depth of several feet. They may puddle easily, and the permeability is lower than that on sagebrush lands, which frequently adjoin *Kochia* associations. Soil moisture is intermediate to high (*SP* 40 to 70), and there may be a high water table. The salinity is moderately low in the first foot (0.12 to 0.3 percent), but it increases with depth so that the second to fourth feet may be strongly saline (0.55 to 1.5 percent). Since *Kochia* tends to have a shallow root system which does not penetrate the more saline deeper portions of the profile, it should not be regarded as especially salt tolerant. Indications: Pure stands of *Kochia* occur in soils that are low in salt in the first foot but have a saline subsoil.

Leaching and drainage are required, and suitability of such land for irrigation agriculture is doubtful.

ALKALI-HEATH (*Frankenia grandifolia* var. *campestris*).—Range: Central and southern California and Nevada. On low-lying lands and alkali flats. Occurs on soils of various textures (sandy loams to fine-textured loams) with soil-moisture conditions which vary from well-drained to wet with a high water table. The salinity is also variable, ranging from low to very high (0.02 to 2.0 percent), and exchangeable sodium is frequently present. Indications: Where alkali-heath is growing luxuriantly in a uniform stand, the soils are generally highly saline and the lands are unsuitable for agriculture unless they are drained and leached. Where growth is sparse, the soil may be much less saline and easier to reclaim.

GREASEWOOD (*Sarcobatus vermiculatus*).—Range: North Dakota to Alberta, Canada, south to California, Arizona, and northern Mexico; rare in California and southern Arizona. Usually occurs on fine-textured soils (clay, clay loam) but occasionally on soils of coarser texture. The moisture content of the soil is intermediate to high (*SP* 45 to 70), especially below the second foot, permeability may be restricted, and frequently the water table is high. The soils are generally saline-alkali; the range of salinity is wide (0.05 to 1.6 percent) and varies with depth; exchangeable sodium is present in most areas and the values are moderate to high. Indications: Greasewood is very salt and alkali tolerant, and usually indicates a fine-textured, relatively impervious soil with high salinity and exchangeable sodium. Drainage and leaching are required, and amendments may be necessary.

CRESSA (*Cressa truxillensis*).—Range: Texas to southern Utah and southern California and Mexico. Occurs on saline flats where the soils are fine-textured, usually moist, with restricted permeability. The salinity is very high (1.0 to 2.0 percent). Indications: Cressa is a good indicator of saline soil and is more reliable than alkali-heath, because the range of salinity under which it grows is less variable. The soils require drainage and leaching.

SALTGRASS (*Distichlis stricta*).—Range: Saskatchewan to Washington, south to Texas, Arizona, and California. On salt flats and wet meadows. Occurs on soils of various textures, but it is most commonly found on loamy soils. The moisture-holding capacity is usually high (*SP* 45 to 90), and the soils are moist or wet throughout much of the year with a high water table. The salt content of the 4-foot profile is usually high (0.8 to 2.0 percent), with the highest content in the first foot. However, good stands may occur on soils containing very small amounts of salt (0.05 percent). Exchangeable sodium may or may not be present. Indications: Usually indicates wet, strongly saline soils with high water tables, but the plant may occur in areas low in salinity. Drainage and leaching are essential.

SALTWORT, or SEEPWEED (*Suaeda* spp.).—Range: Alberta to Oregon, south to northern Mexico. Salt flats and marshes. Occurs on loamy soils of varying textures which may be puddled and underlain with hardpan. Usually found on moist seep lands with high water tables but may occur on better drained land. Moisture-holding capacity is intermediate to high (*SP* 30 to 60). The soils are saline or saline-alkali, with high concentrations of salt in the first foot (0.6 to 3.2 percent) and decreasing amounts with depth, but the average salinity for a 4-foot profile may exceed 1 percent where the growth is luxuriant. The soils may contain exchangeable sodium. Indications: Where virgin growth is vigorous, seepweed is a good indicator of highly saline or saline-alkali soil. Drainage and leaching are essential, and amendments may be required.

ALKALI SACATON, or TUSSOCKGRASS (*Sporobolus airoides*).—Range: South Dakota to Washington, south to Texas, Arizona, and southern California. In low, wet areas, and river valleys. Occurs on loamy and clayey soils that have an intermediate to high moisture-holding capacity (*SP* 45 to 75). The soil surface is moist a great part of the year, and the water table is usually high. The salinity of the soil may vary within wide limits (0.3 to >3.0 percent), the higher values being in the first foot; but the plant grows best in the lower range (0.3 to 0.5 percent). Exchangeable sodium may be present, and this grass is very tolerant to it. Indications: In pure, vigorous stands, this plant is a good indicator of wet, very saline or saline-alkali soils, with a high water table. It may occur on soils without a high moisture content in the subsoil on sites receiving runoff water. The land requires drainage and leaching, and soil amendments may be needed unless gypsum is present.

SAMPHIRE, or GLASSWORT (*Salicornia* spp.).— Range: Saskatchewan to British Columbia, south through Colorado and Nevada. On salt flats and along shores of saline ponds and lakes. Occurs on fine-textured clayey soils that are very wet throughout the profile, with high water tables. The salinity is very high, and this plant grows well where salt may average 1 to 4 percent in the 4-foot profile. Exchangeable sodium may be present in varying amounts. Indications: Soils are usually very wet, with excessive salinity. Useless for agriculture without drainage and prolonged leaching.

PICKLEWEED, or IODINEBUSH (*Allenrolfea occidentalis*).—Range: Oregon to Baja California, Mexico, east through Arizona and New Mexico to western Texas. On saline flats. Occurs on a wide range of soil textures (loamy and clayey soils), but usually on fine-textured soils. The soils are moist or wet throughout the year, with high water tables that may be close to the surface. The soils are excessively saline in the first foot (1.0 to >2.5 percent) and are very saline throughout the 4-foot profile (average 1.0 to 1.5 percent), but the salinity decreases somewhat with depth. Exchangeable sodium may be present in varying amounts. Indications: Soils are usually fine-textured, very wet, and excessively saline. If the stand is good, the land is not suited for agriculture without drainage and prolonged leaching.

Crop Response on Saline Soils

A field of crop plants growing on saline soil usually has barren spots, stunted growth of the plants with considerable variability in size, and a deep blue-green foliage; but these features are not invariable indications of salinity. For example, barren spots may occur in nonsaline fields because of faulty leveling and the resultant inadequacy of irrigation; and retarded growth and abnormal color may result from nutrient deficiencies.

The extent and frequency of bare spots in many areas may be taken as an index of the concentration of salt in the soil. Inasmuch as most plants are more sensitive to salinity during germination than in later stages of growth, barren spots are more indicative of salinity around the seed during germination than they are of the general salinity status of the soil profile. Frequently, cultural practices contribute to an accumulation of salt around the germinating seed with resultant failure in germination. The vigor of the plants adjacent to barren spots may indicate the distribution of salt in the soil. Full-sized vigorous plants immediately adjacent to a bare spot suggest a local concentration of salt, while stunted plants in this position indicate a more general distribution of salinity in the area. If the level of salinity is not sufficiently high to result in barren spots, the major characteristic in the appearance of the crop may be a marked irregularity in vegetative vigor.

Caution should be exercised to avoid confusion between effects of low soil fertility and those caused by salinity. Plants that are stunted because of low fertility are usually yellowish green, whereas those stunted owing to salinity are characteristically blue green. The bluish appearance is the result of an unusually heavy waxy coating on the surface of the leaves, and the darker color to an increase in the chlorophyll content on a surface-area or fresh-weight basis. Sugar beets, crucifers (cabbage, mustards, and related species), alfalfa, some clovers, grasses, and other crops generally develop a noticeable blue-green coloration when grown on saline soils.

There are many regions where plants may develop an intense chlorosis because of certain soil conditions. The causes of chlorosis are not fully understood, but this condition is frequently associated with calcareous soils or, in some cases, with the use of irrigation waters of high bicarbonate content (Harley and Lindner, 1945). Although calcium carbonate is relatively insoluble, much crop injury is associated with its presence. Since this soil condition frequently occurs in the absence of an accumulation of soluble salts, chlorosis cannot be regarded as a definite symptom of salinity.

Some species of plants develop characteristic necrotic areas, tipburn, and firing of the margins of the leaves when grown on saline soil. Many stone fruits, avocado, grapefruit, and some of the less salt-tolerant varieties of cotton belong in this category.

The cupping or rolling of leaves is a common manifestation of moisture deficiency in plants, but these symptoms may be indicative of salinity when they occur in the presence of apparently adequate soil moisture; however, other factors that cause malfunction of the root system, such as root diseases and high water tables, may produce similar leaf symptoms. While the appearance of the crop may, therefore, be indicative of saline conditions, a reliable diagnosis of salinity usually requires additional evidence derived from appropriate soil and plant tests.

Salinity and Water Availability

Numerous laboratory experiments with sand and water cultures have demonstrated the close relationship between plant growth and the osmotic pressure of the culture solution. On a weight or equivalent basis, chloride salts are generally more inhibitory to the growth of plants than sulfate salts, but this difference tends to disappear when concentrations are expressed on an osmotic basis. These relationships indicate that it is the total concentration of solute particles in the solution rather than their chemical nature which is mainly responsible for the inhibitory effects of saline

solutions on the growth of crop plants. Direct experimental evidence of the influence of osmotic concentration on water uptake by plant roots has been reported by Hayward and Spurr (1944). In addition to the osmotic pressure of the solution, the nature of the salts present may exert an important influence on plant growth. Such specific ion effects are discussed in a subsequent section.

There is much evidence to indicate that an increase in the osmotic pressure of the soil solution may result in a decrease in the water uptake by plant roots, but an additional factor must be taken into account in dealing with the soil system; that is, soil-moisture tension, or the molecular attraction of the surface of the soil particles for water. Soil-moisture tension increases as the soil becomes drier and the water films around the soil particles become thinner. This equivalent negative pressure is apparently additive to the osmotic pressure of the soil solution in limiting the availability of water to plant roots. The sum of soil-moisture tension and the osmotic pressure of the soil solution is termed "total soil-moisture stress." Studies on the effects on growth of several moisture treatments and

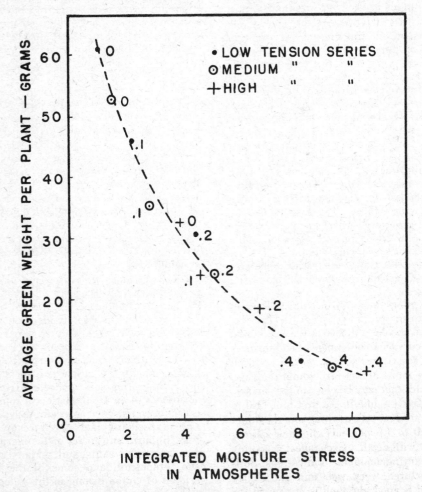

FIGURE 17.—Growth of bean plants as influenced by total soil-moisture stress. The salinity level for each treatment is indicated as percentage on a dry-soil basis (Wadleigh and Ayers, 1945).

salinity levels indicate that plant growth is a function of total soil-moisture stress, regardless of whether this stress arises primarily from salinity or moisture tension (fig. 17).

It is possible to extract the soil solution and determine its osmotic pressure, but this procedure is seldom used because it is simpler to estimate salt concentration by determining the electrical conductivity of the saturation extract (EC_e). Since saturation percentage is related to the field-moisture range, EC_e bears a close relationship to the EC of the soil solution. The relationship between EC and the osmotic pressure of saturation extracts is given in figure 6. The EC_e, therefore, provides information on the concentration of salt in the soil solution and its osmotic properties. The yield of orchardgrass when grown on soil to which various single salts had been added indicated that growth was simply related to salinity, expressed in terms of EC_e for various neutral salts (fig. 18). The response to sodium bicarbonate was, however, exceptional. In this case, calcium and magnesium ions from the soil exchange complex were precipitated as carbonates, thereby greatly increasing the exchangeable-sodium-percentage and producing an alkali soil.

The Scofield scale, in which crop response to salinity under average conditions is expressed in terms of the conductivity of the saturation extract, was discussed in chapter 2. This salinity scale has been widely used for a number of years and has been found to be satisfactory for salinity appraisal. To facilitate the discussion of plant response on saline soils, this salinity scale in its latest modified form is given again.

Salinity effects mostly negligible	Yields of very sensitive crops may be restricted	Yields of many crops restricted	Only tolerant crops yield satisfactorily	Only a few very tolerant crops yield satisfactorily
0 2	4	8	16	

Scale of conductivity (millimhos per centimeter at 25° C.)

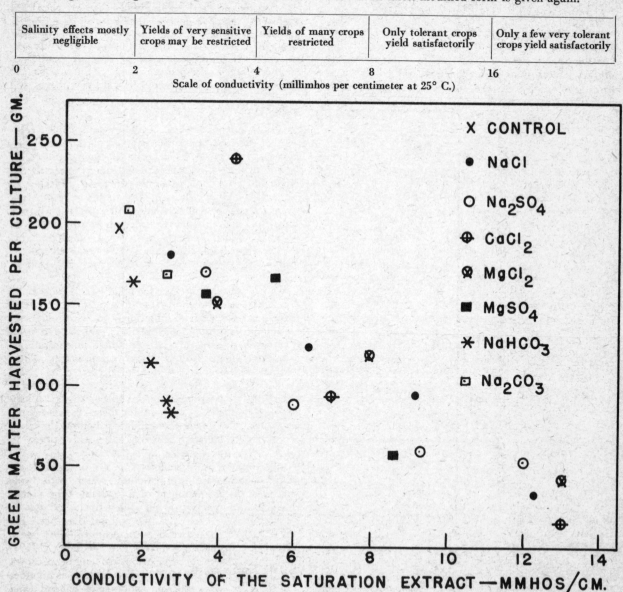

FIGURE 18.—Growth of orchardgrass, as influenced by various salts added to a sandy loam soil (Wadleigh and others, 1951).

It should be emphasized that this classification of plant growth in relation to various salinity levels refers to the salt status of the soil in the active root zone. It is possible to obtain samples from the surface soil around the base of row crops that may contain 5 percent salt or more with EC_e values of 50 mmhos/cm. or higher. This high concentration of salt represents an accumulation in the bed during the growth of the plants and not the salt concentration in the active root zone. Therefore, in correlating crop growth with salinity, care should be exercised to take soil samples from the active root zone that are uncontaminated by surface incrustations of salt. With row crops, the mass of soil making up the bed is frequently more saline than the soil below the furrow, and studies of root distribution and water uptake by plants indicate that under such conditions the major root activity occurs in the less saline parts of the soil, as shown in figure 14. These considerations should be borne in mind in determining the salt status of a soil with reference to plant response.

A technique for measuring the freezing point of soil moisture has been developed that provides a rapid, useful method for obtaining, by a single determination, the total moisture stress in a soil sample at field-moisture conditions (Method 6b). This eliminates errors caused by dilution of the soil solution and the resultant dissolving of moderately soluble salts, such as gypsum. Total soil-moisture-stress values obtained by freezing-point measurements are in good agreement with previously used methods involving determination of EC_e and moisture tension for the soil studied (Wadleigh, 1946, and Ayers and Campbell, 1951).

The experimental evidence cited above supports the concept that decreased growth on saline substrates is related to decreased water availability, but certain relationships between plant and substrate are still not fully understood. Despite marked decreases in growth with increasing concentration of the substrate, osmotic gradients between tops of plants and substrate are sometimes unaffected by increased osmotic pressure or total soil-moisture stress of the substrate. This is caused by increases in osmotic pressure of aerial parts of the plant that parallel increases in osmotic pressure of the substrate (Eaton, 1942). In addition, the osmotic pressure of expressed tissue fluids from the tops of plants does not appear to be correlated with the salt tolerance of some species. It is possible, however, that such measurements of osmotic gradient between plant tops and substrate may not represent the effective osmotic force which limits water absorption by the roots.

Specific Ion Effects

The previous discussion has dealt primarily with the effect of soluble salts in limiting the availability of moisture to plants. Other effects of salt may be equally important in restricting the growth of certain species. Injury or growth depression of plants, which cannot be accounted for on the basis of the osmotic pressure of the solution, will be referred to as a toxic effect of the salt in question. It should be recognized that toxicity so defined need not involve a direct effect of the salt or ions, either on surface membranes of plant roots or in the plant tissues. Frequently, toxicity may be caused, in part, at least, through effects on the uptake or metabolism of essential nutrients. As it is not always possible to distinguish clearly the mechanism underlying specific ion effects, it is convenient to refer to such phenomena as toxicities in contrast to the general osmotic effect of salt on plant growth.

The influence of excessive concentrations of specific salts on plant growth is an extremely complex subject involving many fundamental principles of plant nutrition. It is beyond the scope of this handbook to review the voluminous and diversified literature bearing on this subject. Much of the pertinent literature is cited in a review by Hayward and Wadleigh (1949). Literature citations in the following discussion are restricted mainly to papers of special significance in connection with certain topics not considered in the review cited above.

Ions that are frequently found in excess in saline soils include chloride, sulfate, bicarbonate, sodium, calcium, and magnesium. Less frequently encountered in excessive amounts are potassium and nitrate. The effects of all these ions on plant growth are being investigated by comparing plant response to isosmotic solutions of different salts. Species and even varietal differences among plants make it difficult to generalize regarding the toxicity of various salts or ions. It appears, however, that differences in plant tolerance to excessive concentrations of ions in the substrate are related, in some degree, to specific selectivity in ion absorption and nutrient requirements of the plants. In addition to these factors, there is also a marked difference among species in the amounts of such ions as sodium and chloride that can be accumulated without toxic effects.

Before considering specific toxic effects caused by excessive concentrations of soluble salts, other effects of certain ions deserve some mention. Although not considered essential plant nutrients, sodium and chloride, when present in relatively small concentrations, may stimulate the productivity of certain crops. Thus, Harmer and Benne (1941) have attributed increased yields of beets, celery, Swiss chard, and turnips to sodium. These authors consider sodium to be "nearly as much needed as a nutrient for these crops as is the potassium ion." Other investigators believe the effect of sodium to be more indirect, either substituting to some degree where potassium is deficient (Lehr, 1949; Dorph-Petersen and Steenbjerg, 1950) or limiting excessive accumulation of calcium, which with beets results in the development of a "calcium-type plant" characterized by a blue-green color and stunted growth (Lehr, 1942). Chloride, like sodium, has been observed to increase yields of some crops, notably beets, spinach, and tomato (Hayward and Wadleigh, 1949). On the other hand, chloride salts have long been known to affect adversely the quality of such crops as potatoes and tobacco. However, on saline soils, chloride and sodium ions occur in much higher concentrations than customarily employed in fertilizer studies. Under such conditions the high osmotic pressure of the soil solution tends to obscure specific effects of sodium or chloride on crop yields and quality (Bernstein and others, 1951).

Sodium

Plant species vary greatly in the amounts of sodium that they may accumulate, and many species tend to exclude sodium from their leaves, although they may accumulate it in their stems or roots. Notwithstanding this extreme selectivity in accumulation of sodium by plants, few well-defined instances of sodium toxicity have been reported. Lilleland and coworkers (1945) described a tipburn of almond leaves that is related to sodium content, and Ayers and associates (1951) have described a sodium-scorch of avocado leaves. In both studies, the soils on which affected trees grew were sufficiently low in soluble salts and exchangeable sodium to be regarded as nonsaline and nonalkali. Although sodium salts in water cultures rarely cause toxic plant reactions, stone-fruit trees (Brown and others, 1953) and avocados (Ayers, 1950) evidenced the same types of leaf injury in sand or water cultures containing added sodium salts as were observed in the field, thus confirming the relationship of sodium to leaf injury in these species. Unpublished data by Wadleigh and Gauch indicate that leaf burn in salt-sensitive cotton varieties is closely correlated with the sodium content of leaves.

Sodium in the soil may exert important secondary effects on plant growth through adverse structural modifications of the soil. Thus, if the exchange complex contains appreciable amounts of sodium, the soil may become dispersed and puddled, thereby causing poor aeration and low water availability (McGeorge and Breazeale, 1938). This is especially true in fine-textured soils. Also, if the exchange complex becomes more than 40 to 50 percent saturated with sodium, nutritional disturbances may result (Ratner, 1935; Thorne, 1945). Ratner (1944) stated that under such conditions the exchange complex actually removes calcium from the root tissues of the plant and that death may ensue because of calcium deficiency. Laboratory experiments have shown that the addition of calcium, and sometimes magnesium, to alkali soils can improve plant growth very markedly with an associated increase in the uptake of these added elements by the plants (Bower and Turk, 1946).

Bower and Wadleigh (1949), using amberlite resins, determined the effects of various levels of exchangeable sodium on cationic accumulation and growth of four species of plants. The effect of increasing levels of exchangeable sodium on cationic accumulation varied among the species and between tops and roots of a given species and was related to inherent specificity of the species in accumulating the several cations. In general, increasing the exchangeable-sodium-percentage of the substrate resulted in a decreased accumulation of calcium, magnesium, and potassium in the plants.

Calcium

The effect of high concentrations of calcium ions in saline soil solutions varies with the species. Some species, such as guayule, are more tolerant of added calcium salts than of other neutral salts (Wadleigh and Gauch, 1944). Masaewa (1936), however, found added calcium chloride to be more toxic to soil cultures of flax than added sodium chloride. Wadleigh and coworkers (1951) have reported specific toxicity of calcium salts added to soil cultures of orchardgrass, and unpublished data by Ayers indicate a similar relation for tall fescue. Both the calcium and chloride contents of the grasses from the calcium chloride treatments increased markedly; but since calcium nitrate produced a toxic effect similar to that of calcium chloride, the toxicity was attributed to calcium accumulation rather than to chloride (Wadleigh and coworkers, 1951). Moderate concentrations of calcium chloride are highly toxic to stone fruits in sand culture, and it appears that this toxicity is associated with an accumulation of chloride in the leaves. This chloride accumulation is more pronounced in the presence of excess calcium ions than when sodium occurs in excess (Brown and others, 1953).

Magnesium

High concentrations of magnesium in the substrate are frequently more toxic to plants than isosmotic concentrations of other neutral salts. This toxicity of magnesium may be alleviated by the presence of relatively high concentrations of calcium ions in the substrate.

Potassium

Although the occurrence of high concentrations of potassium in the soil solution is rare, toxic effects of high potassium have been reported. There is evidence to indicate that toxicity of high potassium, like that of high magnesium, may be lessened when balanced by high calcium concentrations. High concentrations of potassium may also induce magnesium deficiency (Boynton and Burrell, 1944) and iron chlorosis (Walsh and Clarke, 1942).

Chloride

As indicated under the discussion of calcium toxicity, the accumulation of chloride ion in plant tissues manifesting toxic symptoms is not an infallible indication of the specific toxicity of chloride. Many plant species are no more sensitive to chloride salts than they are to isosmotic concentrations of sulfate salts. There is good evidence, however, for the specific toxicity of chloride to some tree and vine crops. Hayward and associates (1946) and Brown and coworkers (1953) have found chloride salts to be toxic to peaches and other stone fruits, and Harper (1946) has reported chloride burn of pecan and native tree species of Oklahoma. Chloride burn has also been reported for citrus (Reed and Haas, 1924; Cooper and Gorton, 1951), avocados (Ayers,

1950; Ayers and others, 1951; Cooper, 1951), and grapevines (Thomas, 1934; Ravikovitch and Bidner, 1937).

Reference has been made in the discussion on toxic effects of high concentrations of potassium and magnesium to the ameliorative effects of increased concentrations of calcium. In such cases, high concentrations of potassium or magnesium result in increased absorption of these ions and decreased absorption of calcium; hence, the beneficial effect of increasing the calcium concentration in the substrate. It is pertinent, at this point, to consider whether such effects occur in the anion nutrition of plants; specifically, whether high levels of chloride (or sulfate) may interfere with nitrogen, phosphorus, or sulfur nutrition. Available evidence indicates that such interference in absorption of essential anions from saline substrates is of relatively minor importance and that decreased growth on saline media is not related in any appreciable degree to decreased availability of essential anions. However, Breazeale and McGeorge (1932) have emphasized the importance of decreased availability of phosphorus and nitrogen in calcareous alkali soils.

Sulfate

Specific sensitivity of plants to high sulfate concentrations has been noted for a number of crops, and it appears that such sensitivity is related to the tendency of high sulfate concentrations to limit the uptake of calcium by plants. Associated with this decrease in calcium are increases in the absorption of sodium and potassium, so that harmful effects of high sulfate in the substrate may be related to a disturbance of optimum cationic balance within the plant.

Bicarbonate

Plant species differ markedly in their tolerance to the bicarbonate ion, which sometimes exerts specific toxic effects, resulting in serious injury even at low osmotic concentrations. Beans and Dallis grass are very sensitive, while Rhodes grass and beets are relatively tolerant (Wadleigh and Brown, 1952; Gauch and Wadleigh, 1951). Studies in sand culture indicate that the bicarbonate ion affects the uptake and metabolism of nutrients by plants and that the nature of these effects varies with the plant species. For example, bean plants in the presence of the bicarbonate ion contain less calcium and more potassium than control plants, while the main effects in beets are a decrease in magnesium and an increase in sodium content. The pattern of effects is obviously related to the inherent selectivity of species in relation to mineral nutrition.

The studies by Wadleigh and coworkers cited above are of interest in connection with the problem of lime-induced chlorosis. Chlorotic symptoms and associated divergences in metabolism, involving contents of active iron, organic acid fractions, and essential cations, are very similar for typical cases of lime-induced chlorosis (Iljin, 1951, 1952; McGeorge, 1949) and bicarbonate-induced chlorosis. Since the basic causes of these chloroses are not understood, it would be speculative to suggest any closer relationship of the two disorders than the common features indicate. Thorne and others (1951) have shown that chloroses owing to such diverse causes as development in darkness, zinc deficiency, virus infection, and lime-induced chlorosis may be accompanied by very similar changes in potassium accumulation, water-soluble nitrogen fraction, and other features frequently considered characteristic of lime-induced chlorosis.

Boron

In addition to the elements that frequently occur in relatively high concentrations, boron may cause injury to plants even when present in very low concentrations in the soil solution. Boron is essential to the normal growth of all plants, but the concentration required is very small and if exceeded may cause injury. Plant species vary both in boron requirements and in tolerance to excess boron, so that concentrations necessary for the growth of plants having high boron requirements may be toxic for plants sensitive to boron.

Symptoms of boron injury may include characteristic burning, chlorosis, and necrosis, although some boron-sensitive species do not develop perceptible symptoms. Citrus, avocados, persimmons, and many other species develop a tipburn or marginal burn of mature leaves, accompanied by chlorosis of interveinal tissue. Boron injury to walnut leaves is characterized by marginal burn and brown necrotic areas between the veins. Stone-fruit trees, apples, and pears are sensitive to boron, but they do not accumulate it in high concentration in their leaves nor do they develop typical leaf symptoms. Cotton, grapes, potatoes, beans, peas, and several other plants show marginal burning and a cupping of the leaf that results from a restriction of the growth of the margin.

Boron toxicity occurs in limited, scattered areas in arid or semiarid regions. While its incidence is not restricted to saline or alkali soils, excess boron is frequently present in saline soils.

Plant Analysis

The normal mineral composition of plant parts is frequently altered under saline- or alkali-soil conditions, and analysis of appropriate plant organs may serve for diagnosing mineral excesses as well as for mineral deficiencies of soils. In addition, plant analysis may indicate salt injury in cases where the soil is regarded as nonsaline. This condition may occur with plants that are very sensitive to salt, such as beans and stone fruits, or in cases where the soil salinity is transitory.

Under some conditions, as in the presence of the bicarbonate ion, the entire complex of factors in the mineral composition of plants may be altered, and caution should be exercised in relating malfunction of these plants to a specific ion. Frequently, excessive accumulation of an ion in the plant may be the result of conditions other than high concentration of that ion in the soil solution. Any factors that inhibit plant growth, such as mineral deficiencies and high moisture stress, may result in abnormal accumulation of ions in plant tissues. For example, plants deficient in potassium will often show greater accumulation of calcium, magnesium, or sodium than normal plants (Cooil, 1948). Owing to the high degree of variability in the composition of "normal" plants under diverse growing conditions, the chemical composition of plant parts should usually be considered as only one line of evidence in the diagnosis of crop injury on saline or alkali soils. Appropriate soil tests, as described elsewhere in this handbook, may be used to furnish corroborative evidence.

Eaton (1942) has pointed out that no particular range of salt concentration in the substrate is critical in retarding plant growth. Growth depression is usually progressive as salt concentration increases. This type of relationship is to be expected in cases characterized by a predominance of the osmotic factor in limiting growth on saline substrates. Correspondingly, there is usually a progressive increase in salt concentration in the plant tissues as salinity in the substrate increases, although frequently the curve relating concentration of a specific ion in the leaves to that in the substrate may be exponential rather than linear. Considering the progressive nature of growth depression and ionic accumulation, it becomes apparent that for such cases no critical level of salt concentration in the tissues can be established with reference to the onset of "salt injury." In some instances, however, specific toxic effects of an ion may be of predominant importance in limiting plant growth. In extreme cases, death may ensue, whereas isosmotic concentrations of salts not specifically toxic to the species may cause only minor growth depression. Under such conditions, fairly definite limits of accumulation of ions, such as sodium or chloride, have been observed to be associated with the development of toxic symptoms in certain plant species.

Foliar analysis is commonly used in studying salt accumulation. The relationships between foliar composition and the principal ions that occur in excess in saline soils can be summarized as follows: (1) Chloride concentration in leaves usually bears a close relationship to the chloride concentration of the substrate; (2) excessive sulfate in the substrate causes small relative increases in total sulfur of the leaf tissue; (3) increases in calcium concentration in leaves are frequently associated with excess calcium in the substrate; (4) excess soluble sodium may or may not be reflected in the sodium content of leaf tissues. The influence of high exchangeable-sodium-percentage in depressing the calcium concentration of plant tissues has been mentioned in an earlier section.

Recent studies have furnished information on levels of chloride and sodium accumulation in leaf tissues associated with leaf injury. Rootstock studies by Cooper and Gorton (1951) and Cooper and associates (1951 and 1952) indicate that grapefruit and Valencia orange may develop leaf burn when chloride accumulation reaches about 1.0 to 1.5 percent on a dry-weight

basis, whereas bronzing may occur with even lower chloride accumulation. Avocados appear to be more sensitive than citrus, since leaf tipburn symptoms were reported at chloride concentrations of 0.5 to 0.9 percent (Ayers, 1950; Haas, 1950; Ayers and coworkers, 1951; Cooper, 1951). Cooper and Gorton (1951) have observed tipburn symptoms when chloride was only 0.2 percent. Burning of peach leaves has been noted when chloride content reached 1.0 percent (Hayward and others, 1946); and, in a study of six varieties of stone fruits, leaf burn was not observed until chloride levels reached values of 0.6 to 1.8 percent of the dry weight of the leaves, depending on the variety (Brown and others, 1953). Plum and prune showed leaf-burn symptoms with about 0.6 percent chloride in the leaves, while burning occurred in peach and apricot at 1.0 percent chloride. The leaves of the two almond varieties, Nonpareil and Texas, developed burn at 1.2 and 1.8 percent, respectively. In a study of salt injury to pecans and native trees of Oklahoma, Harper (1946) found approximately 0.6 percent chloride to be associated with the development of leaf-burn symptoms. Thomas (1934) observed leaf burn of grapes having a chloride content of 0.5 percent, and Ravikovitch and Bidner (1937) found 1.2 percent. The latter reported that the variety Chasselas accumulated as much as 3.0 percent chloride in severely burned leaves, while the variety Muscat Hamburg accumulated a maximum of 1.5 percent. Such varietal differences in levels of chloride accumulation doubtless will be found for other crops.

Other factors that may affect the level of accumulated chloride include age of leaf, season, and climatic conditions. Brown and coworkers (1953) and Thomas (1934) reported increasing levels of chloride in leaves of stone fruits and grapes, respectively, as the season progressed. Hot, windy weather may result in very rapid chloride accumulation in leaves in a very short time (Thomas, 1934); and, under such conditions, higher chloride levels may appear to be critical in the development of leaf injury. Although chloride contents of 0.5 to 1.0 percent may be associated with foliar injury of some crops, it should be pointed out that many species of plants, including some possessing no outstanding salt tolerance, such as potatoes, may accumulate as much as 5.0 percent chloride on a dry-weight basis without showing foliar symptoms (Bernstein and associates, 1951).

While the causal relationship between chloride accumulation and leaf symptoms has been demonstrated by means of carefully controlled experiments for some of the crops mentioned in the above discussion, such as avocado and stone fruits, the data for other crops are based only on a close concomitance between chloride accumulation and observed leaf injury.

Few instances of injury related to excessive sodium accumulation have been noted. With some crops sodium injury may be obscured by simultaneous chloride injury, as Ayers and others (1951) have pointed out for avocado. In a water-culture study, Ayers (1950) observed leaf burn of avocado when leaves contained 0.5 percent sodium on a dry-weight basis. Lilleland and associates (1945) have indicated that sodium accumulation of 0.3 percent in almond leaves is associated with incipient leaf-burn symptoms. In sand cultures, Brown and coworkers (1953) have observed tipburn of Texas almond leaves containing 0.4 percent sodium and of plum leaves containing 0.3 percent. Unpublished data by Wadleigh and Gauch have indicated that leaf burn of salt-sensitive cotton varieties may occur in leaves containing 0.2 percent sodium.

Chapman (1949) has indicated that chloride or sodium accumulations of 0.25 percent or higher in citrus leaves should be regarded as excessive. While these values are lower than those at which definite foliar injury may appear, they do emphasize the fact that under some conditions even lower values than those cited in the above discussion may indicate a definite tendency toward excessive accumulations of harmful ions in the plant.

Foliar analysis is useful in the diagnosis of boron injury of many plant species. The boron content of normal, mature leaves of such plants as citrus, avocados, walnuts, figs, grapes, cotton, and of alfalfa tops is about 50 p. p. m. Boron contents of 20 p. p. m. or less indicate deficiency, while values above 250 p. p. m. are usually associated with boron toxicity. Stone-fruit trees, apples, and pears do not accumulate high concentrations of boron in their leaves, although these species are sensitive to excess boron. If due allowance is made for varietal specificity in boron accumulation, foliar analysis may provide a readier basis for diagnosis than analysis of soil or water.

Crop Selection for Saline Soils

Because of saline irrigation water, high water table, or low permeability of the soil, it may not be economically feasible to maintain low salinity. In such instances, the judicious selection of crops that can produce satisfactory yields under saline conditions and the use of special management practices to minimize salinity may make the difference between success or failure.

As has already been pointed out, the availability of water to plants is always a factor under saline conditions. For example, suppose alfalfa is being grown on a loam having a salt content of 0.2 percent sodium chloride and a wilting percentage of 6 when the latter is determined on a nonsaline sample. Under such conditions, because the osmotic effect is additive with soil-moisture tension, alfalfa will stop growing when the soil dries to a moisture content of only 13 percent. In other words, if the soil contains 0.2 percent salt, the alfalfa plant cannot use a large part of the soil moisture that is normally available under nonsaline conditions. The presence of even smaller quantities of salt in this soil would cause a fraction of the soil moisture above the wilting percentage to be unavailable to the plant. More frequent irrigation would be required to decrease the inhibitory effect of the salt on the growth of alfalfa.

Although it has been shown that crop growth on saline soils is definitely benefited by more frequent irrigation, the need for this irrigation may not be indicated by the appearance of the crop (Richards and Wadleigh, 1952). In nonsaline soils, there is usually a relatively abrupt transition from low moisture stress to high moisture stress conditions, and the wilting of the plant indicates the need for irrigation. In saline soils, changes in moisture stress are more gradual and, although the plants may be subjected to high stress, there is no abrupt transition in the turgor condition of the plant and, hence, no sign of the need for irrigation. Nevertheless, experiments have shown that crop growth is greatly improved by more frequent irrigation under such conditions. Careful leveling of the fields to insure more uniform moisture distribution during irrigation will also improve chances for successful crops on saline soils.

Germination

In selecting crops for saline soils, particular attention should be given to the salt tolerance of the crop during germination because poor crops frequently result from a failure to obtain a satisfactory stand. This problem is complicated by the fact that some crop species which are very salt tolerant during later stages of growth may be quite sensitive to salinity during germination (fig. 19). Sugar beets, for example, which are very salt tolerant during later stages of growth, are extremely sensitive during germination. On the other hand, barley has very good salt tolerance during all stages of growth, although it is more sensitive during germination than at later stages (Ayers and others, 1952). Under field conditions, it is possible by modification of planting practices to minimize the tendency for salt to accumulate around the seed and to improve the stand of crops that are sensitive to salt during germination (Heald and coworkers, 1950).

Relative Salt Tolerance of Crop Plants

The salt tolerance of many species and varieties of crop plants has been investigated at the Laboratory. Previously published lists (Magistad and Christiansen, 1944, and Hayward and Magistad, 1946) have been modified on the basis of recent findings and are presented in table 8.

The salt tolerance of a crop may be appraised according to three criteria: (1) The ability of the crop to survive on saline soils, (2) the yield of the crop on saline soils, and (3) the relative yield of the crop on a saline soil as compared with its yield on a nonsaline soil under similar growing conditions. Many previous observations on salt tolerance have been based mainly on the first criterion, ability to survive; but this method of appraisal has very limited practical significance in irrigation agriculture. Although it is recognized that the second criterion is perhaps of greater agronomic importance, the third criterion was used in compiling the present salt-tolerance lists because it provides a better basis of comparison among diverse crops.

The salt-tolerance lists are arranged according to major crop divisions; and, in each division, crops are

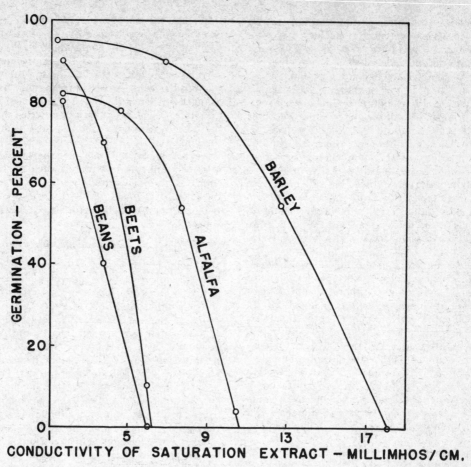

FIGURE 19.—Percent germination of four crops, as related to the conductivity of the saturation extract of the soil, under laboratory conditions (Ayers and Hayward, 1949).

listed in three groups. Within each group, the crops are listed in the order of decreasing salt tolerance, but a difference of 2 or 3 places in a column may not be significant. EC_e values given at the top of a column represent the salinity level at which a 50-percent decrease in yield may be expected as compared to yields on nonsaline soil under comparable growing conditions. For example, for crops with high salt tolerance in the division of field crops, EC_e values of 16 mmhos/cm. occur at the top of the column and 10 mmhos/cm. at the bottom. This indicates that crops near the top of this column will produce about 50 percent as well on a soil having an EC_e of 16 mmhos/cm. as on a nonsaline soil under similar conditions, and crops near the bottom of this column will produce about 50 percent as well on soils having an EC_e of 10 mmhos/cm. as on a nonsaline soil. EC_e values having similar significance have been shown for each group of plants for which such data are available.

In most instances, these data are based on a field-plot technique in which crops are grown on soils that are artificially adjusted to various salinity levels after the seedlings are established. By this method, crop yields were related to EC_e values for comparable saline and nonsaline soils, and the salinity level associated with a 50-percent decrement of yield was determined graphically. In many of these studies, a number of varieties of a given crop were compared. Significant varietal differences were found for cotton, barley, and smooth brome, while for truck crops such as green beans, lettuce, onions, and carrots varietal differences were not of practical significance.

In applying the information in the following table, it is important to remember that climatic conditions may influence profoundly the reaction of plants to salinity. The choice of suitable salt-tolerant varieties and strains will depend on local climatic factors; and, consequently, information on salt-tolerant varieties should be evaluated with reference to the conditions under which the crops are to be grown. The position of each crop in this table reflects its relative salt tolerance under management practices that are customarily employed when this crop is grown under irrigation agriculture and not the inherent physiological ability of the crop to withstand salinity under some given set of conditions that is uniform for all crops.

A salt-tolerance list for some important crops of Holland has recently been prepared by Van den Berg

TABLE 8.—*Relative tolerance of crop plants to salt* [1]

FRUIT CROPS

High salt tolerance	Medium salt tolerance	Low salt tolerance
Date palm	Pomegranate Fig Olive Grape Cantaloup	Pear Apple Orange Grapefruit Prune Plum Almond Apricot Peach Strawberry Lemon Avocado

VEGETABLE CROPS

$EC_e \times 10^3 = 12$	$EC_e \times 10^3 = 10$	$EC_e \times 10^3 = 4$
Garden beets Kale Asparagus Spinach	Tomato Broccoli Cabbage Bell pepper Cauliflower Lettuce Sweet corn Potatoes (White Rose) Carrot Onion Peas Squash Cucumber	Radish Celery Green beans
$EC_e \times 10^3 = 10$	$EC_e \times 10^3 = 4$	$EC_e \times 10^3 = 3$

FORAGE CROPS

$EC_e \times 10^3 = 18$	$EC_e \times 10^3 = 12$	$EC_e \times 10^3 = 4$
Alkali sacaton Saltgrass Nuttall alkaligrass Bermuda grass Rhodes grass Rescue grass Canada wildrye Western wheat-grass Barley (hay) Bridsfoot trefoil	White sweetclover Yellow sweetclover Perennial ryegrass Mountain brome Strawberry clover Dallis grass Sudan grass Hubam clover Alfalfa (California common) Tall fescue Rye (hay) Wheat (hay) Oats (hay) Orchardgrass Blue grama Meadow fescue Reed canary Big trefoil Smooth brome Tall meadow oat-grass Cicer milkvetch Sourclover Sickle milkvetch	White Dutch clover Meadow foxtail Alsike clover Red clover Ladino clover Burnet
$EC_e \times 10^3 = 12$	$EC_e \times 10^3 = 4$	$EC_e \times 10^3 = 2$

FIELD CROPS

$EC_e \times 10^3 = 16$	$EC_e \times 10^3 = 10$	$EC_e \times 10^3 = 4$
Barley (grain) Sugar beet Rape Cotton	Rye (grain) Wheat (grain) Oats (grain) Rice Sorghum (grain) Corn (field) Flax Sunflower Castorbeans	Field beans
$EC_e \times 10^3 = 10$	$EC_e \times 10^3 = 6$	

[1] The numbers following $EC_e \times 10^3$ are the electrical conductivity values of the saturation extract in millimhos per centimeter at 25° C. associated with 50-percent decrease in yield.

(1950). Based on field-plot studies in areas which had been inundated by salt or brackish water in 1944–45, the salinity values ("salt index," expressed as grams NaCl per liter of soil water) associated with 75 percent of normal yields for 14 crops were determined. Despite obvious differences in climate and cultural practices, Van den Berg's results for relative salt tolerance are in good agreement with those in table 8.

Relative Boron Tolerance of Crop Plants

Plant species differ markedly in their tolerance to excessive concentrations of boron. In sections where boron tends to occur in excess in the soil or irrigation water, the boron-tolerant crops may grow satisfactorily, whereas sensitive crops may fail. The relative boron tolerance of a number of crops was determined by Eaton (1935), and his results are reported in table 9 with

TABLE 9.—*Relative tolerance of plants to boron*

[In each group, the plants first named are considered as being more tolerant and the last named more sensitive]

Tolerant	Semitolerant	Sensitive
Athel (*Tamarix aphylla*) Asparagus Palm (*Phoenix canariensis*) Date palm (*P. dactylifera*) Sugar beet Mangel Garden beet Alfalfa Gladiolus Broadbean Onion Turnip Cabbage Lettuce Carrot	Sunflower (native) Potato Acala cotton Pima cotton Tomato Sweetpea Radish Field pea Ragged Robin rose Olive Barley Wheat Corn Milo Oat Zinnia Pumpkin Bell pepper Sweetpotato Lima bean	Pecan Black walnut Persian (English) walnut Jerusalem artichoke Navy bean American elm Plum Pear Apple Grape (Sultanina and Malaga) Kadota fig Persimmon Cherry Peach Apricot Thornless blackberry Orange Avocado Grapefruit Lemon

minor modifications based on field observations. The boron-tolerance lists are analogous to the salt-tolerance lists and subject to much the same limitations in interpretation. Differences in position of a few places may or may not be significant, and there is no sharp division between successive classes. Climate and variety may also be factors in altering the indicated tolerance of a given species under specific conditions.

Available information on boron tolerance does not permit the establishment of definite permissible limits of boron concentration in the soil solution. Irrigation waters are classified on the basis of boron content in table 14, chapter 5, with reference to sensitive, semi-tolerant, and tolerant crops. The effect of a given concentration of boron in the irrigation water on the boron content of the soil solution will be conditioned by soil characteristics and management practices that influence the degree of boron accumulation in the soil. In the discussion of saturation extracts of soils (ch. 2), 0.7 p. p. m. boron in the saturation extract was indicated as the approximate safe limit for sensitive crops.

Chapter 5

Quality of Irrigation Water

The concentration and composition of dissolved constituents in a water determine its quality for irrigation use. Quality of water is an important consideration in any appraisal of salinity or alkali conditions in an irrigated area. Much work has been done on quality of irrigation water. The United States Geological Survey is very active in general quality-of-water studies, and the analyses made by this agency are published at irregular intervals in the USGS Water-Supply Papers. In addition to current programs, analyses dating back to the beginning of irrigation in the western United States are recorded in this series. The Geological Survey took the leadership in preparing an index of water analyses that has proved to be very useful.[13] Agricultural experiment stations in the Western States have also been active in quality-of-water studies and have published a number of bulletins on this subject (Smith, 1949; Smith and others, 1949; Miller, 1950; Jensen and others, 1951; Thorne and Thorne, 1951).

The Rubidoux Laboratory since 1928 has analyzed more than 22,000 samples of irrigation water. Much of the information has been published, and all of it is available in the records of the Laboratory. This work shows that poor quality of both surface and ground waters is a limiting factor in the irrigation of many areas in this country and abroad.

There are many places in western United States, particularly in the desert areas of California, Arizona, Texas, and New Mexico, and also in the other parts of the world, where ground water is available but the quality is questionable or unsatisfactory. Similarly, where surface waters are used, the present rate of increase of irrigation development and changes in management practices are resulting in serious quality-of-water problems. There is the tendency to divert for irrigation all of the available water. This means that over a period of years the downstream diversions may change from uncontaminated river water to a substantial proportion of drainage return-flow of poor quality. To cope with such problems, it is necessary to have detailed information concerning the quality of irrigation water and a background of experience relating to the effect of irrigation waters on soils and crops.

---

[13] U. S. DEPARTMENT OF THE INTERIOR, GEOLOGICAL SURVEY. INVENTORY OF PUBLISHED AND UNPUBLISHED CHEMICAL ANALYSES OF SURFACE WATERS IN THE WESTERN UNITED STATES, NOTES ON HYDROLOGIC ACTIVITIES. Bul. No. 2, October 1948. [Processed.]

Methods of Analysis

The methods used by this Laboratory for the analysis of irrigation waters are given in chapter 8, Methods 70 to 86. The Versenate titration (Method 79) for calcium plus magnesium, the flame photometer method for sodium and potassium (Methods 80b and 81c), and the colorimetric method for boron (Method 73b), make possible rapid determinations without sacrificing accuracy. Also, the volume of water required for an analysis is less, thus simplifying the collection and transportation of samples.

If all of the principal constituents have been determined and expressed in chemical equivalents, the sum of the cations should equal the sum of the anions, and a lack of balance indicates an error. There are a number of ways in which a water analysis can be checked. The numerical value of the ratio—electrical conductivity in micromhos per centimeter divided by cations in milliequivalents per liter—should be about 100 for most waters (fig. 20). This ratio may be as low as 80 for bicarbonate or sulfate waters in which calcium and magnesium are high, but for chloride waters that are high in sodium the ratio may be as high as 110. The numerical value of the ratio—dissolved solids in parts per million divided by conductivity in micromhos per centimeter—should be approximately 0.64 (fig. 21). A third ratio—dissolved solids in parts per million divided by cations in milliequivalents per liter—has a value of approximately 64. These values are averages based on a large number of determinations for natural waters.

Characteristics That Determine Quality

The characteristics of an irrigation water that appear to be most important in determining its quality are: (1) Total concentration of soluble salts; (2) relative proportion of sodium to other cations; (3) concentration of boron or other elements that may be toxic; and (4) under some conditions, the bicarbonate concentration as related to the concentration of calcium plus magnesium.

Electrical Conductivity

The total concentration of soluble salts in irrigation waters can be adequately expressed for purposes of diagnosis and classification in terms of electrical con-

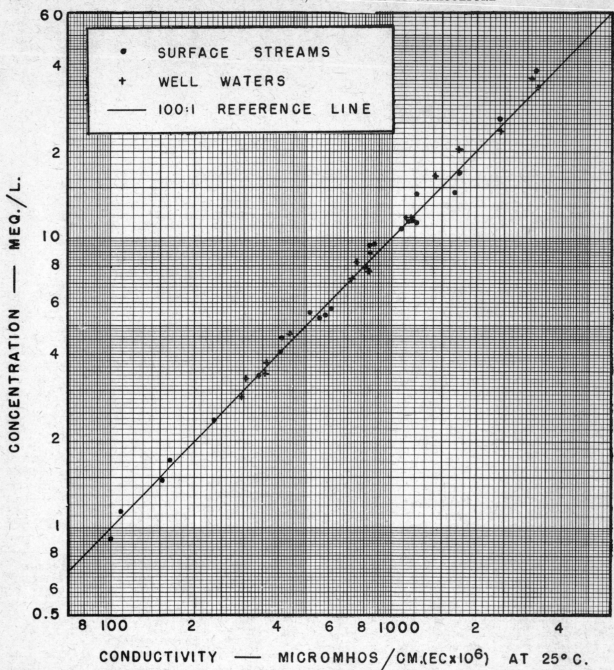

FIGURE 20.—Concentration of irrigation waters in milliequivalents per liter of cations as related to conductivity.

ductivity. The conductivity is useful because it can be readily and precisely determined.

Nearly all irrigation waters that have been used successfully for a considerable time have conductivity values less than 2,250 micromhos/cm. Waters of higher conductivity are used occasionally, but crop production, except in unusual situations, has not been satisfactory.

Saline soils are those in which the conductivity of the saturation extract is greater than 4 millimhos/cm., or 4,000 micromhos/cm. It has been found that the conductivity of the saturation extract of a soil, in the absence of salt accumulation from ground water, usually ranges from 2 to 10 times as high as the conductivity of the applied irrigation water. This increase in the salt concentration is the result of continual moisture extraction by plant roots and evaporation. Therefore, the use of waters of moderate to high salt content may result in saline conditions, even where drainage is satisfactory. In general, waters with conductivity values below 750 micromhos/cm. are satisfactory for irrigation insofar as salt content is concerned, although salt-sensitive crops may be adversely affected by the use of irrigation waters having conductivity values in the range 250 to 750 micromhos/cm.

Waters in the range of 750 to 2,250 micromhos/cm. are widely used, and satisfactory crop growth is obtained under good management and favorable drainage conditions, but saline conditions will develop if leaching and drainage are inadequate. Use of waters with conductivity values above 2,250 micromhos/cm. is the exception, and very few instances can be cited where such waters have been used successfully. Only the more salt-tolerant crops can be grown with such waters and then only when the water is used copiously and the subsoil drainage is good.

As discussed in chapter 3, the steady-state leaching requirement for soils where no precipitation of salts occurs is directly related to the electrical conductivity of the irrigation water and the permissible conductivity

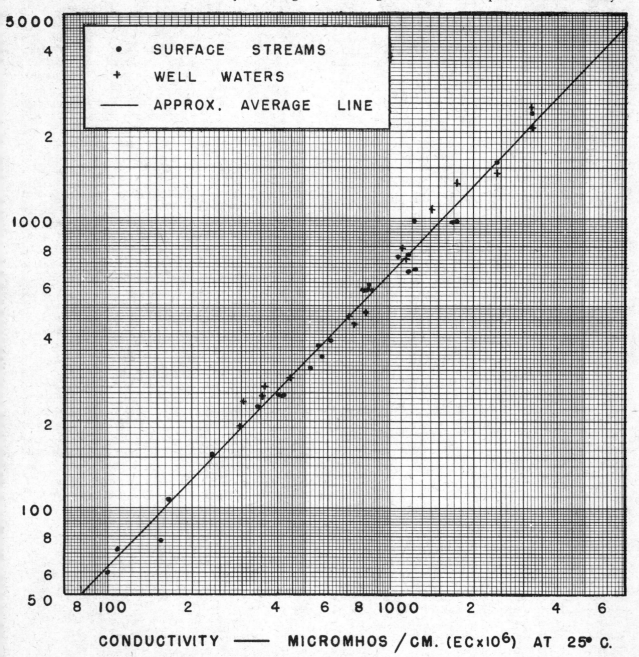

FIGURE 21.—Concentration of irrigation waters in parts per million as related to conductivity.

of the water draining from the root zone. The leaching requirements for specified electrical conductivity values of the irrigation and drainage waters, as determined from equation 2, chapter 3, are given in table 10.

TABLE 10.—*Leaching requirement* [1] *as related to the electrical conductivities of the irrigation and drainage waters*

Electrical conductivity of irrigation waters (micromhos/cm.)	Leaching requirement for the indicated maximum values of the conductivity of the drainage water at the bottom of the root zone			
	4 mmhos/cm.	8 mmhos/cm.	12 mmhos/cm.	16 mmhos/cm.
	Percent	*Percent*	*Percent*	*Percent*
100	2.5	1.2	0.8	0.6
250	6.2	3.1	2.1	1.6
750	18.8	9.4	6.2	4.7
2,250	56.2	28.1	18.8	14.1
5,000		62.5	41.7	31.2

[1] Fraction of the applied irrigation water that must be leached through the root zone expressed as percent.

Although, for reasons stated in chapter 3, these leaching requirement values are probably somewhat high, they illustrate the manner in which the electrical conductivity of irrigation waters influences the leaching requirement under various levels of soil salinity, expressed in terms of electrical conductivity of the soil solution at the bottom of the root zone. It is apparent that the water-transmission and drainage properties of the soil and the salt tolerance of the crop to be grown are important factors in appraising irrigation waters from the standpoint of total salt concentration.

Sodium-Adsorption-Ratio

The soluble inorganic constituents of irrigation waters react with soils as ions rather than as molecules. The principal cations are calcium, magnesium, and sodium, with small quantities of potassium ordinarily present. The principal anions are carbonate, bicarbonate, sulfate, and chloride, with fluoride and nitrate occurring in low concentrations. The alkali hazard involved in the use of a water for irrigation is determined by the absolute and relative concentrations of the cations. If the proportion of sodium is high, the alkali hazard is high; and, conversely, if calcium and magnesium predominate, the hazard is low. The importance of the cationic constituents of an irrigation water in relation to the chemical and physical properties of the soil was recognized even before cation exchange reactions were widely understood. Scofield and Headley (1921) summarized the results of a series of alkali reclamation experiments with the statement: "Hard water makes soft land and soft water makes hard land." Alkali soils are formed by accumulation of exchangeable sodium and are often characterized by poor tilth and low permeability.

In the past the relative proportion of sodium to other cations in an irrigation water usually has been expressed in terms of the soluble-sodium percentage. However, as was shown in chapter 2, the sodium-adsorption-ratio of a soil solution is simply related to the adsorption of sodium by the soil; consequently, this ratio has certain advantages for use as an index of the sodium or alkali hazard of the water. This ratio is defined by the equation:

$$SAR = Na^+ / \sqrt{(Ca^{++} + Mg^{++})/2}$$

where Na^+, Ca^{++}, and Mg^{++} represent the concentrations in milliequivalents per liter of the respective ions. A nomogram for estimating the SAR value of an irrigation water is shown in figure 22. This nomogram is similar to figure 27, but figure 22 has scales more suitable for the cationic concentrations encountered in irrigation waters.

An ESP scale is included in the nomogram opposite the SAR scale. This ESP scale is based on the regression line shown in figure 9, chapter 2, in which the relation between SAR and ESP was given as

$$ESP = \frac{100\,(-.0126 + .01475\,SAR)}{1 + (-.0126 + .01475\,SAR)}$$

This empirical equation was used to relate the ESP scale to the SAR scale in figure 22. After the SAR value of an irrigation water is determined by use of the nomogram, it is possible from the central scale to estimate the ESP value of a soil that is at equilibrium with the irrigation water. It is to be expected, however, that this condition would not often occur in the field, because the soil solution is nearly always appreciably more concentrated than the irrigation water.

The concentration of the soil solution is increased by the extraction of water from the soil by roots and by evaporation. As the quantity of salt absorbed by plants is relatively small, the solution remaining in the soil is more concentrated than the applied irrigation water. At the next irrigation this more concentrated solution may be displaced downward or diluted, and so the concentration of the solution in contact with the soil varies with time and location in the profile. It is not unusual to find shallow ground water or drainage water that is from 2 to 10 times as concentrated as the irrigation water. It is reasonable to assume, however, that for a limited depth of soil, such as the top 12 inches, the concentration of the soil solution is not, on the average, more than 2 or 3 times the concentration of the irrigation water.

Under conditions in soil where it is permissible to neglect precipitation and absorption of soluble salts by roots, it is clear that irrigation water, after entering the soil, becomes more concentrated without change in relative composition, i. e., the soluble-sodium percentage does not change. The SAR value, however, increases in proportion to the square root of the total concentration, i. e., if the concentration is doubled the SAR value increases by a factor of 1.41. If the concentration is quadrupled the SAR value will be doubled.

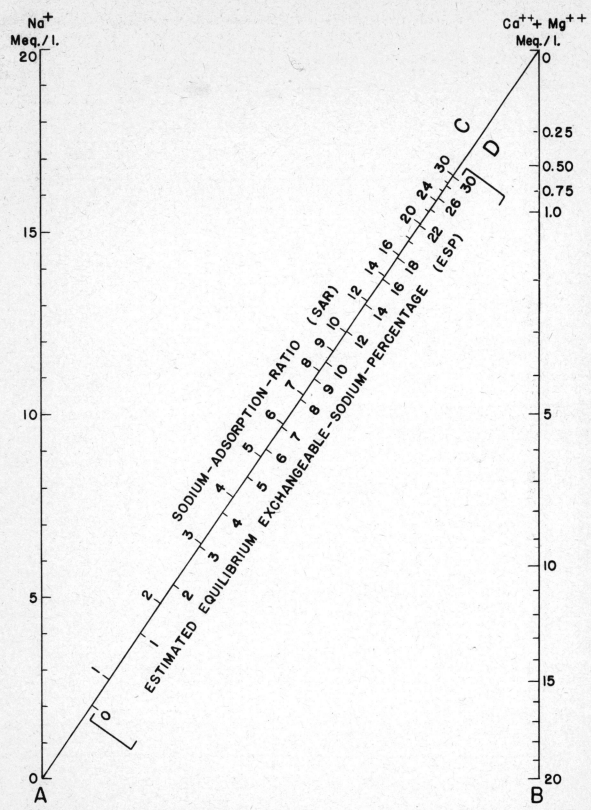

FIGURE 22.—Nomogram for determining the *SAR* value of irrigation water and for estimating the corresponding *ESP* value of a soil that is at equilibrium with the water.

It has been observed that where an irrigation water of relatively constant composition is used and drainage conditions are good, the *ESP* value of soil varies only slightly from season to season or from year to year. This implies that the cation-exchange material of the soil has reached a steady state relative to the cations in the soil solution which are derived from the irrigation water. All suitable data bearing on the relationship between the soluble cations of the irrigation water and the exchangeable cations of the soil have been assembled from the records of the Laboratory. Only

those instances were selected in which the drainage was known to be good and only the surface sample of soil from each site was considered. It was further required that the composition of the irrigation water be relatively invariant with time and that the water must have been used for many seasons in the field experiments or for many irrigations in experiments conducted at the Laboratory.

The relation between the *SAR* value of the irrigation waters and the *ESP* values of the soil samples is shown by the points on the graph in figure 23. The solid

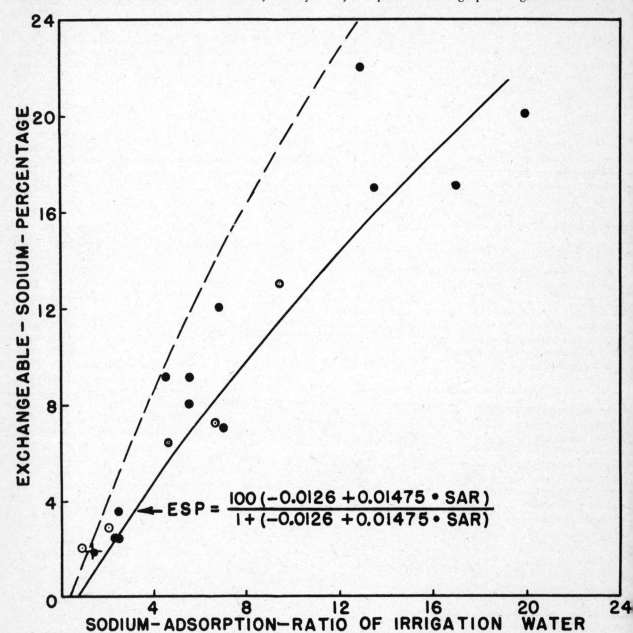

FIGURE 23.—The exchangeable-sodium-percentage volues of samples of surface soil as related to the sodium-adsorption-ratio values of the irrigation waters: ⊙, small lysimeters after 42 irrigation cycles; +, large lysimeters after prolonged leaching; ●, field observations.

curve represents the relation between *SAR* and *ESP* given by the equation shown in the figure, and also indicated by scales C and D in the nomogram of figure 22. It is apparent that, under the conditions existing in the field, the *ESP* values of the soil samples are generally higher than the estimated values. The deviations from the solid curve are undoubtedly owing to the fact that the concentrations of the soil solutions are somewhat higher than the concentrations of the irrigation waters.

The dotted curve in figure 23 shows the *ESP* values that would be attained by the soils, assuming a threefold increase in the concentration of the irrigation waters. In other words, if the soluble-sodium percentages of the irrigation waters after entering the soils remain unchanged but the total concentrations increase by a factor of 3, the *SAR* values would increase by a factor equal to the square root of 3 and the resulting predicted *ESP* values for the samples would lie along the dotted curve in the figure. The distribution of the points on the graph that represent the field samples indicates that the saturation extracts were 1 to 3 times as concentrated as the irrigation waters applied.

More data are needed to explain the relation of exchangeable sodium to water quality and irrigation practices. On the basis of the relationship shown in figure 23, *SAR* appears to be a useful index for designating the sodium hazard of waters used for irrigation.

Boron

Boron is a constituent of practically all natural waters, the concentration varying from traces to several parts per million. It is essential to plant growth, but is exceedingly toxic at concentrations only slightly above optimum. Eaton (1944) found that many plants made normal growth in sand cultures with a trace of boron (0.03 to 0.04 p. p. m.), and that injury often occurred in cultures containing 1 p. p. m.

Bicarbonate

In waters containing high concentrations of bicarbonate ion, there is a tendency for calcium and magnesium to precipitate as carbonates as the soil solution becomes more concentrated. This reaction does not go to completion under ordinary circumstances, but insofar as it does proceed, the concentrations of calcium and magnesium are reduced and the relative proportion of sodium is increased. Eaton (1950) uses three terms in connection with this reaction: (1) Soluble-sodium percentage "found" = $(Na^+ \times 100)/(Ca^{++} + Mg^{++} + Na^+)$; (2) Soluble-sodium percentage "possible" = $(Na^+ \times 100)/((Ca^{++} + Mg^{++} + Na^+) - (CO_3^{--} + HCO_3^-))$, where the $CO_3^{--} + HCO_3^-$ deduction does not exceed $Ca^{++} + Mg^{++}$; (3) "Residual Na_2CO_3" = $(CO_3^{--} + HCO_3^-) - (Ca^{++} + Mg^{++})$. In these relations the ionic constituents are expressed as milliequivalents per liter.

The influence of the bicarbonate ion concentration of irrigation waters upon the exchangeable-sodium-percentage has been studied at the Laboratory. One

experiment involved the growth of Rhodes grass in pots of Hanford loam soil. The soils were irrigated with the waters under test, then allowed to dry to a soil-moisture tension of about 700 to 800 cm. of water between irrigations. There were low- and high-leaching treatments. The high-leaching treatment provided for the application of excess irrigation water so that about 25 percent of the applied irrigation water was collected as percolate after each irrigation. The low-leaching regime provided for the same proportion of leachate every fourth irrigation. Exchangeable-sodium-percentages were somewhat greater with the low-leaching treatments than with the high. Table 11 describes the irrigation waters that were tested and reports the results of the analyses of soil samples from the low-leaching treatments. The soil samples were collected after the 42d and 86th irrigations.

The use of two of the bicarbonate waters, 20b and 10b, gave rise to substantially higher *ESP* values than the corresponding chloride waters, 20a and 10a (table 11). At the end of 42 irrigations, there was no appreciable difference between the 5a and 5b waters, but a significant difference was found after the 86th irrigation. With the remaining waters, there appears to be no difference between the chloride and bicarbonate treatments.

Typical Waters

The analyses of a group of surface waters from western United States that are typical of the waters that are being used for irrigation purposes are presented in table 12. The composition of a surface water may vary considerably, but the analyses shown were selected to represent average conditions.

Ground waters are much more variable in composition than surface waters. With few exceptions, it is not possible to select ground waters that are typical of an area or to generalize about the ground waters of a given basin. Analyses of samples from a large number of wells in the Coachella Valley in Riverside County, California, illustrate this point. Electrical conductivity varies from 208 to 13,200 micromhos/cm; boron from a trace to 3.15 p. p. m., and soluble-sodium percentage (*SSP*) from 21 to 97. Even where wells are only a short distance apart or are pumping from different strata, great variation is sometimes noted. Two wells within a half mile of each other had conductivities of 13,200 and 604 micromhos/cm., and 3.03 and 0.38 p. p. m. boron, respectively. The first of these wells is 565 feet deep and the second 180 feet deep. The quality of the water from different strata tapped by the same well may vary, or the quality may change with length of time of pumping. This change with time is usually associated with overpumping but it does not often occur. The quality of water from a new well should be determined prior to its use for irrigation.

Classification of Irrigation Waters

In classification of irrigation waters, it is assumed that the water will be used under average conditions

TABLE 11.—*The composition of the irrigation waters used and the analyses of soil samples from a bicarbonate experiment at the Laboratory; low-leaching noncalcareous treatments*

| Irrig. water No. | Irrigation water | | | | | | Analyses of soil samples collected after— | | | | | | | |
| | Concentration | Composition | | | | Residual Na_2CO_3 | Irrigation No. 42 | | | | Irrigation No. 86 | | | |
		Ca^{++}	Na^+	HCO_3^-	Cl^-		$EC_e \times 10^3$ at 25° C.	pH_s	ES	ESP	$EC_e \times 10^3$ at 25° C.	pH_s	ES	ESP
	Meq./l.	Percent	Percent	Percent	Percent	Meq./l.			Meq./ 100 gm.				Meq./ 100 gm.	
20a ..	20. 0	25	75	0	100	0	3. 73	6. 8	1. 16	12	5. 30	6. 8	1. 40	16
20b .	20. 0	25	75	50	50	5. 0	5. 94	8. 6	4. 52	52	16. 0	9. 4	6. 45	72
10a ..	10. 0	25	75	0	100	0	2. 22	7. 2	. 80	8. 4	3. 70	7. 3	1. 40	15
10b .	10. 0	25	75	50	50	2. 5	2. 03	8. 6	1. 72	20	7. 30	9. 0	3. 80	42
5a ...	5. 0	25	75	0	100	0	1. 28	6. 8	. 84	9. 0	1. 78	6. 7	1. 12	11
5b ...	5. 0	25	75	50	50	1. 25	1. 18	8. 4	1. 02	10	2. 42	7. 7	1. 98	20
1a ...	1. 0	25	75	0	100	0	. 40	7. 1	. 22	2. 4	. 32	6. 4	. 25	2. 4
1b ..	1. 0	25	75	50	50	. 25	. 36	7. 0	. 24	2. 6	. 34	6. 4	. 22	2. 1
5aL....	5. 0	75	25	0	100	0	1. 02	6. 9	. 22	2. 2	1. 50	6. 1	. 23	2. 2
5bL....	5. 0	75	25	85	15	. 50	. 69	8. 1	. 29	3. 1	1. 05	7. 4	. 36	3. 5
1aL....	1. 0	75	25	0	100	0	. 34	7. 0	. 14	1. 5	. 36	6. 4	. 12	1. 1
1bL....	1. 0	75	25	85	15	. 10	. 33	7. 2	. 14	1. 4	. 34	6. 4	. 13	1. 3

with respect to soil texture, infiltration rate, drainage, quantity of water used, climate, and salt tolerance of crop. Large deviations from the average for one or more of these variables may make it unsafe to use what, under average conditions, would be a good water; or may make it safe to use what, under average conditions, would be a water of doubtful quality. This relationship to average conditions must be kept in mind in connection with the use of any general method for the classification of irrigation waters.

A diagram for classifying irrigation waters was suggested by Wilcox (1948), and this was subsequently modified by Thorne and Thorne (1951) for the classification of the irrigation waters of Utah. Both diagrams have been widely used. In the classification presented below, certain features of both diagrams are used. However, the *SAR* value rather than the soluble-sodium percentage is taken as the index of sodium status or sodium hazard.

Salinity Hazard

Waters are divided into four classes with respect to conductivity, the dividing points between classes being at 250, 750, and 2,250 micromhos/cm. (See figure 25). These class limits were selected in accordance with the relationship between the electrical conductivity of irrigation waters and the electrical conductivity of saturation extracts of soil as discussed previously in this chapter under the heading, Electrical Conductivity. The frequency distribution of the electrical conductivity of three groups of irrigation waters with respect to these four classes has been determined on the basis of number of water sources and acreage irrigated. These three groups of data were compiled from the following sources:

Group 1. Data from Laboratory files for 1,142 irrigation water sources, both surface and ground water.

Group 2. Data estimated from figure 1, page 10, of Utah Agr. Expt. Sta. Bul. 346; Irrigation Waters of Utah, by Thorne and Thorne (1951).

Group 3. All conveniently available data from projects irrigated with surface waters of known and reasonably constant composition.

The frequency distribution of the first two groups is with respect to the number of sources, while distribution of the third group is with respect to acres irrigated. These data are presented in table 13. The frequency-distribution curves for the first two groups of waters are shown in figure 24.

It is apparent that more than half of the waters considered in table 13 have conductivity values below 750 micromhos/cm., the lowest limit used in the earlier schemes of classification. The establishment of a class limit at 250 micromhos/cm. further divides this large group. Considering the first group of data, 11 percent of the sources had conductivity values below 250 micromhos/cm. and are in the low-salinity class. The waters of the medium-salinity class have conductivities of 251 to 750 micromhos/cm. and comprise 47 percent of the sources. The remaining 42 percent represent irrigation waters of high or very high salinity. Distribution of waters in group 2 is similar to those in group 1.

Sodium Hazard

The establishment of water-quality classes from the standpoint of the sodium hazard is more complicated than for the salinity hazard. The problem can be approached from the point of view of the probable ex-

TABLE 12.—*Chemical composition of some river waters used for irrigation in western United States* [1]

River	Location	Date sampled	EC×10^6 at 25° C.	Dissolved solids	Sum of cations	Boron	Milliequivalents per liter								SSP	SAR	Residual Na₂CO₃
				P.p.m.	*Meq./l.*	*P.p.m.*	Ca	Mg	Na	K	CO3	HCO3	SO4	Cl			*Meq./l.*
Missouri [2]	Williston, N. Dak.	11/29/45	838	574	9.48	0.1	3.49	2.38	3.48	0.13	0	3.54	5.39	0.34	37	2.0	0
Yellowstone	Miles City, Mont.	7/22/48	548	368	5.71	.11	2.27	1.22	2.11	.11	(3)	2.40	2.96	.15	37	1.6	0
North Platte [2]	Wyoming-Nebraska lines	10/8/45	828	565	8.99	.03	3.59	1.64	3.61	.15		4.46	3.98	.54	40	2.2	0
South Platte	Englewood, Colo.	7/11/44	406	246	4.07	.12	1.84	.87	1.28	.08	.10	1.99	1.21	.69	31	1.1	0
Platte	Aurora, Nebr.	7/21/51	800	571	7.98	.11	2.96	1.67	3.35		.20	2.85	4.56	.76	42	2.2	0
Arkansas	La Junta, Colo.	7/21/44	1,210	981	14.38	.11	7.18	3.49	3.47	.24	(3)	3.95	9.80	.62	24	1.5	0
Do [4]	Ralston, Okla.	8/16/44	1,670	967	14.52		4.34	2.14	8.04		0	2.79	4.39	7.28	55	4.5	0
Canadian [5]	Conchos Dam, N. Mex.	6/3/43	844	586	9.57		3.64	2.63	3.30		0	2.72	6.33	.51	34	1.9	0
Rio Grande	Otowi Bridge, N. Mex.	6/46	340	227	3.39		1.86	.70	.83		(3)	1.77	1.50	.14	24	.7	0
Do	El Paso, Tex.	6/46	1,160	754	11.54	.14	4.16	1.42	5.96		.05	3.59	5.00	3.10	52	3.6	0
Do	Roma, Tex.	6/46	607	380	5.76	.11	2.49	.86	2.41		0	2.03	1.88	1.88	42	1.9	0
Pecos [2]	Carlsbad, N. Mex.	1945/46	3,210	2,380	38.00		17.27	9.21	11.52		0	3.18	23.11	11.99	30	3.2	0
Gila	Florence, Ariz.	4/10/34	1,720	983	16.85	.26	3.59	1.99	11.27		.20	3.68	3.26	9.95	67	6.7	0
Salt	Stewart Mountain Dam, Ariz.	3/8/34	1,210	664	11.27	.10	2.38	1.20	7.69		.39	2.40	.85	7.65	68	5.7	0
Colorado	Yuma, Ariz.	3/21/43	1,060	740	10.96	.10	4.79	2.11	4.06		(3)	2.64	6.39	2.05	37	2.2	.47
Sevier [6]	Central, Utah	6/5/49	580	338	5.47	.11	2.50	1.23	1.57	.17	.10	4.10	1.12	.74	29	1.1	0
Do [6]	Delta, Utah	6/3/49	2,400	1,574	25.81	.46	3.14	6.90	15.31	.46	.33	4.76	8.44	12.52	59	6.8	0
Weber	Ogden, Utah	10/7/49	510	308	5.58	.03	3.32	1.44	.73	.09	.42	3.66	.82	.54	13	.5	0
Humboldt [7]	Rye Patch, Nev.	8/48	1,173	[8]658	11.55	.62	1.75	1.89	7.91		0	5.20	2.17	4.46	68	5.9	1.56
Sacramento	Tisdale, Calif.	8/15/47	162	108	1.73	.05	.66	.57	.45	.05	0	1.35	.14	.20	26	.6	.12
Kern	Bakersfield, Calif.	9/28/44	234	152	2.36	.20	1.00	.24	1.06	.06	0	1.51	.49	.40	45	1.3	.27
Columbia	Wenatchee, Wash.	11/25/35	151	[8]78	1.48	.05	.90	.39	.19		0	1.26	.21	.07	13	.2	0
Snake [9]	Minidoka, Idaho	1948/49	410	[8]246	4.54		2.15	1.29	.84	.26	.34	2.59	.91	.74	19	.6	0
Payette [9]	Black Canyon, Idaho	1948/49	100	[8]60	.91		.40	.23	.18	.10	0	.63	.18	.12	20	.3	0
Rogue	Medford, Oreg.	9/13/32	108	72	1.15	.09	.54	.26	.33	.02	0	.85	(3)	.25	29	.5	.05

[1] Except as noted, these analyses were made by the Rubidoux Unit, U. S. Salinity Laboratory, Riverside, California.   [2] After U. S. Geol. Survey (1950).   [3] Trace.   [4] After U. S. Geol. Survey (1949).
[5] After U. S. Geol. Survey (1945).   [6] After Thorne and Thorne (1951).   [7] After Miller (1950).   [8] Calculated.   [9] After Jensen and others (1951).

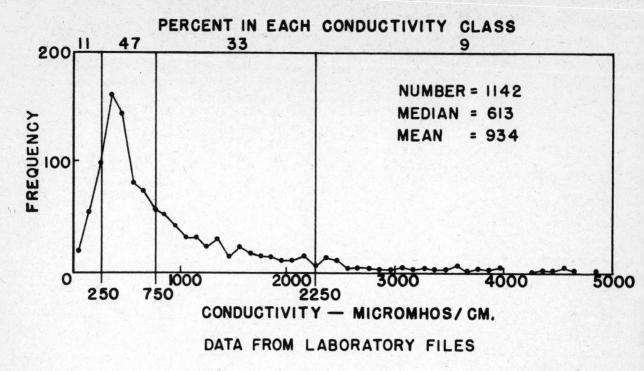

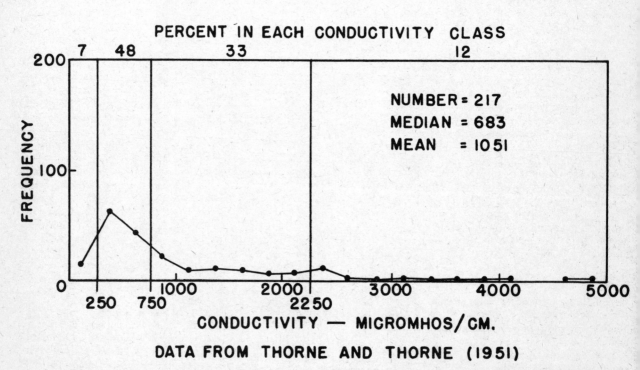

FIGURE 24.—Frequency distribution of two groups of irrigation waters with respect to electrical conductivity.

TABLE 13.—*Distribution of 3 groups of irrigation waters among 4 concentration classes*

Conductivity range (micromhos/cm. at 25° C.)	Group 1		Group 2		Group 3	
	Samples	Percent	Samples	Percent	Acres	Percent
	Number		Number		Thousands	
<250.........	124	11	15	7	453	21
251–750.......	541	47	105	48	977	46
751–2,250......	378	33	71	33	671	32
2,251–5,000.....	99	9	26	12	22	1
Total........	1,142	100	217	100	2,123	100

tent to which soil will adsorb sodium from the water and the rate at which adsorption will occur as the water is applied. Consider the simple case where a nonalkali soil is leached continuously with a high-sodium irrigation water and an increase in concentration of the salts in the solution is prevented by the absence of plant growth and of surface evaporation. Under these conditions the *ESP* which the soil will attain when it and the water are in equilibrium can be predicted approximately from the *SAR* value of the water; the rate at which the equilibrium condition will be attained will depend on the total cation concentration or electrical conductivity of the water. Thus, for this situation, application of waters having the same sodium-adsorption-ratio and variable electrical conductivities would ultimately result in about the same exchangeable-sodium-percentages, but the amount of water required to bring the soil to this ultimate exchangeable-sodium-percentage would vary inversely with the electrical conductivity. In actual practice, the *SAR* value of the water increases in the soil, owing to the increase in concentration of all salts and the possible precipitation of calcium and magnesium salts as the moisture content is decreased by plant extraction and surface evaporation. This results in a somewhat higher *ESP* than would be predicted directly from the *SAR* value of the water (fig. 23). Although the *SAR* value is the best available index of the equilibrium *ESP* of soil in relation to irrigation water, total cation concentration or conductivity is an additional factor and is taken into account in the following classification of sodium hazard.

Diagram for Classifying Irrigation Waters

The diagram for the classification of irrigation waters is shown in figure 25 and is based on the electrical conductivity in micromhos per centimeter and the sodium-adsorption-ratio.

In earlier diagrams curves representing mass-action equations between soluble and exchangeable cations delimited the several sodium classes. The curves in figure 25 can be constructed by the use of the following empirical equations:

Upper curve: $S = 43.75 - 8.87$ (log C);
Middle curve: $S = 31.31 - 6.66$ log C);
Lower curve: $S = 18.87 - 4.44$ (log C);

Where S = sodium-adsorption-ratio; C = electrical conductivity in micromhos per centimeter; log = logarithm to base 10.

These equations plot as straight lines on rectangular coordinate paper when log C is used.

The curves are given a negative slope to take into account the dependence of the sodium hazard on the total concentration. Thus, a water with a *SAR* value of 9 and a conductivity less than 168 is classed, so far as sodium hazard is concerned, as an S1 water. With the same *SAR* value and a conductivity from 168 to 2,250, it becomes an S2 water; with a conductivity greater than 2,250, the water is rated S3. This system by which waters at a constant *SAR* value are given a higher sodium-hazard rating with an increase in total concentrations is arbitrary and tentative, but it seems to be supported by field and laboratory observations.

To use the diagram, the electrical conductivity and the concentrations of sodium and calcium plus magnesium for the irrigation water are required. The determination of conductivity is described in Method 72; sodium in Methods 80a and 80b; and calcium plus magnesium in Method 79. If only the value for calcium plus magnesium is known, sodium can be estimated as follows:

$$Na^+ = (EC \times 10^6/100) - (Ca^{++} + Mg^{++})$$

Conversely, if only sodium is known, calcium plus magnesium can be estimated by the equation:

$$(Ca^{++} + Mg^{++}) = (EC \times 10^6/100) - Na^+$$

The ionic concentrations are expressed in milliequivalents per liter. The sodium-adsorption-ratio may be calculated from the equation defining the value or estimated from the nomogram of figure 22. Using the *SAR* and the *EC* values as coordinates, locate the corresponding point on the diagram. The position of the point determines the quality classification of the water. This is illustrated by the analysis of the water of the Sevier River at Delta, Utah (table 12), in which calcium plus magnesium equals 10.04 meq./l.; sodium, 15.31 meq./l.; and electrical conductivity, 2,400 micromhos/cm. The *SAR* value from the nomogram (fig. 22) is found to be 6.8. The point on the diagram corresponding to these coordinates ($SAR = 6.8$, $EC \times 10^6 = 2,400$) classifies the water as C4–S2.

The significance and interpretation of the quality-class ratings on the diagram are summarized below.

Conductivity

LOW-SALINITY WATER ($C1$) can be used for irrigation with most crops on most soils with little likelihood that soil salinity will develop. Some leaching is required, but this occurs under normal irrigation practices except in soils of extremely low permeability.

MEDIUM-SALINITY WATER ($C2$) can be used if a moderate amount of leaching occurs. Plants with

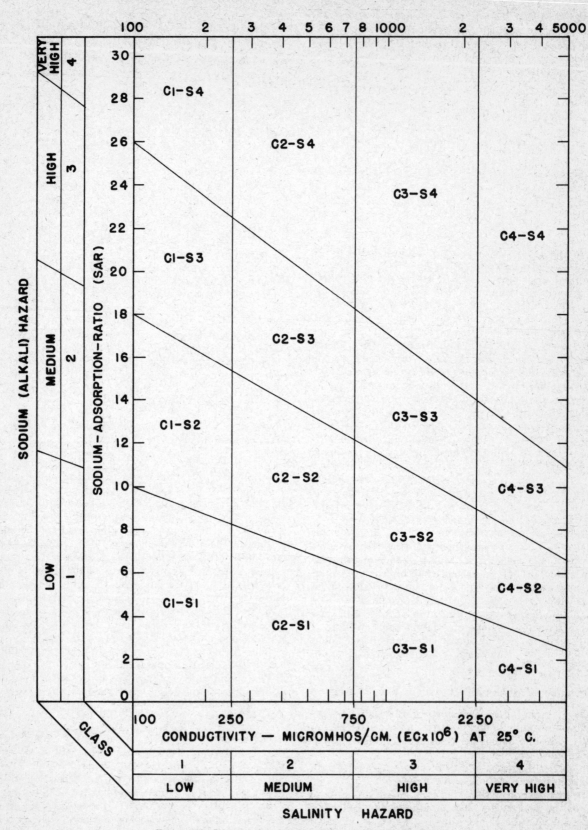

FIGURE 25.—Diagram for the classification of irrigation waters.

moderate salt tolerance can be grown in most cases without special practices for salinity control.

HIGH-SALINITY WATER (C3) cannot be used on soils with restricted drainage. Even with adequate drainage, special management for salinity control may be required and plants with good salt tolerance should be selected.

VERY HIGH SALINITY WATER (C4) is not suitable for irrigation under ordinary conditions, but may be used occasionally under very special circumstances. The soils must be permeable, drainage must be adequate, irrigation water must be applied in excess to provide considerable leaching, and very salt-tolerant crops should be selected.

Sodium

The classification of irrigation waters with respect to SAR is based primarily on the effect of exchangeable sodium on the physical condition of the soil. Sodium-sensitive plants may, however, suffer injury as a result of sodium accumulation in plant tissues when exchangeable sodium values are lower than those effective in causing deterioration of the physical condition of the soil.

LOW-SODIUM WATER (S1) can be used for irrigation on almost all soils with little danger of the development of harmful levels of exchangeable sodium. However, sodium-sensitive crops such as stone-fruit trees and avocados may accumulate injurious concentrations of sodium.

MEDIUM-SODIUM WATER (S2) will present an appreciable sodium hazard in fine-textured soils having high cation-exchange-capacity, especially under low-leaching conditions, unless gypsum is present in the soil. This water may be used on coarse-textured or organic soils with good permeability.

HIGH-SODIUM WATER (S3) may produce harmful levels of exchangeable sodium in most soils and will require special soil management—good drainage, high leaching, and organic matter additions. Gypsiferous soils may not develop harmful levels of exchangeable sodium from such waters. Chemical amendments may be required for replacement of exchangeable sodium, except that amendments may not be feasible with waters of very high salinity.

VERY HIGH SODIUM WATER (S4) is generally unsatisfactory for irrigation purposes except at low and perhaps medium salinity, where the solution of calcium from the soil or use of gypsum or other amendments may make the use of these waters feasible.

Sometimes the irrigation water may dissolve sufficient calcium from calcareous soils to decrease the sodium hazard appreciably, and this should be taken into account in the use of C1–S3 and C1–S4 waters. For calcareous soils with high pH values or for non-calcareous soils, the sodium status of waters in classes C1–S3, C1–S4, and C2–S4 may be improved by the addition of gypsum to the water. Similarly, it may be beneficial to add gypsum to the soil periodically when C2–S3 and C3–S2 waters are used.

Effect of Boron Concentration on Quality

Boron is essential to the normal growth of all plants, but the quantity required is very small. A deficiency of boron produces striking symptoms in many plant species. Boron is very toxic to certain plant species and the concentration that will injure these sensitive plants is often approximately that required for normal growth of very tolerant plants. For instance, lemons show definite and, at times, economically important injury when irrigated with water containing 1 p. p. m. of boron, while alfalfa will make maximum growth with 1 to 2 p. p. m. of boron.

The occurrence of boron in toxic concentrations in certain irrigation waters makes it necessary to consider this element in assessing the water quality. Scofield (1936) proposed the limits shown in table 14.

TABLE 14.—*Permissible limits of boron for several classes of irrigation waters*

Boron class	Sensitive crops	Semitolerant crops	Tolerant crops
	P. p. m.	*P. p. m.*	*P. p. m.*
1	<0.33	<0.67	<1.00
2	0.33 to .67	0.67 to 1.33	1.00 to 2.00
3	.67 to 1.00	1.33 to 2.00	2.00 to 3.00
4	1.00 to 1.25	2.00 to 2.50	3.00 to 3.75
5	>1.25	>2.50	>3.75

The tolerance of crops to boron is discussed in chapter 4 and a boron tolerance list is given in table 9. Boron frequently occurs in toxic concentrations along with the other salts that are present in saline soils. It can be leached from the soil but, if concentrations are high initially, a quantity of boron sufficient to cause trouble may remain after the concentration of other salts is reduced to a safe level. The boron status of saline soils should be determined as a part of a salinity appraisal following Method 17.

Effect of Bicarbonate Ion Concentration on Quality

On the basis of the data given in table 11 and using the "residual sodium carbonate" concept of Eaton (1950), it is concluded that waters with more than 2.5 meq./l. "residual sodium carbonate" are not suitable for irrigation purposes. Waters containing 1.25 to 2.5 meq./l. are marginal, and those containing less than 1.25 meq./l. "residual sodium carbonate" are probably safe. It is believed that good management practices and proper use of amendments might make it possible to use successfully some of the marginal waters for irrigation. These conclusions are based on limited data and are, therefore, tentative.

In appraising the quality of an irrigation water, first consideration should be given to salinity and alkali hazards by reference to figure 25. Then consideration should be given to the independent characteristics, boron or other toxic elements, and bicarbonate, any one of which may change the quality rating. Recommendations as to the use of a water of a given quality must take into account such factors as drainage and management practices.

Chapter 6

Methods for Soil Characterization

Unless otherwise specified, all chemicals referred to in this chapter, as well as in chapters 7 and 8, are "reagent" grade and conform to standards established by the American Chemical Society.

The following concentrated reagents are used.

Reagents:	Percent	Normality	Specific gravity
Acetic acid	99.5	18	
Hydrochloric acid	35–38	12	1.19
Nitric acid	70	16	1.42
Sulfuric acid	95–96	36	1.84
Ammonium hydroxide	28 (NH₃)	15	.90

Dilutions are indicated by (1+2), (1+10), and other proportions. The first figure indicates the volume of concentrated reagent and the second the volume of water.

Several methods involve centrifugation processes that are specified in terms of time and relative centrifugal force (*RCF*), which is the ratio of the acceleration in the centrifuge to the acceleration of gravity, i. e., $RCF = 0.0000112 \times r \times (r.\ p.\ m.)^2$ where r. p. m. is centrifuge speed in revolutions per minute and r is the radius in centimeters from the axis of the centrifuge to the bottom of the centrifuge vessel when in the rotating position.

Sampling, Soil Extracts, and Salinity Appraisal

(1) Soil Sample Collecting, Handling, and Subsampling

A round-nose trenching spade is a convenient tool for sampling surface soil. A soil tube is useful for small subsurface samples, whereas a barrel-type auger can be used when larger subsurface samples are required. Canvas bags are generally used as containers for soil samples, especially for samples of 100 to 200 pounds. For small samples, metal boxes or cardboard cartons can be used. Samples for salinity measurements require special handling, because at field-moisture content the salt in the soil is relatively mobile and moves with the soil water. It has been found that kraft paper nail bags are satisfactory for handling samples of saline soil, providing the bags are first waterproofed by soaking in a 5 or 10 percent solution of paraffin in gasoline or other wax solvent.

Soil should be air-dried before shipping or storing for any extended length of time. Air-dry soils that con-

tain deliquescent salts may accumulate enough moisture during a short shipping or storage period to decompose a canvas bag. A container impervious to water vapor should be used for such soils. Wax-treated bags, as mentioned above, or various types of waterproofed bags used for merchandising foodstuff or other hygroscopic material can be used. Samples in paper bags will withstand usual transportation handling if they are tightly packed in wooden boxes. To guard against accidental confusion of samples, it is desirable to place an identification tag inside the bag, in addition to using an external marking or tag.

The following recommendations will aid in determining the size of sample required:

Measurements to be made:	Soil required in grams
1. Electrical conductivity of the saturation extract, saturation percentage, and pH of soil paste	250
2. Soluble ion analysis (semimicro methods) for—	
Low salinity	500
High salinity	250
3. Exchangeable-cation analysis	15
4. Hydraulic conductivity (disturbed)	400
5. Gypsum and alkaline-earth carbonates	50

The total amount of soil to be obtained for the sample can be determined by adding up the amounts indicated for the individual tests to be made. If measurement 2 is to be made, then no extra soil will be required for measurement 1. Samples twice as large as those indicated above are desirable, if handling facilities permit.

Care must be taken to obtain representative subsamples of a granular material such as soil. Bulk samples at the Laboratory are air-dried before or after passing through a screen with 6-mm. square openings, are mixed, and are stored in galvanized iron containers. An attempt is made to maintain a level surface of soil in a container so that a minimum of segregation of particles or aggregates occurs from rolling. A subsample of the main sample is taken by means of several partial loadings of a hand scoop from different locations on the surface of the soil. The subsample is then screened to the desired size. For exchangeable-cation analysis and other determinations requiring samples of about 5 gm. or less, the soil is ground to pass a 0.5-mm. sieve. For a number of tests relating to moisture retention and moisture transmission, the soil is passed through a 2-mm. round-hole sieve with the aid of a rubber stopper. One purpose of such sieving is to remove rocks larger than 2 mm.; another is to reduce all aggregates to less than 2 mm. In the removal of rocks between 2 mm. and 6 mm., they may be returned to the screened sample if desired. The entire subsample is then placed on a mixing cloth and pulled in such a way as to produce mixing. Some pulling operations will produce segregation instead of mixing, and special care must be exercised to obtain a well-mixed sample. The soil sample is then flattened until the pile is 2 to 4 cm. deep.

For moisture retentivity, hydraulic conductivity, and modulus of rupture tests, 2 to 6 subsamples, each having a fairly definite volume, are required. Use paper cups to hold the individual subsamples. Mark with a pencil line around the inside of the cup the height to which the cup is to be filled to give the correct amount of subsample. Then, using a thin teaspoon or a small scoop, lift small amounts of soil from the pile, placing each in successive cups and progressing around the pile until the cups are filled to the desired level. It is difficult with some soils, especially if they have been passed through a 2-mm. round-hole sieve, to take samples from the pile without allowing the larger particles to roll off the spoon or scoop. This rollback should be avoided because it makes the extracted subsample nonrepresentative. The rollback problem is practically absent from some soils, especially if all the sample has been passed through an 0.5-mm. sieve.

Three data forms, or work sheets, used at the Laboratory are shown herewith. The field data sheet should be at hand during sampling as an aid in recording pertinent information. The other two forms serve as work sheets for recording and calculating laboratory determinations.

(2) Saturated Soil Paste

Apparatus

Container of 250-ml. capacity or greater, such as a cup or moisture box.

Procedure

Prepare the saturated soil paste by adding distilled water to a sample of soil while stirring with a spatula. The soil-water mixture is consolidated from time to time during the stirring process by tapping the container on the workbench. At saturation the soil paste glistens as it reflects light, flows slightly when the container is tipped, and the paste slides freely and cleanly off the spatula for all soils but those with a high clay content. After mixing, the sample should be allowed to stand for an hour or more, and then the criteria for saturation should be rechecked. Free water should not collect on the soil surface nor should the paste stiffen markedly or lose its glistening appearance on standing. If the paste does stiffen or lose its glisten, remix with more water.

Because soils puddle most readily when worked at moisture contents near field capacity, sufficient water should be added immediately to bring the sample nearly to saturation. If the paste is too wet, additional dry soil may be added.

The amount of soil required depends on the measurements to be made, i. e., on the volume of extract desired. A 250-gm. sample is convenient to handle and provides sufficient extract for most purposes. Initially, the sample can be air-dry or at the field-moisture content, but the mixing process is generally easier if the soil is first air-dried and passed through a 2-mm. sieve.

If saturation pastes are to be made from a group of samples of uniform texture, considerable time can be saved by carefully determining the saturation percentage of a representative sample in the usual way. Subsequent samples can be brought to saturation by adding appropriate volumes of water to known weights of soil.

Special precautions must be taken with peat and muck soils and with soils of very fine and very coarse texture.

PEAT AND MUCK SOILS.—Dry peat and muck soils, especially if coarse or woody in texture, require an overnight wetting period to obtain a definite endpoint for the saturated paste. After the first wetting, pastes of these soils usually stiffen and lose the glisten on standing. Adding water and remixing then gives a mixture that usually retains the characteristics of a saturated paste.

FINE-TEXTURED SOILS.—To minimize puddling and thus obtain a more definite endpoint with fine-textured soils, the water should be added to the soils with a minimum of stirring, especially in the earlier stages of wetting.

COARSE-TEXTURED SOILS.—The saturated paste for coarse-textured soils can be prepared in the same manner as for fine-textured soils; however, a different moisture content is recommended for the salinity appraisal of such soils (Method 3b).

Method 27 gives procedures for determining the moisture content of saturated paste, i. e., the saturation percentage.

(3) Soil-Water Extracts

(3a) Saturation Extract

Apparatus

Richards or Buechner funnels, filter rack or flask, filter paper, vacuum pump, extract containers such as test tubes or 1-oz. bottles.

Procedure

Transfer the saturated soil paste, Method 2, to the filter funnel with a filter paper in place and apply vacuum. Collect the extract in a bottle or test tube. Pyrex should not be used if boron is to be determined. If the initial filtrate is turbid, it can be refiltered through the soil or discarded. Vacuum extraction should be terminated when air begins to pass through the filter. If carbonate and bicarbonate determinations are to be made on the extract, a solution containing 1,000 p. p. m. of sodium hexametaphosphate should be added at the rate of one drop per 25 ml. of extract prior

Soil Acc. No. ____

Temporary No. ____

UNITED STATES SALINITY LABORATORY
FIELD DATA FOR SOIL SAMPLES

Sampled by _____ Mail address _____ Date _____

State _____ County _____ Nearest settlement _____

Site location ____ ¼, ____ ¼, Sec. ____; T _____; R _____

Station or farm _____ District or valley _____

Directions for finding site: (Use reverse side for a sketch of roads showing nearest settlement and distance from local landmarks.)

References (Soil Survey Bul., other publications, or correspondence):

Profile description (color, texture, structure, horizons, hardpan, origin, parent material, water table, drainage, and soil series if known):

Topography _____ Surface slope _____ Percent topsoil erosion _____

Microrelief at the sampling site, furrow, ridge, etc. _____

Disturbance from land preparation, leveling, filling, etc. _____

Sample: Depth _____ No. sacks _____ Approx. total wt. (lb.) _____

Composite sample: Depth _____ No. holes _____ Sampling method and pattern_____

_____ Approx. total wt. (lb.) _____

Undisturbed structure sample: Depth _____ No. of replicates _____

Yrs. of cultivation _____ Yrs. of irrigation _____ Source of water _____

Crop data (rotation, yield history, detailed description of plant condition at time of sampling):

Management practices:

(It is expected that not all the above blanks can be filled for every sample but the usefulness of laboratory determinations depends on the completeness and accuracy of the field data.)

Soil sample No. _____ .   Description:

Moisture in air-dry Soil

Can No. _____

	Air-dry	Oven-dry
Gross		
Tare	_____	_____
Net		

$\dfrac{OD}{AD}$ [ ]

P_w
(Oven-dry basis)   [ ]

Saturation Percentage

From Water Added

Can No. _____

Air-dry soil, gm. _____

Oven-dry soil, gm. _____

H_2O, ml. (____ + ____) _____

P_w at sat.   [ ]
(Oven-dry basis)

By Drying

Can No. _____

	Wet	Oven-dry
Gross		
Tare	_____	_____
Net		

P_w at sat.   [ ]
(Oven-dry basis)

---

pH of Saturated Soil Paste

[ ]

pH of Saturation Extract

[ ]

pH of Suspension

Soil _____   [ ]
Water _____

Electrical Conductivity

Saturation Extract

$T^\circ C$. _____

k   _____

R   _____

Millimhos/cm.   [ ]
   at 25° C.

Alkaline-earth Carbonates

(Lime)

(Scale: low, medium, high)

[ ]

Lime

Boron   _____ ml.

____ %T.   _____ p.p.m. B

B   [ ]
p.p.m.

Calcium plus Magnesium
(Versenate titration)

Ca+Mg, sat. ext.   [ ]
  meq./l.

Ca+Mg, dry soil   [ ]
  meq./100 gm.

Sodium

Standard _____ meq./l.

r = _____ = _____ meq./l.

Na, sat. ext.   [ ]
  meq./l.

Na, dry soil   [ ]
  meq./100 gm.

Potassium

Standard _____ meq./l.

r = _____ = _____ meq./l.

K, sat. ext.   [ ]
  meq./l.

K, dry soil   [ ]
  meq./100 gm.

Soil Sample No. _____

1	Centrifuge tube number			
2	Sample, air-dry weight gm.			
3	Sample, oven-dry weight gm.			
	CATION-EXCHANGE-CAPACITY			
	(Saturated with NaAc: Na by flame photometer)			
4	Extracting solution diluted to ml.			
5	Dilution: Solution 4 dilution ratio			
6	Flame photometer standard Na meq./l.			
7	Flame photometer reading			
8	Sodium, from graph meq./l.			
9	Cation-exchange-capacity (OD basis) meq./100 gm.			
	EXCHANGEABLE SODIUM			
10	Extracting solution (NH_4Ac) diluted to ml.			
11	Dilution: Solution 10 dilution ratio			
12	Flame photometer standard Na meq./l.			
13	Flame photometer reading			
14	Sodium, from graph meq./l.			
15	Total sodium (OD basis) meq./100 gm.			
16	Sodium in sat. extract (OD basis) meq./100 gm.			
17	Exchangeable sodium (OD basis) meq./100 gm.			
18	Exchangeable-sodium-percentage			
	EXCHANGEABLE POTASSIUM			
19	Extracting solution (NH_4Ac) diluted to ml.			
20	Dilution: Solution 19 dilution ratio			
21	Flame photometer standard K meq./l.			
22	Flame photometer reading			
23	Potassium, from graph meq./l.			
24	Total potassium (OD basis) meq./100 gm.			
25	Potassium in sat. extract (OD basis) meq./100 gm.			
26	Exchangeable potassium (OD basis) meq./100 gm.			
27	Exchangeable-potassium-percentage			

to stoppering and storing. This prevents the precipitation of calcium carbonate on standing.

For appraising soil salinity for most purposes, the extraction can be made a few minutes after preparing the saturated paste. If the soil contains gypsum, the conductivity of the saturation extract can increase as much as 1 or 2 mmhos/cm. upon standing. Therefore, if gypsum is present, allow the saturated paste to stand several hours before extracting the solution.

If the solution is to be analyzed for its chemical constituents, the saturated paste should stand 4 to 16 hours before extraction.

References

Richards (1949a), Reitemeier and Fireman (1944).

(3b) Twice-Saturation Extract for Coarse-Textured Soils (Tentative)

The following procedure gives a moisture content that is approximately 8 times the 15-atmosphere percentage instead of 4 times, which is a usual factor for the saturation percentage of finer textured soils. The conductivity of the "twice-saturation" extract, therefore, is doubled before using the standard saturation-extract scale for salinity evaluation.

Apparatus

Soil container of 10 to 12 cm. diam. (i. e., 1-lb. coffee can) with a loosely fitting basket formed from galvanized screen with openings approximately 6 mm. square.

Pipet, 2-ml. capacity. Other items are the same as for Method 3a.

Procedure

Place the wire basket in the can, fill the basket with soil to a depth of 2 or 3 cm. Level the soil and by use of a pipet add 2 ml. of water dropwise to noncontiguous spots on the soil surface, cover, and allow to stand for 15 min. Gently sift the dry soil through the wire basket and weigh the moist pellets of soil retained thereon. Calculate the moisture content of the pellets as follows:

$$P_w = (2 \times 100)/(\text{wet weight in grams} - 2)$$

Weigh 250 gm. of air-dry soil and add sufficient water to make the moisture content up to 4 times the value found in the pellets. Use a vacuum filter to obtain the soil extract. For salinity appraisal of coarse-textured soil from which this extract was obtained, determine the electrical conductivity of the extract at 25° C. Multiply this conductivity value by 2 before using the standard saturation-extract salinity scale for interpretation (chs. 2 and 4).

(3c) Soil-Water Extracts at 1:1 and 1:5

Apparatus

Filter funnels, fluted filter paper, and bottles for soil suspensions and filtrates.

Procedure

Place a soil sample of convenient size in a bottle, add the required amount of distilled water, stopper, and agitate in a mechanical shaker for 15 min. Allow the contents to stand at least an hour, agitate again for 5 min., and filter. If shaken by hand, invert and shake bottle vigorously for 30 sec. at least 4 times at 30-min. intervals before filtering.

At a 1:1 soil-water ratio, it may be desirable to correct for hygroscopic moisture. Unless high precision is required, this is done by grouping the air-dried and screened soils roughly according to texture, and determining the percent moisture in 2 or 3 samples from each textural group. It is then possible to weigh out soil samples from the various groups and add sufficient water to bring the samples to approximately 100 percent moisture by weight. For example, an air-dry soil containing 3 percent moisture on an oven-dry basis can be brought to a 1:1 soil-water ratio by adding 97 ml. water to 103 gm. of air-dried soil.

At a soil-water ratio of 1:5 or greater, no allowance is ordinarily made for moisture in the air-dried sample.

(3d) Soil Extract in the Field-Moisture Range

A displacement method such as used by White and Ross (1937) does not require complicated apparatus; however, the pressure-membrane method described here can be used for a wider range of soil textures and a wider range of moisture contents.

Apparatus

Pressure-membrane cell with a cylinder 5 or 10 cm. high, tank of commercial water-pumped nitrogen, cans with watertight lids, plain transparent cellophane No. 600.

Procedure

Prior to use, the sheets of No. 600 cellophane are soaked in distilled water with daily changes of water in order to reduce the electrolyte content of the membrane. Electrical conductivity measurements on the water will indicate when the bulk of these impurities has been removed. Since washed and dried membranes may be somewhat brittle, they are stored wet until ready for use. They should be partially dried before mounting in the pressure-membrane apparatus.

The soil should be brought from the field at the moisture condition desired for the extraction and immediately packed in the pressure-membrane apparatus. If the soil has been air-dried, it may be passed through a 6-mm. screen and wetted to the desired water content with a fine spray of distilled water while tumbling in a mixing can or on a waterproofed mixing cloth. This wetted soil is stored in an airtight container, preferably in a constant-temperature room for 2 weeks and is mixed occasionally during this time. The pressure-membrane apparatus is then assembled, using No. 600

plain transparent cellophane for the membrane. The soil is firmly packed by hand on the membrane in the extraction chamber to a depth of 2 or 4 in., depending upon the height of cylinder available. The chamber is then closed and the extraction process started at 225 lb. per sq. in. (15 atm.) of nitrogen gas.

The extract should be collected in fractions of approximately equal volume. The first fraction is usually discarded to avoid contamination from the membrane. Electrical conductivity measurements can be made on subsequent fractions to determine the degree of uniformity of the extract. The extraction process may require 1 to 4 days.

References

Reitemeier (1946), Reitemeier and Richards (1944), Richards (1947), and White and Ross (1937).

(4) Electrical Conductivity of Solutions

(4a) Standard Wheatstone Bridge

Remarks

Electrical conductivity is commonly used for indicating the total concentration of the ionized constituents of solutions. It is closely related to the sum of the cations (or anions) as determined chemically and usually correlates closely with the total dissolved solids. It is a rapid and reasonably precise determination that does not alter or consume any of the sample.

Apparatus

Wheatstone bridge, alternating current, suitable for conductivity measurements. This may be a 1,000-cycle a. c. bridge with telephone receivers, a 60-cycle a. c. bridge with an a. c. galvanometer, or one of the newer bridges employing a cathode ray tube as the null indicator.

Conductivity cell, either pipet or immersion type, with platinized platinum electrodes. The cell constant should be approximately 1.0 reciprocal centimeter. New cells should be cleaned with chromic-sulfuric acid cleaning solution, and the electrodes platinized before use. Subsequently, they should be cleaned and replatinized whenever the readings become erratic or when an inspection shows that any of the platinum black has flaked off. The platinizing solution contains platinum chloride, 1 gm., lead acetate, 0.012 gm., in 100 ml. water. To platinize, immerse the electrodes in the above solution and pass a current from a 1.5-volt dry battery through the cell. The current should be such that only a small quantity of gas is evolved, and the direction of current flow should be reversed occasionally.

A thermostat is required for precise measurements, but for many purposes it is satisfactory to measure the temperature of the solution and make appropriate temperature corrections.

Reagents

Potassium chloride solution, 0.01 N. Dissolve 0.7456 gm. of dry potassium chloride in water and make to 1 liter at 25° C. This is the standard reference solution and at 25° C. has an electrical conductivity of 1411.8 $\times 10^{-6}$ (0.0014118) mhos/cm.

Procedure

Fill the conductivity cell with the reagent, having known conductivity EC_{25}. Most cells carry a mark indicating the level to which they should be filled or immersed. Follow the manufacturers' instructions in balancing the bridge. Read the cell resistance, R_{25} at 25° C. and calculate the cell constant (k), from the relation,

$$k = EC_{25} \times R_{25}$$

The cell constant will change if the platinization fails, but it is determined mainly by the geometry of the cell, and so is substantially independent of temperature.

Rinse the cell with the solution to be measured. The adequacy of rinsing is indicated by the absence of resistance change with successive rinsings. If only a small amount of the sample is available, the cell may be rinsed with acetone and ventilated until it is dry. Record the resistance of the cell (R_t) and the temperature of the solution ($_t$) at which the bridge is balanced. Keep the cell filled with distilled water when not in use.

Calculations

The electrical conductivity (EC_t) of the solution at the temperature of measurement ($_t$) is calculated from the relation

$$EC_t = k/R_t$$

where

$$k = EC_{25} \times R_{25}$$

For soil extracts and solutions, a temperature conversion factor (f_t), obtained from table 15, can be used for converting conductivity values to 25° C. Thus,

$$EC_{25} = EC_t \times f_t = kf_t/R_t$$

References

Campbell and others (1948), National Research Council International Critical Tables (1929).

(4b) Direct Indicating Bridge

Apparatus

Conductivity sets are available that have a bridge scale and cell design features suggested by the Laboratory especially for use with saturation extracts (fig. 26). This set is convenient to use and has sufficient accuracy for diagnostic purposes. The conductivity cell supplied with this bridge has a constant of 0.5 cm.$^{-1}$ and a capacity of 2 to 3 ml. of solution. With this cell the

TABLE 15.—*Temperature factors* (f_t) *for correcting resistance and conductivity data on soil extracts to the standard temperature of* $25°$ C.

$$EC_{25} = EC_t \times f_t; \quad EC_{25} = (k/R_t) \times f_t; \quad R_{25} = R_t/f_t$$

°C.	°F.	f_t	°C.	°F.	f_t	°C.	°F.	f_t
3.0	37.4	1.709	22.0	71.6	1.064	29.0	84.2	0.925
4.0	39.2	1.660	22.2	72.0	1.060	29.2	84.6	.921
5.0	41.0	1.613	22.4	72.3	1.055	29.4	84.9	.918
6.0	42.8	1.569	22.6	72.7	1.051	29.6	85.3	.914
7.0	44.6	1.528	22.8	73.0	1.047	29.8	85.6	.911
8.0	46.4	1.488	23.0	73.4	1.043	30.0	86.0	.907
9.0	48.2	1.448	23.2	73.8	1.038	30.2	86.4	.904
10.0	50.0	1.411	23.4	74.1	1.034	30.4	86.7	.901
11.0	51.8	1.375	23.6	74.5	1.029	30.6	87.1	.897
12.0	53.6	1.341	23.8	74.8	1.025	30.8	87.4	.894
13.0	55.4	1.309	24.0	75.2	1.020	31.0	87.8	.890
14.0	57.2	1.277	24.2	75.6	1.016	31.2	88.2	.887
15.0	59.0	1.247	24.4	75.9	1.012	31.4	88.5	.884
16.0	60.8	1.218	24.6	76.3	1.008	31.6	88.9	.880
17.0	62.6	1.189	24.8	76.6	1.004	31.8	89.2	.877
18.0	64.4	1.163	25.0	77.0	1.000	32.0	89.6	.873
18.2	64.8	1.157	25.2	77.4	.996	32.2	90.0	.870
18.4	65.1	1.152	25.4	77.7	.992	32.4	90.3	.867
18.6	65.5	1.147	25.6	78.1	.988	32.6	90.7	.864
18.8	65.8	1.142	25.8	78.5	.983	32.8	91.0	.861
19.0	66.2	1.136	26.0	78.8	.979	33.0	91.4	.858
19.2	66.6	1.131	26.2	79.2	.975	34.0	93.2	.843
19.4	66.9	1.127	26.4	79.5	.971	35.0	95.0	.829
19.6	67.3	1.122	26.6	79.9	.967	36.0	96.8	.815
19.8	67.6	1.117	26.8	80.2	.964	37.0	98.6	.801
20.0	68.0	1.112	27.0	80.6	.960	38.0	100.2	.788
20.2	68.4	1.107	27.2	81.0	.956	39.0	102.2	.775
20.4	68.7	1.102	27.4	81.3	.953	40.0	104.0	.763
20.6	69.1	1.097	27.6	81.7	.950	41.0	105.8	.750
20.8	69.4	1.092	27.8	82.0	.947	42.0	107.6	.739
21.0	69.8	1.087	28.0	82.4	.943	43.0	109.4	.727
21.2	70.2	1.082	28.2	82.8	.940	44.0	111.2	.716
21.4	70.5	1.078	28.4	83.1	.936	45.0	113.0	.705
21.6	70.9	1.073	28.6	83.5	.932	46.0	114.8	.694
21.8	71.2	1.068	28.8	83.8	.929	47.0	116.6	.683

bridge scale reads directly from 0.15 to 15 mmhos/cm. The bridge is operated by alternating current and makes use of a cathode ray tube null indicator. When the temperature of the solution is set on the temperature-compensating dial, the main dial, at balance, indicates electrical conductivity at 25° C.

The accuracy of calibration of the bridge scale should be checked with a saturated solution of calcium sulfate dihydrate. With the temperature-compensation dial correctly set, the bridge should read 2.2 mmhos/cm. with this solution.

Procedure

Obtain the saturation extract in accordance with Method 3a. Read the temperature of the extract. Rinse and fill the conductivity cell. Set the temperature compensation dial. Close the contact switch on the cell briefly while balancing the bridge with the main dial. Read and record the electrical conductivity in millimhos per centimeter at 25° C.

If the bridge will not balance, the conductivity of the extract may be below 0.15 or above 15 mmhos/cm. If above, estimate conductivity by adding 9 parts of distilled water to 1 part of extract, by volume, and balancing the bridge with the diluted extract in the cell. The conductivity of the undiluted extract will be approximately 10 times the conductivity reading obtained on the diluted extract.

Alternatively, for concentrated extracts, a cell with a constant higher than 0.5 may be used. If, for example, the value of the cell constant is 5.0, then the scale reading of the bridge must be multiplied by 10.

FIGURE 26.—Bridge and cell for measuring the conductivity of saturation extracts and irrigation waters.

(5) Resistance of Soil Paste and Percent Salt in Soil

Apparatus

Bureau of Soils electrode cup, alternating current Wheatstone bridge, and thermometer.

Procedure

Fill the electrode cup with saturated soil paste prepared in accordance with Method 2. Tap the soil cup on the workbench to remove air bubbles and strike off the soil paste level with the upper surface of the cup. Measure the resistance and the temperature of the soil paste in the cup. Use table 16 to convert the resistance reading to the temperature of 60° F. Then, by means of table 17, convert the paste resistance at 60° to approximate percent salt. Inasmuch as the saturation percentage varies with soil texture, it is necessary to estimate the textural class of the sample and to select the appropriate column in the table for making the conversion from resistance to percent salt.

References

Davis and Bryan (1910), Soil Survey Manual (1951).

(6) Freezing-Point Depression

(6a) Freezing-Point Depression of Solutions

Apparatus

Wheatstone bridge with approximately the following characteristics: 1,000 ohms equal arm ratio, 10,000-ohm decade balancing resistance adjustable to 1 ohm; galvanometer: type E, Leeds and Northrup DM–2430–c, or equivalent. Use a 2-volt lead cell for the bridge voltage supply. Thermistor: type 14B, Western Electric. Freezing bath: with either refrigerating coil or salt-ice mixture. Freezing tube: test tube 1.5 cm. inside diameter × 15 cm. long with rubber stopper. Air-jacket: test tube 2.9 cm. outside diameter × 20 cm. long. Use cork bushings cut by means of a grinding

TABLE 16.—*Bureau of Soils data for reducing soil paste resistance readings to values at 60° F. (Whitney and Means, 1897)*[1]

°F.	Ohms								
	1,000	2,000	3,000	4,000	5,000	6,000	7,000	8,000	9,000
40..............	735	1,470	2,205	2,940	3,675	4,410	5,145	5,880	6,615
42..............	763	1,526	2,289	3,052	3,815	4,578	5,341	6,104	6,867
44..............	788	1,576	2,364	3,152	3,940	4,728	5,516	6,304	7,092
46..............	814	1,628	2,442	3,256	4,070	4,884	5,698	6,512	7,326
48..............	843	1,686	2,529	3,372	4,215	5,058	5,901	6,744	7,587
50..............	867	1,734	2,601	3,468	4,335	5,202	6,069	6,936	7,803
52..............	893	1,786	2,679	3,572	4,465	5,358	6,251	7,114	8,037
54..............	917	1,834	2,751	3,668	4,585	5,502	6,419	7,336	8,253
56..............	947	1,894	2,841	3,780	4,735	5,682	6,629	7,576	8,523
58..............	974	1,948	2,922	3,896	4,870	5,844	6,818	7,792	8,766
60..............	1,000	2,000	3,000	4,000	5,000	6,000	7,000	8,000	9,000
62..............	1,027	2,054	3,081	4,108	5,135	6,162	7,189	8,216	9,243
64..............	1,054	2,108	3,162	4,216	5,270	6,324	7,378	8,432	9,486
66..............	1,081	2,162	3,243	4,324	5,405	6,486	7,567	8,648	9,729
68..............	1,110	2,220	3,330	4,440	5,550	6,660	7,770	8,880	9,990
70..............	1,140	2,280	3,420	4,560	5,700	6,840	7,980	9,120	10,260
72..............	1,170	2,340	3,510	4,680	5,850	7,020	8,190	9,360	10,530
74..............	1,201	2,402	3,603	4,804	6,005	7,206	8,407	9,608	10,809
76..............	1,230	2,460	3,690	4,920	6,150	7,380	8,610	9,840	11,070
78..............	1,261	2,522	3,783	5,044	6,305	7,566	8,827	10,088	11,349
80..............	1,294	2,598	3,882	5,176	6,470	7,764	9,058	10,352	11,646
82..............	1,327	2,654	3,981	5,308	6,635	7,962	9,289	10,616	11,943
84..............	1,359	2,718	4,077	5,436	6,795	8,154	9,513	10,872	12,231
86..............	1,393	2,786	4,179	5,572	6,965	8,358	9,751	11,144	12,537
88..............	1,427	2,854	4,281	5,708	7,135	8,562	9,989	11,416	12,843
90..............	1,460	2,920	4,380	5,840	7,300	8,760	10,220	11,680	13,140
92..............	1,495	2,990	4,485	5,980	7,475	8,970	10,465	11,960	13,455
94..............	1,532	3,064	4,596	6,128	7,660	9,192	10,724	12,256	13,788
96..............	1,570	3,140	4,710	6,280	7,850	9,420	10,990	12,560	14,130
98..............	1,611	3,222	4,833	6,444	8,055	9,666	11,277	12,888	14,499

[1] Example: Suppose the observed resistance is 2,568 ohms at 50° F. In the table at that temperature, we find that 2,000 ohms is equal to 1,734 ohms at 60° F., 5,000 ohms is equal to 4,335 ohms at 60° F., hence 500 ohms would be equal to 434 ohms. Similarly, 60 ohms would be one-hundredth of 6,000 ohms in the table and therefore equal to approximately 52 ohms at 60° F., while 8 ohms would be equal to about 7 ohms. These separate values are added together thus,

2,000	1,734
500	434
60	52
8	7

2,568 ohms at 50° = 2,227 ohms at 60°

machine to center and suspend the freezing tubes in the air-jackets. Mount the thermistor on a glass tube with plastic spacers so as to hold the thermosensitive bead at the center of a 5-ml. sample of the solution to be frozen. Plot a resistance-temperature calibration curve for the thermistor over the range from 1 to −5° C., using a standard thermometer or other source of reference temperature.

Procedure

Place 5-ml. samples of solutions in the freezing tubes and mount the tubes in the air-jacket in the freezing bath. An undercooling of approximately 2° C. has been found convenient for soil extracts and plant saps.

Place the thermistor in one of the samples when the sample has attained the bath temperature as indicated by the bridge resistance reading. Induce freezing by touching the solution with a metal probe cooled with solid carbon dioxide. Follow the course of the freezing by keeping the bridge approximately balanced until the minimum resistance (maximum temperature) is attained. With an undercooling of 2° C., a time of about 2 min. is required to attain the maximum observed freezing temperature. The minimum resistance value is recorded as the freezing resistance. The thermistor can then be transferred rapidly to the next sample so that ice crystals carried over in the process may initiate freezing. Include a tube of distilled

TABLE 17.—*Bureau of Soils data for relating the resistance of soil paste at 60° F. to percentage of "mixed neutral salts" in soil (Davis and Bryan, 1910)*

Resistance at 60° F. (ohms)	Salts in—			
	Sand	Loam	Clay loam	Clay
	Percent	*Percent*	*Percent*	*Percent*
18	3.00	3.00		
19	2.40	2.64	3.00	
20	2.20	2.42	2.80	3.00
25	1.50	1.70	1.94	2.20
30	1.24	1.34	1.46	1.58
35	1.04	1.14	1.22	1.32
40	.86	.94	1.04	1.14
45	.75	.78	.88	.98
50	.67	.71	.77	.86
55	.60	.64	.69	.77
60	.55	.58	.63	.70
65	.51	.54	.57	.63
70	.48	.50	.53	.59
75	.45	.47	.50	.55
80	.42	.44	.47	.51
85	.39	.42	.44	.48
90	.37	.39	.41	.45
95	.35	.37	.39	.42
100	.33	.35	.37	.39
105	.31	.33	.35	.37
110	.30	.32	.33	.35
115	.28	.29	.31	.33
120	.27	.28	.29	.32
125	.25	.26	.28	.30
130	.24	.25	.26	.28
135	.23	.24	.25	.27
140	.22	.23	.24	.26
145	.21	.22	.23	.25
150	.21	.21	.22	.24
155	.20	.21	.21	.23
160	.20	.20	.21	.22
165	.19	.20	.20	.21
170	.19	.19	.20	.20

water with each batch of samples to provide a check on the resistance thermometer.

Calculations

By means of the standard curve constructed for the particular thermistor in use, convert the freezing resistance to degrees centigrade. Correct for undercooling, using the following relationship:

$$\triangle T = \triangle T_o (1 - 0.0125u)$$

where $\triangle T$ is the corrected freezing-point depression, $\triangle T_o$ is the observed freezing-point depression, and u is the undercooling in degrees centigrade. A table of factors for correction for undercooling is given by Harris (1925). Calculate osmotic pressure from the equation:

$$OP = 12.06 \triangle T - 0.021 \triangle T^2$$

where OP is the osmotic pressure in atmospheres and $\triangle T$ is the freezing-point depression in degrees centigrade. Harris and Gortner (1914) present a table of osmotic pressures in atmospheres covering the range of 0 to 2.999° C. freezing-point depression.

References

Richards and Campbell (1948, 1949).

(6b) Freezing-Point Depression of Water in Soil Cores

Apparatus

Use the same resistance thermometer as in Method 6a, except the thermistor must be enclosed in a thin-walled metal tube sealed at the lower end and fastened at the upper end to the glass mounting tube. The calibration curve should be plotted for this thermistor after mounting in the protective metal jacket.

Soil sampling tube to deliver soil cores 1.7 cm. in diameter. Freezing tubes—glass test tube 2.0 cm. inside diameter (2.2 cm. outside diameter) × 17.0 cm. long with rubber stoppers. Soil core holders of rigid tubular material (hard rubber), 1.7 cm. inside diam. (1.9 cm. outside diameter) × 5.1 cm. long. Covers for soil core holders are disks of hard plastic material (Lucite), 1.9 cm. diam. × 3 mm. thick. One-half of the peripheral surface is turned to a smaller diameter (approximately 1.7 cm.) to give a snug fit in the ends of the soil core holders. A tapered hole large enough to accommodate the jacketed thermistor is drilled in one-half of the covers just described.

The Wheatstone bridge, galvanometer, freezing bath, and air-jacket tubes are as described in Method 6a. It is convenient to construct wooden racks to hold about 30 freezing tubes each.

Procedure

Soil cores are pushed from the sampling tube into the soil core holders and cut to length. A solid disk cover is placed on the bottom and a disk with a hole is placed on the top of the soil core holder. The disks are then pressed into position and are held there by the shoulder machined for that purpose. The cores are placed in the freezing tubes that are closed with rubber stoppers bearing the sample numbers. If the samples are to be stored for some time before freezing, both ends of the core holder may be dipped into melted paraffin to prevent moisture loss.

Prior to freezing the sample, a hole is drilled in the center of the soil core. The diameter of this hole should be slightly smaller than the thermistor jacket. The disturbance caused by insertion of the thermistor in an undercooled sample will then initiate freezing. The hole is drilled by hand with a twist drill mounted in a plastic rod having a free fit in the freezing tube.

The freezing tubes containing the samples to be frozen are centered and suspended in the air-jacket tubes by means of a cork bushing. The thermistor is inserted into a soil core when the freezing bath is initially loaded so that the approach of the temperature of the cores to the bath temperature can be followed. The bath temperature should be held constant $\pm 0.1°$ C. at approximately 1.5° below the expected freezing points for the batch of cores. When the samples attain the bath temperature, freezing of the first core is induced by a twist of the thermistor. Succeeding samples usually start to freeze at the time the thermistor is inserted into the sample. Frozen samples can be replaced in the bath with unfrozen samples, so that for a bath with capacity for 30 samples there is no waiting for undercooling of samples after the initial batch. An interval of about 1 hour is usually sufficient for samples at room temperature to come to bath temperature.

As with the solutions, the change in resistance (temperature) is followed by means of the galvanometer, and the minimum resistance (maximum temperature) recorded as the freezing resistance.

Calculations

The freezing resistance is converted to observed freezing-point depression in degrees centigrade by means of the calibration curve of the thermistor. No convenient method seems to be available at present for making an undercooling correction for water in soil. There is experimental indication that the undercooling correction is small for undercooling of 1.5° C. or less. Freezing-point depression is related to the sum of the tension (suction) and osmotic pressure of water in soil. Calculate the total soil-moisture stress (SMS) in atmospheres from the observed freezing-point depression ($\triangle T_o$) of water in soil cores by the relation,

$$SMS = 12 \triangle T_o$$

References

Ayers and Campbell (1951), Campbell (1952), Richards and Campbell (1949), and Schofield and Bothelho da Costa (1938).

Soluble Cations and Anions

(7) Calcium and Magnesium by Titration With Ethylenediaminetetraacetate (Versenate)

Reagents

A. Ammonium chloride-ammonium hydroxide buffer solution. Dissolve 67.5 gm. of ammonium chloride in 570 ml. of concentrated ammonium hydroxide and make to 1 liter.

B. Sodium hydroxide, approximately 4 N. Dissolve 160 gm. of sodium hydroxide in 1 liter of water.

C. Standard calcium chloride solution, 0.01 N. Dissolve 0.500 gm. of pure calcium carbonate (calcite crystals) in 10 ml. of approximately 3 N (1+3)

hydrochloric acid and dilute to a volume of exactly 1 liter.

D. Eriochrome black T indicator. Dissolve 0.5 gm. of Eriochrome black T (F 241) and 4.5 gm. of hydroxylamine hydrochloride in 100 ml. of 95 percent ethanol. This indicator is available under several different trade names.

E. Ammonium purpurate indicator. Thoroughly mix 0.5 gm. of ammonium purpurate with 100 gm. of powdered potassium sulfate.

F. Ethylenediaminetetraacetate (Versenate) solution, approximately 0.01 N. Dissolve 2.00 gm. of disodium dihydrogen ethylenediaminetetraacetate and 0.05 gm. of magnesium chloride hexahydrate in water and dilute to a volume of 1 liter. Standardize the solution against reagent C, using the titration procedures given below. The solution is standardized, using each of the indicators D and E, as the normality with E is 3 to 5 percent higher than with D.

Procedure

PRETREATMENT OF SOIL EXTRACTS.—Ammonium acetate and dispersed organic matter, when present in appreciable amounts, must be almost entirely removed from soil extracts prior to titration with Versenate. Evaporation of an aliquot of the soil extract to dryness followed by treatment with aqua regia (3 parts conc. hydrochloric acid + 1 part conc. nitric acid), and a second evaporation to dryness usually suffices for the removal of ammonium acetate and organic matter. Very dark colored soil extracts may require additional treatment with aqua regia. Dissolve the residue in a quantity of water equal to the original volume of the aliquot taken for treatment.

CALCIUM.—Pipet a 5- to 25-ml. aliquot containing not more than 0.1 meq. of calcium into a 3- or 4-inch diameter porcelain casserole. Dilute to a volume of approximately 25 ml. Add 0.25 ml. (5 drops) of reagent B and approximately 50 mg. of E. Titrate with F, using a 10-ml. microburet. The color change is from orange red to lavender or purple. When close to the end point, F should be added at the rate of about a drop every 5 to 10 seconds, as the color change is not instantaneous. A blank containing B, E, and a drop or two of F aids in distinguishing the end point. If the sample is overtitrated with F, it may be back-titrated with C.

CALCIUM PLUS MAGNESIUM.—Pipet a 5- to 25-ml. aliquot containing not more than 0.1 meq. of calcium plus magnesium into a 125-ml. Erlenmeyer flask. Dilute to a volume of approximately 25 ml. Add 0.5 ml. (10 drops) of reagent A and 3 or 4 drops of D. Titrate with F, using a 10-ml. microburet. The color change is from wine red to blue or green. No tinge of the wine-red color should remain at the end point.

Calculations

Milliequivalents per liter of Ca or Ca+Mg= (ml. of Versenate solution used × normality of Versenate solution as determined by appropriate indicator × 1,000)/ (ml. in aliquot).

Remarks

Iron, aluminum, and manganese, when present in concentrations greater than 20 p. p. m., and copper, when present in concentrations greater than several tenths of a p. p. m., interfere with the performance of the Eriochrome black T indicator. Usually the concentrations of these metals in water and ammonium acetate extracts of soils of arid regions are insufficient to cause interference. If interference is encountered, it may be overcome as described by Cheng and Bray (1951).

References

Cheng and Bray (1951), Diehl and coworkers (1950).

(8) Calcium by Precipitation as Calcium Oxalate

Apparatus

Centrifuge and 12-ml. conical tubes.

Reagents

(Keep reagents B, C, D, and E in Pyrex bottles.)

A. Methyl orange, 0.01 percent in water.

B. Hydrochloric acid, approximately 6 N (1+1).

C. Oxalic acid, approximately 0.2 N. Dissolve 12.6 gm. of oxalic acid dihydrate in water and make to 1 liter.

D. Ammonium hydroxide, approximately 7 N (1+1).

E. Ammonium hydroxide in ethanol and ether. Mix 20 ml. of conc. ammonium hydroxide with 980 ml. of a mixture of equal volumes of ethanol, ether, and water.

F. Perchloric acid, 4 N. Dilute 340 ml. of 70 percent perchloric acid or 430 ml. of 60 percent perchloric acid to 1 liter.

G. Nitro-ferroin indicator (5-nitro-1,10-phenanthroline ferrous sulfate solution, 0.001 M).

H. Ammonium hexanitrate cerate, 0.01 N in perchloric acid, 1 N. Dissolve 5.76 gm. of ammonium hexanitrate cerate in 250 ml. of 4 N perchloric acid and dilute to 1 liter. The reagent should be standardized in the following manner: Pipet 5 or 10 ml. of fresh standard 0.01 N sodium oxalate into a small beaker containing 5 ml. of reagent F, add 0.2 ml. of G, and titrate with the cerate solution to the pale-blue end point. Determine a blank titration correction on a similar sample minus the oxalate solution. The milliliters of oxalate used multiplied by 0.01 and divided by the corrected milliliters of cerate provide the normality of the cerate. Do not attempt to adjust the solution to exactly 0.01 N. Restandardize each time the reagent is used if more than 2 days have elapsed since the last standardization. Keep in a dark bottle away from light.

Procedure

Pipet an aliquot containing 0.005 to 0.08 meq. of calcium into a 12-ml. conical centrifuge tube, dilute or evaporate [14] to 5 ml., and add 1 drop of reagent A, 2 drops of B, and 1 ml. of C. Heat to the boiling point in a water bath. While twirling the tube, add D dropwise until the solution just turns yellow. Replace in the bath, and, after 30 min., cool the tube in air or in water. If necessary, add more D to keep the solution just yellow.

Centrifuge at $RCF = 1,000$ for 10 min. Carefully decant the supernatant liquid into another 12-ml. conical centrifuge tube and save for the magnesium determination. Stir the precipitate and rinse the sides of the tube with a stream of 5 ml. of reagent E blown from a pipet. Centrifuge at $RCF = 1,000$ for 10 min. Decant and drain the tube by inversion on filter paper for 10 min. Wipe the mouth of the tube with a clean towel or lintless filter paper.

Blow into the tube 3 ml. of reagent F from a pipet. When the precipitate is dissolved, add 0.1 ml. of G. Titrate with H from a 10-ml. microburet to the pale-blue end point. If more than 5 ml. of H is required, transfer the sample to a small beaker and complete the titration. Determine the blank correction in the same manner; it is usually about 0.03 ml.

Calculations

Milliequivalents per liter of Ca = (corrected ml. of cerate solution × normality of cerate × 1,000) / (ml. in aliquot).

Reference

Reitemeier (1943).

(9) Magnesium by Precipitation as Magnesium Ammonium Phosphate

Apparatus

Centrifuge, 12-ml. conical tubes, and photoelectric colorimeter.

Reagents

A. Ammonium chloride, 3 percent solution. Dissolve 3 gm. of ammonium chloride in water and dilute to 100 ml. Filter before use.

B. Ammonium dihydrogen phosphate, 5 percent solution. Dissolve 5 gm. of ammonium dihydrogen phosphate in water and dilute to 100 ml. Filter before use.

C. Phenolphthalein, 1 percent in 60 percent ethanol.

---

[14] Evaporation operations carried on with centrifuge tubes in a water bath may be speeded up by the use of an air blower. For this, a bank of glass nozzle-tubes in an array to match positions in the centrifuge tube rack is supplied with air from a compressed air system. A stream of air is thus introduced into each drying tube.

D. Ammonium hydroxide, conc.

E. Ammonium hydroxide in ethanol and ether. Mix 20 ml. of conc. ammonium hydroxide with 980 ml. of a mixture of equal volumes of ethanol, ether, and water.

F. Magnesium sulfate solution, approximately 0.01 N, standardized. This is best prepared by dilution of a more concentrated solution of magnesium sulfate that has been standardized by gravimetric determination of magnesium (Method 78).

G. Sulfuric acid. Approximately 5 N (1+6).

H. Ammonium vanadate, 0.25 percent solution. Dissolve 2.5 gm. of ammonium vanadate in 500 ml. of boiling water, cool somewhat, and then add 60 ml. of reagent G. Cool to room temperature and dilute to 1 liter. Store in a brown bottle.

I. Ammonium molybdate, 5 percent solution. Dissolve 50 gm. of ammonium molybdate in 1 liter of water. Store in a brown bottle.

Procedure

To the 12-ml. conical centrifuge tube containing the calcium-free sample from Method 8, add 1 ml. each of reagents A and B and 1 drop of C. Heat to 90° C. in a water bath and then add D until permanently pink. After 15 min., add an additional 2 ml. of D. Stopper and let stand overnight.

Centrifuge at $RCF = 1,000$ for 10 min., decant carefully, drain on filter paper for 10 min., and wipe the mouth of the tube with a clean towel or lintless filter paper. Wash the precipitate and sides of the tube with a stream of 5 ml. of reagent E from a pipet equipped with a rubber bulb or by a similar arrangement. Centrifuge at $RCF = 1,000$ for 5 min., decant, drain for 5 min., and wipe the mouth of the tube. Repeat this washing procedure once.

Pipet 10 ml. of reagent G into the tube and twirl for a few seconds. After 5 min. wash the contents into a 100-ml. volumetric flask. Dilute to about 60 ml. and pipet 10 ml. each of H and I into the flask while twirling rapidly. Dilute to the mark and mix. After 10 min. measure the difference in light transmission of the sample and water, using optical cells and a 460-mμ filter.

Starting at the beginning of the Procedure above, prepare a photometer calibration curve on semilogarithmic graph paper, for 0, 0.5, 1, 2, 3, 4, and 5 ml. of reagent F. One ml. of 0.2 N oxalic acid should be added to each tube of standard before precipitating the magnesium. The amount of magnesium in the aliquot is obtained by simple interpolation on the curve.

Calculations

Milliequivalents per liter of Mg = (meq. of Mg found by interpolation $\times$ 1,000)/(ml. in Ca aliquot $\times$ 0.98). The factor of 0.98 corrects for magnesium lost in the washings from the calcium precipitate.

References

Kitson and Mellon (1944), Reitemeier (1943).

(10) Sodium

(10a) Sodium by Flame Photometer

Apparatus

Perkin-Elmer model 52 flame photometer with acetylene or propane burner.

Reagents

A. Ammonium acetate, approximately 1 N. To 700 or 800 ml. of water add 57 ml. of conc. acetic acid and then 68 ml. of conc. ammonium hydroxide. Dilute to a volume of 1 liter and adjust to pH 7.0 by the addition of more ammonium hydroxide or acetic acid.

B. Sodium chloride, 0.04 N. Dissolve 2.338 gm. of dry sodium chloride in water and dilute to exactly 1 liter.

C. Sodium chloride, 0.04 N in 1 N ammonium acetate. Dissolve 2.338 gm. of dry sodium chloride in reagent A. Dilute to exactly 1 liter with additional A.

D. Lithium chloride, 0.05 N. Dissolve 2.12 gm. of dry lithium chloride in water and dilute to exactly 1 liter.

Procedure

Using reagents B and D prepare a series of standard sodium chloride solutions, each containing the same concentration of lithium chloride. Prepare a similar series of standard sodium chloride solutions, using reagents C and D, and use A for dilution. Recommended concentrations of sodium chloride are 0, 0.2, 0.4, 0.6, 0.8, 1, 2, 3, and 4 meq./l. The optimum concentration of lithium chloride varies with individual flame photometers but is usually 5 to 10 meq./l. Standard solutions made up with water are employed for the analysis of waters and water extracts of soils; whereas, standard solutions made up in ammonium acetate solutions are used for the analysis of ammonium acetate extracts of soils. Calibrate the flame photometer for operation over the concentration range 0 to 1 meq./l. of sodium, using the first 6 standard solutions of the appropriate series. Use the first and the last 4 solutions of the appropriate series to calibrate the instrument for operation over the concentration range 0 to 4 meq./l. of sodium.

Pipet an aliquot of the solution to be analyzed, containing less than 0.2 meq. of sodium, into a 50-ml. volumetric flask. Add an amount of reagent D that, when diluted to a volume of 50 ml., will give a concentration of lithium chloride exactly equal to that in the standard sodium chloride solutions. Dilute to volume with water, or with A, if ammonium acetate extracts are being analyzed. Mix and determine the sodium concentration by use of the flame photometer and the appropriate calibration curve.

Calculations

Milliequivalents per liter of Na in water or extract = (meq./l. of Na as found by interpolation on calibration curve $\times$ 50)/(ml. in aliquot).

(10b) Sodium by Precipitation as Sodium Uranyl Zinc Acetate

Apparatus

Centrifuge and 12-ml. conical tubes.

Reagents

A. Uranyl zinc acetate. Weigh 300 gm. of uranium acetate dihydrate, 900 gm. of zinc acetate dihydrate, and 10 mg. of sodium chloride into a large flask. Add 82 ml. of glacial acetic acid and 2,618 ml. of water. Stir or shake until the salts are dissolved, leaving only a small amount of sodium uranyl zinc acetate precipitate. Filter before use.

B. Acetic acid-ethanol. Mix 150 ml. of glacial acetic acid with 850 ml. of 95 percent ethanol. Shake with an excess of *sodium* uranyl zinc acetate crystals. Filter before use. *Sodium* uranyl zinc acetate crystals may be prepared as follows: Add 125 ml. of reagent A to 5 ml. of 2 percent sodium chloride solution, stir, and after 15 min. collect the precipitate in a porous-bottomed porcelain crucible. Wash several times with glacial acetic acid, then several times with ether, and finally dry in a desiccator.

C. Ether, anhydrous.

Procedure

Pipet an aliquot containing 0.003 to 0.07 meq. of sodium into a 12-ml. conical centrifuge tube. Evaporate on a water bath to 0.5 ml. Cool, add 8 ml. of reagent A, and mix by stirring with an aluminum wire bent into a loop. Let stand 1 hour. Centrifuge at $RCF=1,000$ for 10 min. Decant and drain on filter paper for 10 min. Wipe the mouth of the tube with a clean towel or lintless filter paper. Suspend the precipitate and wash the sides of the tube, using 5 ml. of B blown from a pipet equipped with a rubber bulb. Centrifuge for 10 min., decant, and drain for 1 min. Wipe the mouth of the tube. Wash with 5 ml. of C, but centrifuge for only 5 min. Decant carefully without draining. Repeat washing and centrifuging once. Clean the outside of tube with chamois, dry for an hour or more at 60° C., cool in a desiccator, and weigh. Add 10 ml. of water, stir with the wire until the sodium precipitate is dissolved, centrifuge for 5 min., decant carefully, and drain for 5 min. on filter paper. Suspend the insoluble precipitate and wash the sides of the tube with 5 ml. of B blown from a pipet. Centrifuge for 5 min., and decant. Wash with 5 ml. of C, centrifuge for 5 min., clean tube with chamois, dry for an hour at 60°, cool in a desiccator, and weigh. The difference between the two weights is the weight of the sodium precipitate.

Calculations

Milliequivalents per liter of Na = (gm. of Na precipitate×650.2)/(ml. in aliquot).

Reference

Reitemeier (1943).

(11) Potassium

(11a) Potassium by Flame Photometer

Apparatus

Perkin-Elmer model 52 flame photometer with acetylene or propane burner.

Reagents

A. Ammonium acetate, approximately 1 N. To 700 or 800 ml. of water add 57 ml. of conc. acetic acid and then 68 ml. of conc. ammonium hydroxide. Dilute to a volume of 1 liter and adjust to pH 7.0 by the addition of more ammonium hydroxide or acetic acid.

B. Potassium chloride, 0.02 N. Dissolve 1.491 gm. of dry potassium chloride in water and dilute to a volume of exactly 1 liter.

C. Potassium chloride, 0.02 N in 1 N ammonium acetate. Dissolve 1.491 gm. of dry potassium chloride in reagent A. Dilute to a volume of exactly 1 liter with additional A.

D. Lithium chloride, 0.05 N. Dissolve 2.12 gm. of dry lithium chloride in water and dilute to 1 liter.

Procedure

Using reagents B and D, prepare a series of standard potassium chloride solutions, each containing the same concentration of lithium chloride. Prepare a similar series of standard potassium solutions using reagents C and D, and use A for dilution. The concentrations of potassium chloride are 0, 0.1, 0.2, 0.3, 0.4, 0.5, 1, 1.5, and 2 meq./l. The optimum concentration of lithium chloride varies with individual flame photometers but is usually 5 to 10 meq./l. Standard solutions made up in water are employed for the analysis of waters and water extracts of soils; whereas, those made up in ammonium acetate solution are used for the analysis of ammonium acetate extracts of soils. Calibrate the flame photometer for operation over the concentration range 0 to 0.5 meq./l. of potassium, using the first 6 standard solutions of the appropriate series. Use the first and the last 4 solutions of the appropriate series to calibrate the instrument for operation over the concentration range 0 to 2 meq./l. of potassium.

Pipet an aliquot of the solution to be analyzed containing less than 0.1 meq. of potassium into a 50-ml. volumetric flask. Add an amount of reagent D which, when diluted to a volume of 50 ml., will give a concentration of lithium chloride exactly equal to that in the standard potassium chloride solutions. Dilute to volume with water or with A, if ammonium acetate extracts are being analyzed, mix, and determine the potassium concentration by use of the flame photometer and the appropriate calibration curve.

Calculations

Milliequivalents per liter of K in water or extract = (meq./. of K as found by interpolation on calibration curve×50)/(ml. in aliquot).

(11b) Potassium by Precipitation as Potassium Dipicrylaminate

Apparatus

Photoelectric colorimeter, centrifuge, and 12-ml. conical tubes.

Reagents

A. Lithium dipicrylaminate solution. Dissolve 1.65 gm. of lithium carbonate in 250 ml. of water. Warm to 50° C. and then add 9 gm. of dipicrylamine. After the dipicrylamine has dissolved, filter and dilute 200 ml. of this solution to 1 liter. To the remaining portion of approximately 50 ml., add 0.25 gm. of potassium chloride. Separate and wash the resulting potassium dipicrylaminate precipitate with a few milliliters of water by means of a centrifuge. Add the potassium salt to the warm solution of lithium dipicrylaminate and shake for 30 min. Filter the solution before use.

B. Potassium chloride, 0.010 N. Dissolve 0.7456 gm. of dry potassium chloride in water and dilute to exactly 1 liter.

C. Phenolphthalein, 1 percent in 60 percent ethanol.

D. Sodium hydroxide, approximately 1 N. Dissolve 40 gm. of sodium hydroxide in water and dilute to 1 liter.

Procedure

Pipet an aliquot containing 0.005–0.035 meq. of potassium into a 12-ml. conical centrifuge tube. Add 1 drop of reagent C and then D until pink. Evaporate to dryness. This insures removal of ammonium. Cool and then add exactly 2 ml. of A. Grind the salt residue in the bottom of the tube by means of a glass rod and allow 1 hour for precipitation. Centrifuge the tube at $RCF = 1,000$ for 1 min. Remove a 0.2-ml. aliquot from the supernatant liquid by means of a blood pipet and dilute to a volume of 50 ml. Compare the light transmission in an optical cell through a 510-mμ filter with that of water in similar cell. Prepare a calibration curve for each set of samples by carrying a series of 0.5, 1, 1.5, 2, 2.5, 3, 3.5 ml. of B through the same operations. The amount of potassium in the sample is found by interpolation on this curve. When plotted on a linear scale the curve should be slightly S-shaped. The temperature at which the calibration curve is prepared should be within 2° C. of that at which the unknown determinations are made.

Calculations

Milliequivalents per liter of K = (meq. of K in aliquot as found by interpolation × 1,000)/(ml. in aliquot).

Reference

Williams (1941).

(12) Carbonate and Bicarbonate by Titration With Acid

Reagents

A. Phenolphthalein, 1 percent in 60 percent ethanol.
B. Methyl orange, 0.01 percent in water.
C. Sulfuric acid, approximately 0.010 N, standardized.

Procedure

Pipet an aliquot containing 0.005 to 0.04 meq. of chloride into a 15-ml. wide-mouthed porcelain crucible or a small porcelain casserole. Chloride is specified here because the same sample is subsequently used for the chloride determination in Method 13. Add 1 drop of reagent A. If the solution turns pink, add C from a 10-ml. microburet dropwise at 5-second intervals until the color just disappears. Designate this buret reading as y. Add 2 drops of B and titrate to the first orange color. Designate the new buret reading as z. Save the titrated sample for the chloride determination.

An indicator correction blank using boiled water should be determined and applied if it is not negligible. The lighting should be adequate for the recognition of the various colors. The use of comparison color standards at the correct end points is helpful.

Calculations

1. Milliequivalents per liter of $CO_3 = (2y \times$ normality of $H_2SO_4 \times 1,000)/($ml. in aliquot$)$.
2. Milliequivalents per liter of $HCO_3 = (z-2y) \times$ normality of $H_2SO_4 \times 1,000/($ml. in aliquot$)$.

Reference

Reitemeier (1943).

(13) Chloride by Titration With Silver Nitrate

Reagents

A. Potassium chromate, 5 percent solution. Dissolve 5 gm. of potassium chromate in 50 ml. of water and add 1 N silver nitrate dropwise until a slight permanent red precipitate is produced. Filter and dilute to 100 ml.

B. Silver nitrate, 0.005 N. Dissolve 0.8495 gm. of silver nitrate in water and dilute to exactly 1 liter. Keep in a brown bottle away from light.

Procedure

To the sample preserved from the carbonate-bicarbonate determination, add 4 drops of reagent A. While stirring, titrate under a bright light with B from a 10-ml. microburet to the first permanent reddish-brown color. The titration blank correction varies with the volume of the sample at the end point, and usually increases regularly from about 0.03 to 0.20 ml. as the volume increases from 2 to 12 ml.

Calculations

Milliequivalents per liter of $Cl = (ml.$ of $AgNO_3 - ml.$ of $AgNO_3$ for blank) $\times 0.005 \times 1,000/(ml.$ in aliquot).

Reference

Reitemeier (1943).

(14) Sulfate

(14a) Sulfate by Precipitation as Barium Sulfate

Apparatus

Centrifuge and 12-ml. conical tubes.

Reagents

A. Methyl orange, 0.01 percent in water.
B. Hydrochloric acid, approximately 1 N.
C. Barium chloride, approximately 1 N. Dissolve 122 gm. of barium chloride dihydrate in water and dilute to 1 liter.
D. Ethanol, 50 percent by volume.

Procedure

Pipet an aliquot containing 0.05 to 0.5 meq. of sulfate into a clean 12-ml. conical centrifuge tube of known weight. Dilute or evaporate to about 5 ml. Add 2 drops of reagent A, then B dropwise until pink, and then 1 ml. of B in excess. Heat to boiling in water bath. While twirling the tube add 1 ml. of C dropwise. Return to the hot water bath for 30 min. and then cool at least an hour in air.

Centrifuge at $RCF = 1,000$ for 5 min. Carefully decant and let drain by inversion on filter paper for 10 min. Wipe the mouth of the tube with a clean towel or lintless filter paper.

Stir the precipitate and rinse the sides of the tube with a stream of 5 ml. of reagent D blown from a pipet. If necessary, loosen precipitate from bottom of tube by means of a wire bent in appropriate shape. Centrifuge for 5 min. and decant, but do not drain. Repeat this washing and decanting operation once. Wipe the outside of tube carefully with chamois and do not subsequently touch with fingers. Dry overnight in an oven at 105° C. Cool in a desiccator and weigh.

Calculations

Milliequivalents per liter of $SO_4 = (mg.$ of $BaSO_4$ precipitate $\times 8.568)/(ml.$ in aliquot).
(Note. Care must be taken in the preparation or concentration of the unknowns so as not to precipitate foreign material which might be weighed as barium sulfate.)

(14b) Sulfate by Precipitation as Calcium Sulfate

Apparatus

Wheatstone bridge, conductivity cell, centrifuge, and 50-ml. conical tubes.

Reagents

A. Acetone.
B. Calcium chloride, approximately 1 N. Dissolve 74 gm. of calcium chloride dihydrate in water and dilute to 1 liter.

Procedure

Pipet an aliquot containing 0.05 to 0.5 meq. of sulfate into a 50-ml. conical centrifuge tube. Dilute or concentrate to a volume of 20 ml. Add 1 ml. of reagent B and 20 ml. of A. Mix the contents of the tube and let stand until the precipitate flocculates. This usually requires 5 to 10 min. Centrifuge at $RCF = 1,000$ for 3 min., decant the supernatant liquid, invert the tube, and drain on filter paper for 5 min. Disperse the precipitate and rinse the wall of the tube with a stream of 10 ml. of A blown from a pipet. Again centrifuge at $RCF = 1,000$ for 3 min., decant the supernatant liquid, invert the tube, and drain on filter paper for 5 min. Add exactly 40 ml. of distilled water to the tube, stopper, and shake until the precipitate is completely dissolved. Measure the electrical conductivity of the solution, using Method 4b, and correct the conductivity reading to 25° C. Determine the concentration of $CaSO_4$ in the solution by reference to a graph showing the relationship between the concentration and the electrical conductivity of $CaSO_4$ solutions. This graph may be constructed by means of the following data from the International Critical Tables.

$CaSO_4$ concentration (meq./l.):	Electrical conductivity at 25° C. $Mmhos/cm.$
1	0.121
2	.226
5	.500
10	.900
20	1.584
30.5	2.205

Calculations

Milliequivalents per liter of $SO_4 = (meq./l.$ of $CaSO_4$ from electrical conductivity reading) $\times (ml.$ in aliquot/ml. of water used to dissolve precipitate).

Reference

Bower and Huss (1948).

(15) Nitrate by Phenoldisulfonic Acid

Apparatus

Photoelectric colorimeter.

Reagents

A. Phenoldisulfonic acid. Dissolve 25 gm. of phenol in 150 ml. of conc. sulfuric acid, add 75 ml. of fuming sulfuric acid (13 to 15 percent SO_3), and heat at 100° C. for 2 hours.

B. Potassium nitrate, 0.010 N. Dissolve 1.011 gm. of dry potassium nitrate in water and dilute to exactly 1 liter.

C. Silver sulfate, 0.020 N. Dissolve 3.12 gm. silver sulfate in 1 liter of water.

D. Ammonium hydroxide, approximately 7 N (1+1).

E. Calcium oxide.

Procedure

First determine the concentration of chloride in an aliquot as directed under Method 13. Pipet another aliquot containing 0.004 to 0.04 meq. of nitrate into a 25-ml. volumetric flask. Add an amount of reagent C equivalent to the amount of chloride present. Dilute to volume and mix. Transfer most of the suspension to a 50-ml. centrifuge tube and separate the precipitate by centrifuging. After transferring the solution to another centrifuge tube, flocculate any suspended organic matter by adding about 0.1 gm. of E and clear by again centrifuging. Pipet a 10-ml. aliquot representing 2/5 of the sample into an 8-cm. evaporating dish. Evaporate the aliquot to dryness, cool, and dissolve the residue in 2 ml. of A. After 10 min., add 10 ml. of water and transfer to a 100-ml. volumetric flask. Make alkaline by the addition of D, dilute to volume, and mix. Measure the light transmission through a 460-mμ filter in an optical cell against that of water in a similar cell.

Prepare a calibration curve by pipeting 0, 0.2, 0.4, 0.8, 1.2, and 1.6 ml. portions of reagent B into evaporating dishes and treating as above omitting the additions of C and E, and the clarifying procedure.

Calculations

Milliequivalents per liter of NO_3 = (meq. of NO_3 in aliquot as found by interpolation on NO_3 curve) × 1,000/(ml. in aliquot).

(16) Silicate as Silicomolybdate

Apparatus

Photoelectric colorimeter.

Reagents

A. Ammonium molybdate, 10 percent solution. Dissolve 10 gm. of ammonium molybdate in water and dilute to 100 ml.

B. Sulfuric acid, approximately 5 N (1+6).

C. Sodium silicate, 0.01 N. Dissolve 1.5 gm. of $Na_2SiO_3 \cdot 9H_2O$ in 1 liter of water. Determine the silicate (SiO_3) concentration of this solution, using a 100-ml. aliquot and Method 76a (ch. 8). Adjust the remaining solution to exactly 0.01 N by the addition of a calculated amount of water. Store in a plastic bottle.

Procedure

Pipet an aliquot containing 0.005 to 0.05 meq. of silicate into a 50-ml. volumetric flask. Dilute to a volume of 40 to 45 ml. with water. Add 2 ml. of reagent A and then 1 ml. of B. Dilute to 50 ml., mix, and after 15 min. measure the light transmission through a 420-mμ filter in an optical cell against water in a similar cell. Prepare a calibration curve by carrying a series of 0, 1, 2, 3, 4, and 5 ml. of C through the same operations.

Calculations

Milliequivalents per liter of SiO_3 = (meq. of SiO_3 in aliquot as found by interpolation × 1,000)/(ml. in aliquot).

Reference

Snell and Snell (1936).

(17) Boron

Determine boron as directed in Method 73b. If the solution is colored, transfer an aliquot to a platinum dish, make alkaline with NaOH, reagent A, and evaporate to dryness in an oven at 95° C. Ignite over an open flame until the residue fuses. Cool, add 5 ml. dilute HCl, reagent C, and complete as suggested in Method 73b under paragraph, Boron Concentration Too Low.

Exchangeable Cations

(18) Exchangeable Cations

Apparatus

Centrifuge, 50-ml. round-bottom, narrow-neck centrifuge tubes, and reciprocating shaker.

Reagents

A. Ammonium acetate solution, 1.0 N. To 700 or 800 ml. of water add 57 ml. of conc. acetic acid and then 68 ml. of conc. ammonium hydroxide. Dilute to a volume of 1 liter and adjust to pH 7.0 by the addition of more ammonium hydroxide or acetic acid.

B. Nitric acid, conc.

C. Hydrochloric acid, conc.

D. Acetic acid, approximately 0.1 N.

Procedure

Ammonium acetate extractable cations: Samples for this determination should be approximately 4 gm. for medium- and fine-textured soils and 6 gm. for coarse-textured soils. Weigh samples to an accuracy of 1 percent and correct for the air-dry moisture content. Place the sample in a centrifuge tube. Add 33 ml. of reagent A to the tube, stopper, and shake for 5 min. Remove the stopper and centrifuge at $RCF = 1,000$ until the supernatant liquid is clear. This usually requires 5 min. Decant the supernatant liquid as completely as possible into a 100-ml. volumetric flask. Extract with A a total of 3 times by this procedure, decanting into the same flask. Dilute to volume, mix, and determine the amounts of the various extracted cations by flame photometric or chemical methods. Flame photometric analyses may be made directly upon aliquots of the extract. If chemical methods are to be employed for the determination of cations, pretreat the extract in the following manner: Transfer to a 250-ml. beaker and evaporate to dryness on a hot plate or steam bath. Wash down the walls of the beaker with a small quantity of water and again evaporate to dryness. Add 1 ml. of B and 3 ml. of C, evaporate, and dissolve the residue in 20 ml. of D. Filter through low-ash content filter paper into a 50-ml. volumetric flask, using water to wash the beaker and filter paper. Dilute to volume.

Soluble cations: Prepare a saturated soil paste as described in Method 2, using a 200- to 1,000-gm. sample of soil. The weight of soil will depend upon the number of cations to be determined, the analytical methods employed, and the salt content of the soil. Determine the saturation percentage by Method 27. Obtain the saturation extract as described under Method 3a and determine the soluble cation concentrations by flame photometric or chemical methods.

Calculations

Ammonium acetate extractable cations in meq./100 gm. = (cation conc. of extract in meq./l. × 10) / (wt. of sample in gm.).

Soluble cations in meq./100 gm. = (cation conc. of saturation extract in meq./l.) × (saturation percentage) /1,000.

Exchangeable cations in meq./100 gm. = (extractable cations in meq./100 gm.) − (soluble cations in meq./100 gm.).

Reference

Bower and others (1952).

(19) Cation-Exchange-Capacity

Apparatus

Centrifuge, 50-ml. round-bottom, narrow-neck centrifuge tubes, and reciprocating shaker.

Reagents

A. Sodium acetate solution, 1.0 N. Dissolve 136 gm. of sodium acetate trihydrate in water and dilute to a volume of 1 liter. The pH value of the solution should be approximately 8.2.

B. Ethanol, 95 percent.

C. Ammonium acetate solution, 1.0 N. To 700 or 800 ml. of water add 57 ml. of conc. acetic acid and then 68 ml. of conc. ammonium hydroxide. Dilute to a volume of 1 liter and adjust to pH 7.0 by the addition of more ammonium hydroxide or acetic acid.

Procedure

Samples for this determination should be approximately 4 gm. for medium- and fine-textured soils and 6 gm. for coarse-textured soils. Weigh samples to an accuracy of 1 percent and correct for the air-dry moisture content. Place the sample in a centrifuge tube. Add 33 ml. of reagent A, stopper the tube, and shake for 5 min. Unstopper and centrifuge at $RCF = 1,000$ until the supernatant liquid is clear. This usually requires 5 min. Decant the supernatant liquid as completely as possible and discard. Treat the sample in this manner with 33-ml. portions of A a total of 4 times, discarding the supernatant liquid each time. Add 33 ml. of B to the tube, stopper, shake for 5 min., unstopper, and centrifuge until the supernatant liquid is clear. Decant and discard the supernatant liquid. Wash the sample with 33-ml. portions of B a total of 3 times. The electrical conductivity of the supernatant liquid from the third washing should be less than 40 micromhos/cm. Replace the adsorbed sodium from the sample by extraction with three 33-ml. portions of C and determine the sodium concentration of the combined extracts after dilution to 100 ml. as described under Method 18.

Calculations

Cation-exchange-capacity in meq./100 gm. = (Na conc. of extract in meq./l. × 10) / (wt. of sample in gm.).

Reference

Bower and others (1952).

(20) Exchangeable-Cation Percentages

(20a) Exchangeable - Cation Percentages by Direct Determination

Procedure

Determine the exchangeable-cation contents and the cation-exchange-capacity, using Methods 18 and 19.

Calculations

Exchangeable-cation percentage = (exchangeable-cation content in meq./100 gm. × 100) / (cation-exchange-capacity in meq./100 gm.).

(20b) Estimation of Exchangeable-Sodium-Percentage and Exchangeable-Potassium-Percentage From Soluble Cations

Procedure

Prepare a saturation extract of the soil as described under Methods 2 and 3a. Determine the calcium plus magnesium, sodium, and potassium concentrations of the saturation extract, using Methods 7, 10, and 11, respectively.

Calculations

Exchangeable-sodium-percentage

$$=\frac{100\,(-0.0126+0.01475x)}{1+(-0.0126+0.01475x)}$$

where x is equal to the sodium-adsorption-ratio.

Exchangeable-potassium-percentage

$$=\frac{100\,(0.0360+0.1051x)}{1+(0.0360+0.1051x)}$$

where x is equal to the potassium-adsorption-ratio. The sodium-adsorption-ratio and the potassium-adsorption-ratio are calculated as follows:

Sodium-adsorption-ratio $=Na^+/\sqrt{(Ca^{++}+Mg^{++})/2}$

and

Potassium-adsorption-ratio $=K^+/\sqrt{(Ca^{++}+Mg^{++})/2}$

where Na^+, K^+, Ca^{++}, and Mg^{++} refer to the concentrations of designated cations expressed in milliequivalents per liter.

A nomogram, which relates soluble sodium and soluble calcium plus magnesium concentrations to the sodium-adsorption-ratio, is given in figure 27. Also included in the nomogram is a scale for estimating the corresponding exchangeable-sodium-percentage, based on the linear equation given in connection with figure 9 (ch. 2). To use this nomogram, lay a straightedge across the figure so that the line coincides with the sodium concentration on scale A and with the calcium plus magnesium concentration on scale B. The sodium-adsorption-ratio and the estimated exchangeable-sodium-percentage are then read on scales C and D, respectively.

Supplementary Measurements

(21) pH Determinations

(21a) pH Reading of Saturated Soil Paste

Apparatus

pH meter with glass electrode.

Procedure

Prepare a saturated soil paste with distilled water as directed in Method 2 and allow paste to stand at least 1 hour. Insert the electrodes into the paste and raise and lower repeatedly until a representative pH reading is obtained.

(21b) pH Reading of Soil Suspension

Procedure

Prepare a soil suspension, using distilled water, shake intermittently for an hour, and determine pH reading.

(21c) pH Reading of Waters, Solutions, Soil Extracts

Procedure

Determine pH reading by means of a glass electrode assembly with the solution in equilibrium with a known CO_2 atmosphere.

Remarks

Opinion varies as to the proper method for making pH readings. It is desirable to select a definite procedure and follow it closely, so that the readings will be consistent and have maximum diagnostic value. The method used should be described accurately so as to aid others in the interpretation of results.

The CO_2 status influences pH readings, and should be controlled or specified. Ordinarily, readings are made at the CO_2 pressure of the atmosphere. A special high-pH glass electrode should be used for pH values appreciably above 9.0.

(22) Gypsum

(22a) Gypsum by Precipitation With Acetone (Qualitative)

Reagent

Acetone.

Procedure

Weigh 10 to 20 gm. of air-dried soil into an 8-oz. bottle and add a measured volume of water sufficient to dissolve the gypsum present. Stopper the bottle and shake by hand 6 times at 15-min. intervals or agitate for 15 min. in a mechanical shaker. Filter the extract through paper of medium porosity. Place about 5 ml. of the extract in a test tube, add an approximately equal volume of acetone, and mix. The formation of a precipitate indicates the presence of gypsum in the soil.

Remarks

The soil should not be oven-dried, because heating promotes the conversion of $CaSO_4 \cdot 2H_2O$ to $CaSO_4 \cdot 0.5H_2O$. The latter hydrate has a higher solubility in water for an indefinite period following its solution.

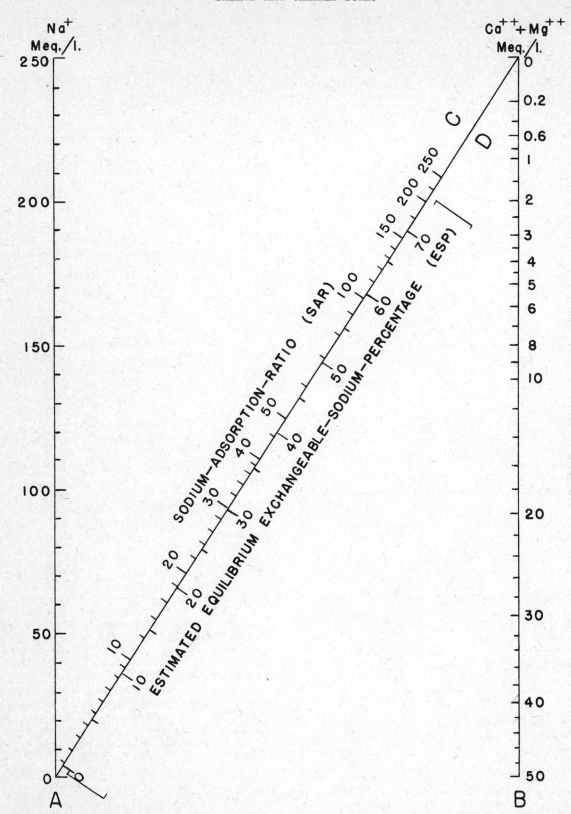

FIGURE 27.—Nomogram for determining the *SAR* value of a saturation extract and for estimating the corresponding *ESP* value of soil at equilibrium with the extract.

(22b) Gypsum by Precipitation With Acetone (Quantitative)

Apparatus

Centrifuge, 50-ml. conical centrifuge tubes, conductivity cell, and Wheatstone bridge.

Reagent

Acetone.

Procedure

Transfer a 20-ml. aliquot of the filtered extract obtained as described in Method 22a into a 50-ml. conical centrifuge tube. Add 20 ml. of acetone and mix. Let stand until the precipitate flocculates. This usually requires 5 to 10 min. Centrifuge at $RCF = 1,000$ for 3 min., decant the supernatant liquid, invert the tube, and drain on filter paper for 5 min. Disperse the precipitate and rinse the wall of the tube with a stream of 10 ml. of acetone blown from a pipet. Again, centrifuge for 3 min., decant the supernatant liquid, invert the tube, and drain on filter paper for 5 min. Add exactly 40 ml. of distilled water to the tube, stopper, and shake until the precipitate is completely dissolved. Measure the electrical conductivity of the solution, using Method 4b, and correct the conductivity reading to 25° C. Determine the concentration of gypsum in the solution by reference to a graph showing the relationship between the concentration and the electrical conductivity of gypsum solutions. This graph may be constructed by means of the following data from the International Critical Tables.

$CaSO_4$ concentration (meq./l.):	Electrical conductivity at 25° C. $Mmhos/cm.$
1	0.121
2	.226
5	.500
10	.900
20	1.584
30.5	2.205

Calculations

Milliequivalents of $CaSO_4$ in aliquot $=$ (meq./l. of $CaSO_4$ from conductivity reading) $\times$ (ml. of water used to dissolve precipitate)/1,000.

Milliequivalents of gypsum per 100 gm. of soil $= 100 \times$ (meq. of $CaSO_4$ in aliquot)/(soil: water ratio $\times$ ml. of soil-water extract used).

Remarks

Sodium and potassium sulfates when present in sufficiently high concentrations are also precipitated by acetone. The maximum concentrations of sodium sulfate and of potassium sulfate that may be tolerated are 50 and 10 meq./l., respectively.

At a 1:5 soil-water ratio, water will dissolve approximately 15 meq. of gypsum per 100 gm. of soil. If it is found that the gypsum content of the soil approaches 15 meq./100 gm. by use of a 1:5 soil-water extract, the determination should be repeated, using a more dilute extract.

Reference

Bower and Huss (1948).

(22c) Gypsum by Increase in Soluble Calcium Plus Magnesium Content Upon Dilution

Procedure

Determine the saturation percentage and obtain a saturation extract of the soil using Methods 27 and 3a. Prepare another water extract of the soil, using a moisture content sufficient to dissolve the gypsum present as described under Method 22a. Determine the calcium plus magnesium concentrations of the two extracts by Method 7.

Calculations

Soluble $Ca + Mg$ at the saturation percentage in meq./100 gm. $=$ ($Ca + Mg$ conc. of saturation extract in meq./l.) $\times$ (saturation percentage) /1,000.

Soluble $Ca + Mg$ at the high moisture percentage in meq./100 gm. $=$ ($Ca + Mg$ conc. of dilute extract in meq./l.) $\times$ (moisture percentage) /1,000.

Gypsum in meq./100 gm. of soil $=$ (soluble $Ca + Mg$ at the high moisture percentage in meq./100 gm.) $-$ (soluble $Ca + Mg$ at the saturation percentage in meq./100 gm.).

(22d) Gypsum Requirement [15]

Reagent

A. Approximately saturated gypsum solution of known calcium concentration. Place about 5 gm. of $CaSO_4 \cdot 2H_2O$ and 1 liter of water in a flask, stopper, and shake by hand several times during a period of 1 hr., or for 10 min. in a mechanical shaker. Filter and determine the calcium concentration of a 5-ml. aliquot of the solution by Method 7. The calcium concentration should be at least 28 meq./l.

Procedure

Weigh 5 gm. of air-dried soil into a 4-oz. bottle. Add 100 ml. of reagent A by means of a pipet. Stopper the bottle and shake by hand several times during a period of 30 min. or for 5 min. in a mechanical shaker. Filter part of the suspension and determine the calcium plus magnesium concentration of a suitable volume of the clear filtrate using Method 7.

---

[15] SCHOONOVER, W. R. EXAMINATION OF SOILS FOR ALKALI. University of California Extension Service, Berkeley, California. 1952. (Mimeographed.)

Calculations

Gypsum requirement, meq./100 gm.=(Ca conc. of added gypsum solution in meq./l.—Ca+Mg conc. of filtrate in meq./l.) ×2.

(23) Alkaline-Earth Carbonates (Lime)

(23a) Alkaline-Earth Carbonates by Effervescence With Acid

Reagent

A. Hydrochloric acid, 3N (1+3).

Procedure

Place several grams of soil on a small watchglass. By means of a pipet add sufficient water to saturate the soil. This displaces most of the soil air so that its loss upon the addition of acid will not be confused with effervescence of lime. Add a few drops of reagent A to the soil and note any effervescence that occurs. The soil may be termed slightly, moderately, or highly calcareous in accordance with the degree of effervescence obtained.

(23b) Alkaline-Earth Carbonates by Gravimetric Loss of Carbon Dioxide

Reagent

A. Hydrochloric acid, 3 N (1+3).

Procedure

Pipet 10 ml. of reagent A into a 50-ml. Erlenmeyer flask, stopper with a cork, and weigh. Transfer a 1- to 10-gm. sample of soil containing 0.1 to 0.3 gm. of calcium carbonate to the flask, a little at a time, so as to prevent excessive frothing. After effervescence has largely subsided, replace the stopper *loosely* and swirl the flask. Let stand with occasional swirling until the weight of the flask and contents does not change more than 2 or 3 mg. during a 30-min. period. The reaction is usually complete within 2 hours. Prior to weighing, displace any accumulated carbon dioxide gas in the flask with air. This is important and may be done by swirling with the stopper removed for 10 to 20 sec.

Calculations

Weight of CO_2 lost= (initial wt. of flask+acid+soil) − (final wt. of flask+acid+soil).
$CaCO_3$ equivalent in percent= (wt. of CO_2 lost× 227.4)/wt. of soil sample.

Remarks

The accuracy of this method depends to a large extent upon the sensitivity of the balance used for weighing. Using a torsion-type balance capable of detecting weight differences of 2 to 3 mg., the relative error is about ±10 percent.

(23c) Alkaline-Earth Carbonates From Acid Neutralization

Reagents

A. Hydrochloric acid, 0.5 N, standardized.
B. Sodium hydroxide, 0.25 N, standardized.
C. Phenolphthalein, 1 percent in 60 percent ethanol.

Procedure

Place 5 to 25 gm. of soil in a 150-ml. beaker, add 50 ml. of reagent A by means of a pipet, cover with a watchglass, and boil gently for 5 min. Cool, filter, and wash all the acid from the soil with water. Determine the amount of unused acid by adding 2 drops of C and back-titrating with B.

Calculations

$CaCO_3$ equivalent in percent= (meq. HCl added− meq. NaOH used) ×5/weight of sample in gm.

Remarks

The calculation gives the $CaCO_3$ equivalent. This is the amount of $CaCO_3$ required to react with the acid. This value usually is somewhat high, because soil constituents other than lime may react with the acid.

(24) Organic Matter

Apparatus

Erlenmeyer flasks, 500-ml., thermometer, 200° C.

Reagents

A. Potassium dichromate, 1 N. Dissolve 49.04 gm. of potassium dichromate in water and dilute to 1 liter.
B. Sulfuric acid, conc., containing silver sulfate. Dissolve 25 gm. silver sulfate in a liter of acid.
C. Ferroin indicator (ortho-phenanthroline ferrous sulfate, 0.025 M). Dissolve 14.85 gm. *o*-phenanthroline monohydrate and 6.95 gm. ferrous sulfate in water and dilute to 1 liter.
D. Ferrous sulfate, 0.5 N. Dissolve 140 gm. of $FeSO_4 \cdot 7H_2O$ in water, add 15 ml. of conc. sulfuric acid, cool, and dilute to 1 liter. Standardize this solution daily against 10 ml. of reagent A, as directed in the procedure below.

Procedure

Grind the soil to pass 0.5-mm. screen, avoiding contact with iron or steel. Transfer a weighed sample, not exceeding 10 gm. and containing from 10 to 25 mg. of organic carbon, to a 500-ml. Erlenmeyer flask. Add 10 ml. of reagent A followed by 20 ml. of B. Swirl the flask, insert thermometer, and heat gently so as to attain a temperature of 150° C. in a heating period of about 1 min. Keep contents of flask in motion in order to prevent local overheating, which results in error caused by thermal decomposition of dichromate. After the 150° temperature is reached, place the flask on an asbestos pad, and allow to cool. Add 200 ml. of water and 4 or 5 drops of C. Titrate with D until the color changes from green to red.

Since some soils adsorb *o*-phenanthroline indicator, the titration may be improved by a prior filtration, using a rapid filter paper on a Buechner funnel. If more than 80 percent of the dichromate solution is reduced, the determination should be repeated with less soil.

Calculations

Organic carbon in percent = (meq. of $K_2Cr_2O_7$ added − meq. of $FeSO_4$ used) × 0.336/wt. of sample in gm.

Organic matter in percent = organic carbon in percent × 1.72.

Remarks

This modification of Walkley's rapid method (1935, 1947) for the determination of organic carbon in soils has been found to give approximately 89 percent recovery of carbon, as compared to the dry-combustion method. The conversion factor 0.336 was obtained by dividing 0.003, the milliequivalent weight of carbon, by 89 and multiplying by 100 to convert to percent. Chloride interference is eliminated by the addition of the silver sulfate to the digesting acid as indicated. Nitrates up to 5 percent and carbonates up to 50 percent do not interfere.

References

Walkley (1935, 1947).

(25) Total and External Ethylene Glycol Retention

Apparatus

Vacuum pump, Central Scientific Company Hyvac or equivalent.

Vacuum desiccators, inside diameter 250 mm., with external sleeve or glass stopcock and porcelain plates.

Muffle furnace with automatic temperature control.

Aluminum moisture boxes, 2½ in. in diameter and ¾ in. high, with lids.

Reagents

A. Hydrogen peroxide, 10 percent solution.
B. Anhydrous calcium chloride, 8 or 12 mesh, technical.
C. Phosphorus pentoxide.
D. Ethylene glycol (Eastman). Redistill under reduced pressure, discarding the first and last 10 percent of the distillate.

Procedure

Soil preparation. Grind the soil sample to pass a 60-mesh sieve. The increase in surface area brought about by this degree of grinding is negligible. Treat approximately 10 gm. of the sieved soil with reagent A for the removal of organic matter (see Method 41). Transfer the treated soil to a 5- to 8-cm. diameter Buechner funnel fitted with filter paper and leach with several small portions of distilled water, using suction. Allow the soil to air-dry, then pass through a 60-mesh sieve.

Total ethylene glycol retention. Weigh 2.10 gm. of the 60-mesh soil into an aluminum moisture box. The tare weight of the box and its lid should be known. Spread the soil evenly over the bottom of the box. Place the box in vacuum desiccator over about 250 gm. of reagent C, apply vacuum by means of a Hyvac or equivalent pump, and dry the soil to constant weight. This usually requires 5 to 6 hours. Determine the weight of vacuum-dried soil. By means of a pipet, having a tip drawn to a fine point, distribute 1 ml. of D dropwise over the soil surface. Place the box in a second vacuum desiccator over 250 gm. of B and allow to stand overnight to obtain uniform wetting of the soil. Connect the desiccator to a Hyvac pump and evacuate at a temperature of 25±2° C. until excess ethylene glycol is removed from the soil. Depending upon the temperature and vacuum conditions attained, this usually requires from 5 to 7 hours when 8 samples are present in a desiccator. In practice, the box is weighed after 5 hours in the vacuum desiccator and at intervals of 1 hour thereafter until the loss of weight per hour interval is less than 3 or 4 percent of the weight of ethylene glycol remaining on the soil. The next to the last weight taken is used to calculate ethylene glycol retained.

External ethylene glycol retention. Weigh exactly 2.10 gm. of the 60-mesh soil into an aluminum moisture box. Spread the soil evenly over the bottom of the box and heat at a temperature of 600±15° C. for 2 hours in a muffle furnace having automatic temperature control. Remove the box, cover, cool in a desiccator containing reagent B, and weigh. Apply 1 ml. of D to the soil, let stand overnight, and remove the excess ethylene glycol by evaporation in vacuum as described previously for the determination of total ethylene glycol retention.

Calculations

Assuming that 3.1×10^{-4} gm. of ethylene glycol are required for the formation of a monolayer on 1 sq. m. of surface, as indicated by Dyal and Hendricks (1950), the formulas for calculation of total, external, and internal surface areas are as follows:

Total surface area, m.²/gm. = wt. of ethylene glycol retained by unheated soil, gm./(wt. of vacuum-dried unheated soil, gm. × 0.00031).

External surface area, m.²/gm. = wt. of ethylene glycol retained by heated soil, gm./(wt. of vacuum-dried unheated soil, gm. × 0.00031).

Internal surface area = (total surface area) − (external surface area).

Remarks

The Hyvac pump and desiccators are connected by means of tight-fitting vacuum rubber tubing. A glass tube filled with reagent B is inserted in the vacuum line to prevent undesirable vapors from entering the pump. The tube also permits the introduction of dry air into the desiccators to release the vacuum. High-vacuum stopcock lubricant should be used to seal the glass joints.

The adequacy of the vacuum system for removing excess ethylene glycol can be checked by determining the rate of evaporation of this liquid from a free surface. The average rate of evaporation over a 5-hour period from an aluminum moisture box of the size specified above and containing ethylene glycol should be at least 1 gm. per hour.

For greatest accuracy in the determination of internal surface area, removal of excess ethylene glycol from heated and unheated soil should be performed concurrently. Four unheated and the corresponding 4 heated samples are ordinarily placed together in a desiccator. The occasional inclusion of a standard sample having a known retention value serves as a useful control on procedure.

The anhydrous calcium chloride placed in the desiccator to absorb ethylene glycol should be renewed after each set of 8 determinations. The phosphorus pentoxide used for drying under vacuum may be used until it absorbs sufficient water to develop a syrupy consistency.

References

Bower and Gschwend (1952), Dyal and Hendricks (1950, 1952).

Soil Water

(26) Soil-Moisture Content

Procedure

Transfer a representative subsample of the soil to a tared can with lid. For accuracy, it is desirable where possible to use at least a 25-gm. sample. Weigh, dry to constant weight at 105° C., and weigh again.

Calculations

Moisture content in percent, P_w = (loss in weight on drying) $\times 100$/(weight of the oven-dry soil).

(27) Saturation Percentage

(27a) Saturation Percentage From Oven-Drying

Procedure

Transfer a portion of the saturated soil paste, prepared according to Method 2, to a tared soil can with lid. Determine the moisture content by Method 26.

Calculations

Saturation percentage (SP) = (loss in weight on drying) $\times 100$/(weight of the oven-dry soil).

(27b) Saturation Percentage From Volume of Water Added

Remarks

When the air-dry moisture content of the sample is known, as it usually is when exchangeable-cation analyses are made, the saturation percentage can be determined as follows:

Procedure

Transfer a known weight of air-dry soil to a mixing cup. Add distilled water from a buret or graduated cylinder with stirring until the soil is saturated as described in Method 2. Record the volume of water added.

Calculations

Weight of oven-dry soil = (weight of air-dry soil) $\times 100$/(100 + air-dry moisture percentage).

Total water = (water added) + (water in air-dry soil) = (weight of water added) + (weight of air-dry soil) − (weight of oven-dry soil).

$SP = 100 \times$ (total weight of water)/(weight of oven-dry soil).

(27c) Saturation Percentage From the Weight of a Known Volume of Paste

Remarks

By this method, the saturation percentage is calculated from the weight of a known volume of saturated soil paste. It is assumed that the soil particles have a density of 2.65 gm./cm.^{3}, and that the liquid phase has a density of 1.00 gm./cm.^{3}.

Apparatus

Balance, accurate to 0.1 gm.

A cup of known volume. This measurement can be combined with the soil-paste resistance measurement using the same loading of the Bureau of Soils electrode cup.

Procedure

Determine the volume and weight of the cup. Fill the cup with saturated soil paste, jarring it during filling to exclude air, and strike off level with the top. Weigh and subtract the cup weight to get the net weight of the paste.

Calculations

$$SP = \frac{100\ (2.65V - W)}{2.65\ (W - V)}.$$

where SP = saturation percentage; V = volume of saturated soil paste, in cm.³, = a constant; and W = net weight of V cm.³ of saturated soil paste, gm. Calculations are simplified by the use of a table or graph relating values of W and SP for a given value of V.

Reference

Wilcox (1951).

(28) Infiltration Rate

Remarks

Infiltration rate (infiltration capacity) is the rate of water entry into the soil where water covers the surface at a shallow depth and downward flow into and through the soil is nondivergent. The latter condition is satisfied by rainfall or if the ponded area is infinitely large. For practical purposes, the subsidence rate of the free-water surface in a large basin is taken as a measure of the infiltration rate. The effect of divergent flow increases as the ponded area decreases. If small basins or cylinders are used, it is difficult to determine the true infiltration rate. For soils in which permeability increases with depth, errors from flow divergence may be negligible; but, if the permeability decreases with depth, the effect of flow divergence may be considerable. Flow divergence that occurs with small plots or cylinders may be minimized by ponding water in a guard ring or border area around the plot or cylinder.

If infiltration measurements are made under conditions where divergent flow may not be negligible, the water-intake rate should be reported as infiltration velocity and accompanied by a description of the measuring method.

Under some conditions the evaporation rate may not be negligible and must be taken into account in infiltration measurements. In small basins or where cylinders are used, evaporation may be minimized by covering the water surface with a film of oil.

There is no single method best suited to all field conditions. Experience and judgment are required in obtaining and evaluating infiltration measurements. (See discussion in chapter 2.)

(28a) Basin

Apparatus

Gage for measuring water elevation, and watch.

Procedure

Pond water on an area of soil enclosed by dikes or ridges. Measure the rate of subsidence of the water surface with a staff gage (a linear scale standing in the water), hook gage, or water-stage recorder.

The infiltration rate will depend on the time and depth of water that has entered the soil.

Calculations

A curve showing the depth of water that has entered the soil as a function of time can be plotted from the water elevation and time readings or taken from a water-stage recorder. Average or instantaneous values of the infiltration rate can be taken from this curve, depending on the purpose of the measurement. Express infiltration rate in centimeters per hour or in inches per hour.

(28b) Cylinder

Apparatus

Cylinders 11 to 14 in. in diameter and 16 in. long. The cylinders can be rolled from 16-gage sheet iron. Butt-weld and grind the weld smooth. Reinforce the upper end with 1/8-in. by 1-in. iron strip, welded to cylinder. Galvanize cylinders after fabrication. For ease in transportation, cylinders can be made with different diameters so that they will fit, one within another.

Circular driving cap and hammer. Torch-cut the driving cap from 1/2-in. steel plate and screw in a 1/2-in. central rod to serve as the hammer guide. The hammer can consist of a 50- to 80-lb. block of iron. This should have a central pipe to slide on the guide rod of the cap. Attach crosshandles to the pipe.

Hook gage or staff gage, watch, thin metal tamp, splash guard of rubber sheet or burlap, field source of water.

Procedure

Drive the cylinders into the soil to a depth of 6 or 8 in. Alternatively, the cylinders can be jacked into the soil, if a heavy tractor or truck is available. Care should be exercised to keep the sides of the cylinder vertical and to avoid disturbance of the soil column within the cylinder. Tamp soil into the space between the soil column and the cylinder. If this space is greater than 1/8 in., the cylinder should be reset. Cover the soil with a splash guard and apply 4 to 6 in. of water. Record the elevation of the water surface and the time at convenient intervals. A staff gage is often satisfactory, but a hook gage should be used if the subsidence rate is low. Several adjacent cylinders are usually installed. These need not be carefully leveled if a mark is placed on each cylinder for locating the base of the hook gage.

While the wetting front is in the cylinder, the water-subsidence rate corresponds to the infiltration rate. When the wetting front passes below the cylinder, more or less divergence of flow will occur and the subsidence rate then should be designated as intake rate or infiltration velocity. Divergent flow is minimized by installing cylinders in plots or within larger diameter rings in which the soil is kept flooded.

Where desired, water-entry rates into subsurface soil layers can be measured by excavating to the desired depth before setting the cylinders.

Calculations

Express infiltration rate and infiltration velocity in centimeters per hour or in inches per hour, using values averaged over time intervals appropriate to the purposes of the measurement.

(29) 1/10-Atmosphere Percentage

Apparatus

Pressure-plate apparatus. Retainer rings approximately 1 cm. high and 6 cm. in diameter to hold at least 25-gm. samples. Balance, drying oven, and moisture boxes.

Remarks

Install the pressure plates to be used for the test in a pressure cooker, fill the cooker with water, fasten the lid on the cooker, and measure the rate of outflow of water from the ceramic plates at a pressure of 15 lb. in.$^{-2}$. This rate should be about 1 cc. per cm.^{2} per hr. per atm. pressure difference or greater for satisfactory operation of the porous plates. Next check the pressure plates for entry value as follows: release the air pressure, empty excess water from the cooker pot and the plates, close the cooker pot, and apply a pressure of $\frac{1}{2}$ atm. or other appropriate value. After a few minutes, the outflow of water from the plate outlets will cease and there should be no bubbling of air from these outlets, thus indicating that the entry values for the plates are above the value of the pressure applied to the pressure cooker. At the conclusion of the entry-value test, submerge the pressure cooker in water while the pressure is on or make other equivalent tests to make sure that there are no air leaks at the cooker gasket or attendant connections. Air leaks from the cooker cause troubles with air-pressure control and may also cause serious errors in retentivity determinations through direct loss of water vapor from the soil samples.

Procedure

Prepare duplicate 25-gm. samples that have been passed through a 2-mm. round-hole sieve, using the subsampling procedure outlined in Method 1. Place the sample retainer rings on the porous plate. In order to avoid particle-size segregation, dump *all* of the soil sample from each container into a ring and level. Allow the samples to stand at least 16 hours with an excess of water on the plate. Close the pressure cooker and apply a pressure of 100 cm. of water. Samples 1 cm. high can be removed any time after 48 hours from initiating the extraction or when readings on a buret indicate that outflow has ceased from all of the samples on each plate. Some soils will approach equilibrium in 18 to 20 hours. Before releasing the air pressure in the pressure cooker, put a pinch clamp on the outflow tube for each plate. This prevents backflow of water to the samples after the pressure is released. To avoid changes in the moisture content of the samples, transfer the samples quickly to moisture boxes. Determine the moisture content by drying to constant weight at 105° C. Express the moisture content as percent, dry-weight basis.

References

Richards and Weaver (1944), and Richards (1949b).

(30) ⅓-Atmosphere Percentage

Apparatus

Same as in Method 29.

Procedure

Same as in Method 29, except that the extraction pressure is 345 cm. of water.

(31) 15-Atmosphere Percentage

Apparatus

Pressure-membrane apparatus with sausage-casing membrane. Rubber soil-retaining rings 1 cm. high and approximately 6 cm. in diameter that hold about 25 gm. of soil. Balance, drying oven, and moisture boxes.

Procedure

Prepare duplicate 25-gm. samples that have been passed through a 2-mm. round-hole sieve, using the subsampling procedure outlined in Method 1. Moisten the cellulose membrane, install in the apparatus, and trim the edge by running a knife around the brass cylinder. Place the soil-retaining rings on the membrane. In order to avoid particle-size segregation, dump *all* of the soil sample from each sample container into one ring. Pouring out part of the sample and leaving part in the container will give a nonrepresentative sample. Level the sample in the ring, cover with a square of waxed paper, and allow the samples to stand at least 16 hours with an excess of water on the membrane. Remove excess water from the membrane with a pipet or rubber syringe, close the pressure-membrane apparatus and admit air to the soil chamber at a pressure of 15 atm. (220 lbs. in.$^{-2}$).

After a few hours, there is a marked decrease in the rate of water outflow from the soil, the outflow rate then being limited mainly by the low capillary conductivity of the soil rather than the low membrane permeability. At this time, the soil samples have sufficient rigidity to resist plastic flow and compaction and so a 4 lb. in.$^{-2}$ pressure differential may be applied to the rubber diaphragm at the top of the soil chamber. This diaphragm action holds the sample firmly in contact with the membrane and considerably hastens moisture extraction for fine-textured soils that shrink appreciably. The diaphragm is unnecessary for medium- and coarse-textured soils.

Remove the samples any time after 48 hours from the commencement of the extraction or when the readings on an outflow buret indicate equilibrium has been attained. Most soils will approach hydraulic equilibrium with the membrane in 18 to 20 hours, but some soils may require a considerably longer time. In order to avoid changes in the moisture content, transfer the samples to moisture boxes as soon as possible after releasing the extraction pressure. Determine the moisture content by drying to constant weight at 105° C. Express moisture content as percent, dry-weight basis.

Remarks

Care must be taken to keep soil away from the lower gasket of the cell. Otherwise, gasket flow that occurs when the cell is closed may press sand particles into the membrane and cause leaks.

References

Richards (1947), Richards and Weaver (1944).

(32) Moisture-Retention Curve

Each sample, with disturbed or undisturbed structure, is contained in a retainer consisting of a brass cylinder, a plastic lid, and a porous ceramic bottom plate, all held together with rubber bands. Various moisture equilibria and weighings are thus made possible with a minimum of disturbance to the sample.

Apparatus

Pressure-plate apparatus, pressure-membrane apparatus, balance, drying oven, large straight-edged carving knife, and aluminum moisture boxes with lids, $3\frac{1}{2}$ in. diameter by 2 in. high.

Soil sampling tube with retainer cylinders cut from brass tubing $2\frac{1}{4}$ in. outside diameter by 19-gage wall. The core retainer cylinders are 3 cm. high, and while in the sampling tube have guard rings 1 cm. high at each end. (See drawing of apparatus in the Appendix.)

Plastic and ceramic disks serve as lids and bottoms for the core retainer. The lids are cut from $\frac{1}{8}$ in. transparent plastic sheet and are $2\frac{1}{4}$ in. in diameter. The ceramic disks are $2\frac{1}{4}$ in. in diameter by $\frac{3}{16}$ in. thick, with a peripheral groove to attach two hooks formed from twisted wire at points on the disk 180° apart. The porous ceramic body should be like that used for tensiometer cups. The entry value should be greater than 1 atm., and the hydraulic conductivity should be equal to or greater than 8×10^{-4} cm./hr.

A layer of cheesecloth and sieved soil make capillary contact between the retainers and the control membranes. The cheesecloth should be treated with a bactericide such as Dowicide No. 4. The fraction of a loam soil that passes a 60-mesh screen makes a good capillary contact medium.

A complete core-retainer set consists of a moisture box with lid, a brass cylinder, a plastic lid, two strong rubber bands, and a ceramic plate. All of the parts in a retainer set should bear the same identifying number. The tare weight of each retainer set with the ceramic disk *saturated with water* should be determined and recorded.

Procedure

Take the cores with the sampling tube when the soil is moist. Remove the 1-cm. guard rings from either end of the 3-cm. retainer cylinder. Roughly trim the cores in the field and transport to the laboratory in the aluminum moisture boxes. Trim the cores accurately in the laboratory with the carving knife. Fasten the plastic lids and ceramic plates to the brass cylinders by stretching the rubber bands across the lids and attaching the bands to the hooks at the opposite edges of the ceramic plates.

Place the core retainers on a porous brick with a free water surface 1 or 2 mm. below the surface of the brick. After 24 hours, wipe the excess water from the retainers, place each in its moisture box, and weigh. Replace the retainers on the brick with the water surface set for 10 cm. After 24 hours, weigh again. These two weighings will not represent equilibrium values, but high precision is usually not required at 0 and 10 cm. of suction. Prepare the pressure-plate apparatus as indicated in Method 29. Spread approximately a 3-mm. layer of screened loam soil on the pressure plate and cover with a single layer of treated cheesecloth. Moisten the soil and cloth with water and set the retainers firmly in contact. Close the pressure cooker and adjust the pressure for the next suction value.

Follow the approach to hydraulic equilibrium at each pressure by connecting the outflow tube from each plate or membrane to the lower end of a buret and recording the buret readings occasionally. When equilibrium is attained, clamp off the outflow tubes and release the air pressure in the cooker or membrane cell. Lift the core retainers from the membrane, brush off any adhering soil, place each in its numbered moisture box, and weigh. For a retention curve, weighings can be made at tensions of 0, 10, 30, 100, and 345 cm. of water and 1, 3, and 15 atm. Other suction values can be used, depending on the information desired.

The porous-ceramic retainers used at the Laboratory have an entry value of 1 atm. and do not change appreciably in moisture content at suction values up to 3 atm. Therefore, the gross tare for a core-retainer set is the same for all weighings at suction values up to and including 3 atm. At the 15-atmosphere equilibrium, the ceramic retainer is removed before the weighing, and a correspondingly different tare weight is used. Determine the weight of the soil core when oven-dried at 105° C.

Calculations

Determine the volume of the core retainer and calculate the bulk density of the soil in the core. From the gross weights at each suction, the tare weights, and the known weight of soil, calculate both the mass of water and the volume of water (numerically the same when c. g. s. units are used) in the core at each suction value. From the foregoing data, calculate the grams of water per 100 gm. of dry soil and the cubic centimeters of water per 100 cm.^{3} of soil at each suction value. The latter may be taken as the depth percentage, i. e., the depth of free water per 100 units of depth of soil. Plot these values on linear coordinates with moisture retention as the dependent variable, and suction or soil-moisture tension as the independent variable.

References

Richards (1947, 1948, 1949b, 1952).

(33) Field-Moisture Range

Remarks

Plants can grow in soil over a range of moisture contents referred to as the available range. The practical upper boundary for this range, sometimes referred to as field capacity, is characteristic of the field situation, and the best method for its determination is based on field sampling. The determination should be made after the soil has been wetted and the rate of downward drainage has decreased, but before appreciable moisture is lost from the profile by evaporation and root extraction. This determination loses significance or requires special interpretation if drainage is restricted or if a water table is close to the soil surface.

Apparatus

Soil tube or soil auger, watertight moisture boxes, balance, and drying oven.

Procedure

One to 3 days after the soil profile is thoroughly wetted with rain or irrigation water, take samples by horizons, by textural layers, or at 1-foot-depth intervals throughout the wetted zone. Determine the moisture content of the samples by drying to constant weight at 105° C. Express the results as moisture percentage, dry-weight basis, or as depth percentage if the bulk density can be determined. The available range for the soil at any given depth is then found by subtracting the 15-atm. percentage from the field determination of the upper limit of available water. The available range can be expressed either as a dry-weight percentage or as a depth percentage.

(34) Hydraulic Conductivity

(34a) Hydraulic Conductivity of Soil Cores

Thin-walled cylinders or cans may be pressed into the soil in the field to obtain samples of soil of substantially undisturbed structure. More often, soil cores are obtained in metal sleeves that fit into a sampling tube, and, after the samples have been taken, the sleeves serve as the core retainers. Power-driven machines are available for taking undisturbed cores of 4- and 6-in. diameter. Such cores are encased in the field for transportation and subsequent water-flow measurements. Various casing methods have been used, such as painting the core with wax or plastic cement before and after wrapping in cloth.

Procedure

In the laboratory, the cores are mounted vertically and supported on a porous outflow surface such as sand or filter paper and metal screen. A shallow depth of water is usually maintained over the soil surface by a siphon tube from a constant-level reservoir. Flow tests should be conducted with water of the same quality as that which occurs in the field. If discharge rates are low, care must be taken to avoid errors arising from evaporation of the percolate. If possible, flow tests should be conducted at or near constant temperature.

Where desirable, especially for long cores, manometers can be attached at various points along the core. These should be installed at transition zones between horizons or at textural discontinuities.

Calculations

Water flow takes place in accordance with the equation:

$$\frac{Q}{t} = k \, A \frac{\triangle H}{\triangle L}$$

where Q is the volume of water passing through the core in time (t), A is the area of the core, and k is the average hydraulic conductivity in the soil interval

($\triangle L$), over which there is a hydraulic head difference of $\triangle H$. Solving for k gives $k = Q \triangle L / At \triangle H$. Hydraulic conductivity (k) will be in centimeters per hour if t is expressed in hours, Q in cm.[3], A in cm.[2], and $\triangle H$ and $\triangle L$ are both in the same units.

References

Bower and Peterson (1950), Kelley and coworkers (1948), Marsh and Swarner (1949), and Richards (1952).

(34b) Hydraulic Conductivity of Disturbed Soil

Apparatus

Soil containers are made from 20-gage seamless brass tubing, 3 in. outside diameter, and 4 in. in length. The bottoms of the containers are machined from 20-gage brass sheet and are soldered into a recess or counterbore in the cylinders. The central outflow tubes are 2 in. long, are cut from $\frac{1}{2}$ in. outside diameter by 20-gage brass tubing, and are attached with solder.

Supports for soil and filter paper consist of circles of 20-mesh or coarser bronze screen cut so as to fit loosely on the inside of the soil container.

Packing block is made from a heavy wooden block approximately 4 by 4 by 8 in. A hole is made in the block to accommodate the outflow tube of the soil container, and guide rods are mounted in the block to keep the cylinder vertical and to insure square impacts. One rod is cut 2.5 cm. above the cylinder so that a finger placed over this rod gives a convenient index of height for the packing process.

Sharkskin filter paper, rack for supporting a number of soil containers, constant-level water supply, siphon tubes to connect soil containers to water supply, graduated cylinders, 2-mm. round-hole sieve, soil grinder, and mixing cloth.

Procedure

Air-dry the soil and pass it through a 2-mm. round-hole screen. A power grinder may be used for hard soils, but the grinding process must be standardized, with the plates set to reduce only the larger particles. Obtain representative 200-gm. subsamples in accordance with Method 1. Dump the entire subsample in one motion into the soil container that has been fitted with a screen and filter paper. This method of transferring the soil is used to prevent particle-size segregation. The cylinder containing the soil is dropped 20 times through a distance of 2.5 cm. onto the packing block. Place a filter paper on the soil surface and introduce water into the container with a minimum of soil disturbance. Record the time of application of water and, if possible, the time of the initial outflow. Collect the percolate in a suitable receptacle and measure the volume at convenient time intervals. Tests ordinarily are run until the volume of water that has passed

through the soil corresponds to approximately 12 cm. of depth of water on the soil surface. Calculate hydraulic conductivity and plot against accumulated equivalent depth of percolate. With soils having extremely low percolation rates, an attempt should be made to obtain at least one flow measurement, and time rather than depth of water is used to determine when to discontinue tests on such soils.

Remarks

While, according to theory, neither the diameter nor the height of the soil column to be tested needs to be within prescribed limits, it has been found that with many soils satisfactory results are not obtained unless the height is less than the diameter of the soil column. This is particularly important if the soil swells appreciably on wetting. Experience indicates that the cylinder should have at least a 7.5-cm. diameter for a 5-cm. depth of soil.

Hydraulic-conductivity measurements should be made in the temperature range from 65° to 75° F. (18° to 24° C.). For the most part, the effect of temperature on hydraulic conductivity in this range is small compared with effects arising from such factors as quality of the water and the base status and salinity of the soil. The standard temperature for laboratory determination of hydraulic conductivity is usually taken as 68° F. (20° C.). Corrections for viscosity effects on measurements at temperatures other than 68° F. can readily be calculated, but it has been observed that temperature has other and not always predictable effects upon the hydraulic conductivity of soils in addition to those arising from viscosity.

The hydraulic gradient is usually set in the range from 1 to 4, although values as high as 10 do not seem to affect the results significantly.

In general the water that will be used on the soil in the field should be used for the laboratory determinations, because small changes in water quality can produce large changes in rate of moisture movement.

Measurements are usually made in triplicate. The samples are discarded and the test repeated if the range of values is greater than 50 percent of the mean hydraulic-conductivity value. Between soils or treatments, average differences in conductivity of less than 15 or 20 percent are not considered significant.

Calculations

Water flow takes place in accordance with the equation:

$$\frac{Q}{t} = kA \frac{\triangle H}{\triangle L}$$

where Q is the volume of water passing through the material in time (t); A is the area of the soil column, and k is the average hydraulic conductivity in the soil interval ($\triangle L$) over which there is a hydraulic-head difference ($\triangle H$). Solving for hydraulic conductivity:

$$k = \frac{Q \triangle L}{t A \triangle H}$$

It should be noted that $\triangle H$ must be measured from the surface of water standing on the soil to the elevation at which water will stand during the flow test in a riser or manometer connected at the bottom of the soil column. For experimental setups sometimes used, this elevation may be quite different from the elevation of the bottom of the soil column. The length of the soil column $\triangle L$ should be measured during or after water flow and not when the soil is dry.

References

Christiansen (1947), Fireman (1944), and Richards (1952).

(34c) Hydraulic Conductivity From Piezometer Measurements

Equipment

The piezometer pipe may be of any convenient diameter. The length will be governed by the depth at which measurements are to be made. The wall thickness should be as thin as practical to minimize soil disturbance during installation. Thin-walled electrical conduit, 1 to 2 in. inside diameter, has been found suitable for hydraulic-conductivity measurements at depths up to 10 ft. Other pieces of equipment needed for this measurement are: a screw-type soil auger having a free-fit inside the piezometer pipe; a hammer, such as is used for soil tubes or for steel fence posts, may be used for driving the pipe; a pump, such as a hand-operated pitcher pump, with a flexible hose attached to the inlet is needed to remove water and sediment from the pipe and the soil cavity; an electrical sounder is convenient for measuring the depth to the water surface within the pipe (see Method 35a); an ordinary watch is satisfactory for measuring time, except, if the rate of rise is rapid, two stop watches may be required to obtain a continuous rate-of-rise record; a soil-tube jack or other tube puller is useful in recovering the piezometer pipe.

Remarks

Hydraulic-conductivity measurements by this method are limited to soils below a water table. An auger hole is cased with a length of pipe and a cylindrical cavity is formed at the lower end of the pipe. Ground water flows into the cavity when water is pumped from the pipe, and the rate at which the water level rises in the pipe is a measure of hydraulic conductivity. Although the development of the equation is based upon an idealized condition of homogenous isotropic soil, this method may be used for determining the hydraulic conductivity of nonuniform soils and of individual soil layers. Information regarding water-table level and nature and position of subsoil layers should be available prior to installation of piezometer pipes to assist in determining proper placement of pipes and construction of cavities. For most purposes, the extremities of the cavity should not be closer than one cavity length from either the top or bottom of the particular soil layer for which the determination is made.

This method is applicable only where a cavity of known shape can be maintained throughout the test. In many fine-textured soils, cavities will stand without support, but in sands and other noncohesive materials a supporting porous structure may be required.

Procedure

Remove grass sod or debris from the soil surface and install the pipe to any desired depth by alternately augering and driving. Auger to a depth of 6 to 12 in. below the end of the pipe from within the pipe, then drive or push the pipe to the bottom of the drilled hole. This is done to minimize soil disturbance as the pipe is driven. When the pipe has been installed to the desired depth, auger out a cavity below the pipe. Cavity lengths of 4 to 8 in. have been found convenient, with pipes 1 and 2 in. in diameter. The length of cavity can be accurately controlled by use of a screw clamp on the auger handle. The cavity should be formed with a minimum of disturbance to the surrounding soil.

Remove seepage water and sediment from the cavity by pumping several times. Measure the depth to the water in the pipe after allowing enough time for the water to rise in the pipe to the equilibrium level. In highly permeable soils the equilibrium level may be attained in a few minutes; in some fine-textured soils several days may be required. Pump the water from the pipe and measure the rate at which ground water rises in the pipe. The rate of rise should be measured as soon as practicable after pumping, since, it is assumed, in the development of the theory, that the drawdown of the water table is negligible. Rate of rise may be measured at any point between the water-table level and the lower end of the pipe, but measurements near the equilibrium level should be avoided. The rise increment should be selected to give convenient and measurable time intervals.

If hydraulic-conductivity determinations are desired at several depths, measurements can be made with the same pipe by successively augering to a greater depth following each determination.

Calculations

Hydraulic conductivity is calculated by use of the equation given by Kirkham (1946) as follows:

$$k = \frac{2.30 \; \pi \; R^2}{A \; (t_2 - t_1)} \; \log_{10} \; (h_1/h_2)$$

where k is hydraulic conductivity; R is the radius of tube; A is a geometrical factor (the A-function), which may be read from figure 28; h_1 is the distance from the water table to the water level in pipe at time t_1; h_2 is the distance from the water table to the water level in pipe at time t_2; $t_2 - t_1$ is the time interval for water to rise from h_1 to h_2. Hydraulic conductivity (k) will be

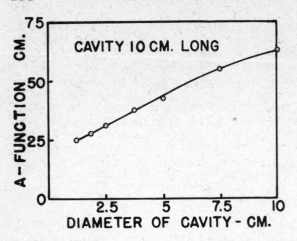 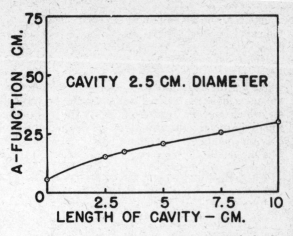

FIGURE 28.—Relation of the A-function to the length and diameter of the cavity for the piezometer method of measuring hydraulic conductivity. (Redrawn from Luthin and Kirkham, 1949.)

in centimeters per hour if R and A are in centimeters; h_1 and h_2 are both in the same units, and $(t_2 - t_1)$ in hours. However, any consistent system of units may be used. For values of the A-function not shown in the illustrations see Luthin and Kirkham (1949).

The hydraulic conductivity can also be calculated from an approximate equation that eliminates the use of logarithms. The constant inflow-rate equation of Kirkham (1946), slightly modified, is as follows:

$$k = \frac{\pi R^2}{A (t_2 - t_1)} \frac{\triangle h}{h_{av}}$$

where $\triangle h$ is the increment of rise of the water level in the pipe in time $t_2 - t_1$; h_{av} is the average head, i. e., $h_{av} = (h_1 + h_2)/2$; and the other terms are as previously defined.

This approximate equation is sufficiently accurate for the usual values of $\triangle h$ and h_{av} and may be used to simplify calculations. The error introduced by using this equation is small if the ratio $\triangle h/h_1$ is small, but increases as the ratio increases. The error in k is less than 4 percent for ratios of $\triangle h/h_1 < 0.5$ and less than 10 percent for ratios as large as 0.7.

References

Johnson, Frevert, and Evans (1952), Kirkham (1946), Luthin and Kirkham (1949), and Reeve and Kirkham (1951).

(34d) Hydraulic Conductivity From Auger-Hole Measurements

Equipment

Soil auger; any convenient size may be used, but it should permit making a hole below the water table with a minimum of soil disturbance. Water-level sounder; an electrical sounder mounted on a frame or tripod is convenient for measuring depth to water in an auger hole. In large-diameter auger holes, water levels can be measured with a rule or tape. A rule attached to a float provides a convenient means for measuring the rate of rise of water in an auger hole.

A hand-operated pitcher pump with a flexible hose attached to the inlet may be used to pump water and sediment from the auger hole. In addition, a stop watch is needed for time measurements.

Remarks

This method is limited to measurements in the soil profile below a water table and is applicable only where a cavity of known shape can be maintained throughout the test.

Procedure

Drill an auger hole to the desired depth below a water table with as little disturbance to the soil as possible. Insert the pump intake hose to the bottom of the auger hole and empty the cavity several times. This is done to remove suspended sediment and to reopen soil pores in the wall that may have been altered by the auger. Measure the depth to water in the hole when equilibrium with the surrounding ground water is attained. In highly permeable soils the equilibrium level may be reached in a few minutes; whereas, in some clays several days may be required. Pump the water from the hole and measure the rate at which the water rises in the hole while the water level is near the bottom of the auger hole or at the time that the auger hole is half full. The rate of rise should be determined as soon as practical after the water level is pumped down, since it is assumed in the development of the theory that the drawdown of the water table is negligible. A small rise increment should be used since the A-function varies as the hole fills up. The formula given below involves this assumption.

Calculations

Hydraulic conductivity is calculated by use of the

equation given by Van Bavel and Kirkham (1949) as follows:

$$k = \frac{\pi \, a^2}{A \,(d-h)} \frac{\triangle h}{\triangle t}$$

where k is the hydraulic conductivity; a is the radius of the auger hole; A is the A-function, a geometrical factor which may be read from figure 29, for the case where the auger hole is empty and where it is half full; d is the depth of auger hole below the water table; h is the depth of water in the auger hole; $\triangle h$ is the increment of rise of the water level in the hole in the time interval $\triangle t$.

Hydraulic conductivity (k) will be in centimeters per hour if a, d, h, and A are in centimeters and t is in hours. However, any consistent system of units may be used.

In selecting values of the A-function (fig. 29), information on the depth (s) to an impermeable layer below the bottom of the auger hole is required. When an impermeable layer occurs at a depth in the range from $s=0$ to $s=d$, the A-function should be selected

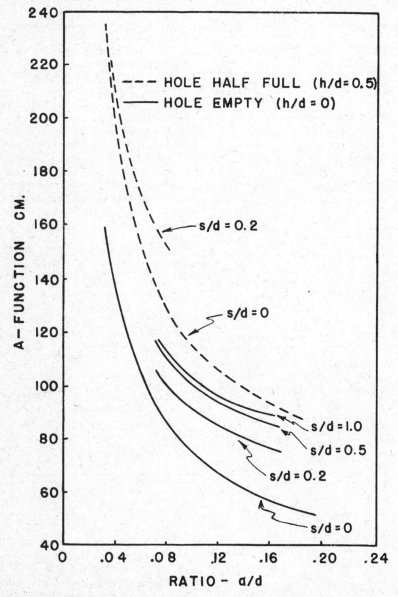

FIGURE 29.—Relation of the value of the A-function to the ratio a/d, for the auger-hole method of measuring hydraulic conductivity: a, radius of the hole; d, depth of the hole below the water table; h, depth of water in the hole; s, depth of an impervious layer below the bottom of the hole. The A values in the figure are for auger holes having a radius equal to 5 cm. For any other radius (x), multiply the A value read from the figure $x/5$. (Redrawn from Van Bavel and Kirkham, 1949.)

from the curve for the nearest value of s/d. When $s/d > 1$, use the curve for $s/d = 1$. The depth(s) to an impermeable layer is not a critical factor for the usual values of a/d. See Van Bavel and Kirkham (1949) for discussion of errors involved when, without knowledge of the depth to an impermeable layer, arbitrary values of s/d are used.

References

Diserens (1934), Hooghoudt (1936), Johnson, Frevert, and Evans (1952), Kirkham and Van Bavel (1949), Reeve and Kirkham (1951), and Van Bavel and Kirkham (1949).

(35) Hydraulic-Head Measurements in Saturated Soil

(35a) Piezometers Installed by Driving

Equipment

Iron pipe, $\frac{3}{8}$ in., galvanized or black, cut in 7, 10.5, 14 ft., or other lengths as desired; hand-operated driving hammer (Christiansen, 1943) or pneumatic driving hammer (Donnan and Christiansen, 1944); rivets, structural iron, $\frac{3}{8}$ in. in diameter by 1 in.; rivet punch-out rods (several lengths of $\frac{1}{8}$ in. in diameter iron .pipe with male and female flush connections, or other rods to fit); 25 to 50 ft. of semirigid plastic tubing, 5/16 in. in diameter;[16] hand-operated bucket pump; 5-gal. water bucket; and carpenter's level.

After installation it is necessary to measure the depth to water in the piezometer. This can be done with a steel tape or other sounding device. Tapes with a dark oxidized surface show the water-level mark readily, or chalk can be used to make the water mark more visible.

If many readings are to be made, it is worth while to construct an electrical water-level sounder. For this, a length of flexible insulated wire is wound on a reel that has a socket for mounting on the top of the piezometer pipe. A straight segment of the wire slightly longer than 1 ft. should be exposed to view between the reel and the top of the pipe. The lower end of the wire is weighted with metal tubing to keep the wire taut, and the upper end is grounded to the reel and pipe through a battery and high-resistance voltmeter. The insulated wire is marked at 1-ft. intervals. Fractions of a foot can be read to the nearest 0.01 ft. from a scale attached to the reel mount. Readings are taken on the first mark on the wire appearing above the top of the pipe when the voltmeter indicates the lower end of the wire is at the water surface.

Procedure

With an iron rivet in lower end of pipe, drive first length of pipe into soil. Additional lengths can be added with standard pipe couplings as driving pro-

gresses until pipe reaches the desired depth. Leave pipe extending approximately 1 ft. above ground surface. If hydraulic-head readings are desired at several depths at a given location, drive pipes of different lengths into the soil, spacing the pipes laterally with a separation of about 1 ft. Use the carpenter's level to set the tops of all pipes to the same elevation. This makes it convenient to record and interpret hydraulic-head readings. Pipe lengths up to 16 ft. long can be installed by driving if a stepladder is used. In some soils, the pipe can be pushed into the ground 5 or 6 ft. before driving is required so that 21-ft. lengths can sometimes be used. Insert punch-out rod in pipe and punch rivet a distance of 3 to 6 in. out of the end of the pipe. Push the plastic tubing, previously marked with paint or tape to indicate the pipe length, to the bottom of the pipe and by pumping water through the tube with the hand pump, flush out a cavity 3 to 6 in. long below the end of the pipe. Soil material and water will return to the surface in the annular space between the tubing and pipe. After the cavity at the base of the pipe is formed, test the piezometer for response rate by filling with water and observing the rate at which the water level drops. If the rate of change in the level of the water in the pipe is very low, repeat the flushing operation. In sands and gravels, the rate of drop may be so rapid that no overflow can be obtained during flushing; whereas, in clays the rate of drop may be so slow that it is hardly noticeable. In any event, the flushing should be repeated without unduly extending the plastic tube below the end of the pipe until the rate of change of the water level in the pipe after filling is perceptible. The level of the water in the piezometer should then be allowed to come to equilibrium with the ground water. It is important to make this test of the responsiveness of each piezometer because the reliability of readings depends directly upon the readiness with which the water level in the pipe responds to hydraulic-head changes in the ground water at the bottom of the pipe. Piezometers should be retested for responsiveness periodically and reflushed, if necessary.

In some soils, the rivet in the end may not be necessary. When the piezometer is driven, a soil plug from 3 to 12 in. in length may form in the lower end of the pipe, which can be removed by the flushing operation. In many soils, this soil plug can be flushed out in much less time than is required to punch out the rivet.

After the piezometers have been installed, flushed, and allowed to come to equilibrium with the ground water, the depth to water surface from the top of the pipe is measured and recorded.

Remarks

The hydraulic head of ground water at any given point, i. e., at the bottom of the pipe, is the equilibrium elevation of the surface of the water in the piezometer. This elevation can be referenced to any standard datum. All hydraulic-head readings in a single ground-water system or locality should be referenced to the same

---

[16] Saran tubing, manufactured by the Dow Chemical Co., is suitable for this use and is often locally available at hardware stores.

datum, mean sea level being commonly used. Water elevations at each site can be recorded as read from the top of the pipe. The elevations of the top of the pipe and the adjacent soil surface are determined by standard surveying methods.

The hydraulic gradient is the change in hydraulic head per unit distance in the direction of the maximum rate of decrease in head. The vertical component of the hydraulic gradient at a site where piezometers have been installed at several depths is equal to the difference in the equilibrium elevation of the water surface in two pipes divided by the difference in the elevation of the cavities at the bottoms of the pipes. This is an average value for the vertical component of the hydraulic gradient in the depth interval. (See Method 36 for graphical procedures that are useful in the interpretation of hydraulic-head readings.)

References

Christiansen (1943), Donnan and Christiansen (1944), and Richards (1952).

(35b) Piezometers Installed by Jetting

Equipment

Iron pipe, $\frac{3}{8}$-in. in diameter, galvanized or black, 10.5-ft. lengths, threaded at both ends; power-driven pump, 300 to 600 lb./in.^{2}, 10 to 15 gal./min. capacity with a water tank of 300-gal. capacity, truck- or trailer-mounted (an auxiliary 300-gal. water tank, truck-mounted, is also desirable); 25 to 50 ft. high-pressure hose, $\frac{3}{4}$-in. in diameter, with a swivel coupling for attachment to the pipe; driller's mud; and steel measuring tape or electrical sounder.

Procedure

The installation of piezometers by the jetting technique makes use of the eroding and lubricating properties of a stream of water issuing from the end of the pipe for opening a passage into the soil. Piezometers may be installed by hand or with simple hoisting and handling equipment, such as has been used in Coachella Valley, California, and described by Reger and associates (1950). During installation, the pipe is oscillated up and down from 1 to 2 ft. to facilitate the jetting. Water and soil material in suspension return to the surface around the outside of the pipe. The return flow acts as a lubricant for the upward and downward movement of the pipe and serves as a means for logging materials penetrated. An adjustable measuring tape used with the Coachella jetting rig serves to indicate depth of penetration to ±0.1 ft. If the jetting is done without a rig, the pipe should be marked at 1-ft. intervals to facilitate logging.

An estimate of texture and consolidation of the material is made from (a) the nature of the vibrations in the pipe that are transmitted to the hands of the operator, (b) the rate of downward progress, (c) examination of sediments carried by the effluent, and (d)

observation of color changes of the effluent. Logging subsurface layers by this method requires experience that can be gained and checked by jetting in profiles for which data on stratigraphy are available from independent logging procedures.

Return flow may be lost and penetration may stop in permeable sands and gravels. A commercial preparation, Aquagel, a form of driller's mud, was found by Reger and associates (1950) to be effective for maintaining return flow in coarse materials. Approximately 10 lb. per 100 gal. of water was sufficient for jetting conditions encountered in the Coachella Valley. It is necessary to add this preparation to the water supply slowly and to agitate thoroughly as it is added.

A record of the depth and nature of material penetrated is kept as the jetting progresses. Where several hydraulic-head measurements are desired at different depths, the deepest pipe is usually installed first. The log from the first pipe serves for selecting depths at which additional pipes are to be installed. It is often desirable to terminate piezometers in sandy lenses to increase the rate at which they respond to hydraulic-head changes in the soil. Jetting is stopped immediately as each pipe reaches the desired depth, so that excessive washing of material from around the pipe will not occur. The material in suspension settles back around the pipe and usually provides a satisfactory seal. Several pipes that terminate in the soil at different depths may be installed as close as 1 ft. apart. Experience has shown that, under most conditions, the effect of leakage along the pipe or from one pipe to another is negligible.

After the piezometers are installed, they are flushed, reference elevations are set, and readings are made as outlined in Method 35a. (For details of jetting-equipment construction, refer to the article by Reger and others (1950).)

References

Pillsbury and Christiansen (1947), Reeve and Jensen (1949), and Reger and others (1950).

(35c) Observation Wells, Uncased or With Perforated Casing

Equipment

Soil auger; perforated tubing or pipe; steel tape, or electrical sounder.

Procedure

It is desired to measure depth to water table. An uncased auger hole can often be used to measure depth to water table. Where soils are sandy and will not stand or where a more permanent well is desired, an auger hole may be cased with perforated casing. Sometimes it is necessary to install the casing during the augering process.

Water-table observation wells are usually installed to a depth great enough to reach the minimum expected position of the water table. As a result, observation wells are sometimes installed to considerable depths and perforated throughout a portion or all of the underwater length. Under many conditions, water-level readings in such wells coincide with the water-table level, but if there is a vertical flow component of water in the soil, either upward or downward, water-level readings in an open or perforated casing well may not represent the true water-table level. Where vertical-flow conditions occur, the water level in a perforated cased well represents a steady-state flow condition within the well itself, and may not give useful information. Such a condition is more likely to occur where an observation well penetrates layers that differ greatly in permeability. Where such conditions occur or where there is any question about water-table readings, hydraulic-head determinations should be made at several depths in the profile by the use of piezometers.

The elevation of the water table can be determined by a graphical method as follows. Plot the elevation of the terminal points of the piezometers in the soil as a function of the corresponding pressure heads, i. e., the lengths of the columns of water standing in the piezometers. Extrapolate this curve to zero pressure-head to obtain the water-table elevation. Abrupt changes in soil permeability with depth in the vicinity of the water table complicate the use of this method and make it necessary to install piezometers at or near the water table.

(36) Ground-Water Graphical Methods

(36a) Water-Table Contour Maps

Equipment

Drafting instruments and supplies.

Procedure

On a scale map of the area being investigated, write in the water-table elevations at locations at which water-table level measurements have been made. By standard mapping procedures used for ground-surface contour plotting, i. e., interpolation and extrapolation, draw in lines of equal water-table elevations. The principles that apply in surface contour mapping also apply for water-table contours. Where slopes change abruptly, more points are required to locate the contours accurately. Conversely, in areas of little change in slope, measurement points may be farther apart. In areas of rolling or varied topography where water tables in general follow surface slopes, the number of data required to construct water-table contours may be prohibitive. A water-table contour line is the locus of points on the water-table surface for which the hydraulic head is constant. In a three-dimensional flow system, such a line represents the intersection of an equal hydraulic-head surface with the surface of the water table.

Water-table contour maps provide direct visual information on the slope of the water table, and it is to be expected that generally there is a horizontal movement of ground water in the direction of slope of the water table. In the absence of subsurface artesian conditions and if the areal application of water to the soil surface is uniform, a region of steep slope of the water table would be expected to occur where barriers to the horizontal movement of ground water occur or where the hydraulic conductance of the soil strata below the water table is low. On the other hand, areas of low slope in the ground-water table may indicate the presence of aquifers that permit the ready transfer of ground water in the horizontal direction. Such information is pertinent to the analysis and solution of drainage problems.

(36b) Water-Table Isobath Maps

Equipment

Drafting instruments and supplies.

Procedure

On a scale map of the area, write in depths to water table from the ground surface at locations at which water-table and ground-surface elevations have been obtained. Construct isobath lines, i.e., lines of equal depth to water table, by the standard mapping procedures that are used for ground-surface and water-table contour mapping, i. e., interpolation and extrapolation, and other procedures. Where either surface topography or water-table slopes change abruptly, more points of measurement are required for accurate construction of equal depth-to-water lines.

Depth to water table may also be shown by circumscribing areas within which depth to water table is in a specified range. On a scale map, note depths to water table as above. Select a convenient number of depth ranges, such as 0 to 2, 2 to 4, 4 to 10, 10 to 20, > 20, and delineate areas within which depth to water table is in the designated ranges. Distinguish between areas with a crosshatch, color, or other convenient code system. Maps such as the foregoing provide graphic information on the adequacy of drainage and, therefore, aid in showing areas in which artificial drainage may be needed.

(36c) Profile Flow Patterns for Ground Water

Equipment

Drafting instruments and supplies.

Procedure

On a profile section showing the soil surface and available information on subsoil stratigraphy, write in hydraulic-head values at points where hydraulic-head

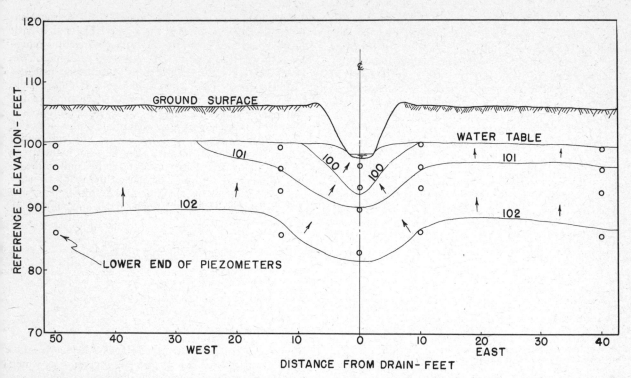

FIGURE 30.—Equal hydraulic-head lines below a water table on a profile section in the vicinity of an open drain. Example from Delta area, Utah. The direction of the hydraulic gradient is represented by arrows and indicates upward water movement from an underlying source.

measurements have been made, i. e., points where piezometers terminate in the soil (fig. 30). By standard methods, which are used for contour mapping, interpolation, and extrapolation, draw lines to connect points of equal hydraulic head. Convenient hydraulic-head intervals may be selected, extending over the range of measured values for hydraulic head. Usually an interval is selected that allows a number of equal hydraulic-head lines to be sketched on the same profile. The component of flow in the plane of the profile is normal to lines of equal hydraulic head, if the profile section is plotted to a 1 : 1 scale. With the 1 : 1 scale, flow lines can be sketched in at right angles to the equal hydraulic-head lines, with arrows to show the direction of flow. If the vertical scale is exaggerated, the relation between stream lines and equal hydraulic-head lines on the plotted profile is no longer orthogonal. Where the vertical and horizontal scales are not equal, therefore, the hydraulic-head distribution may be properly plotted, but flow lines should not be indicated.

For cases where hydraulic head changes in a vertical direction, indicating a vertical component of flow, the elevation of the water table can be determined by piezometers that terminate at the water-table level, or by extrapolation from a series of known points below the water table, as outlined in Method 35c. Draw equal hydraulic-head lines to intercept the water table at the respective equal hydraulic-head elevations.

An equal hydraulic-head line may intercept the water table at any angle, depending upon the flow direction. The water table is not necessarily a flow line as is often assumed, although it may be. A component of upward flow that exists below the water table may continue upward through the soil above the water table to the soil surface by capillarity. Likewise, downward flow may occur in the unsaturated soil above a water table.

References

Christiansen (1943), Reeves and Jensen (1949).

(36d) Water-Table Isopleths for Showing Time Variations in the Elevation of the Water Table

Equipment

Drafting instruments and supplies.

Procedure

A large seasonal variation in the water table often occurs in irrigated areas. In such cases it may be useful to show graphically the variations, both in space and time, by the use of water-table isopleths.[17] By this

[17] Private communication from M. Ram, Water Utilization Division, Ministry of Agriculture, Tel Aviv, Israel.

method a series of observation wells is established on a straight line across the area under investigation and water-table elevations are recorded over a period of time.

The graphical representation of the data is accomplished as follows: On a vertical scale at the left margin of a sheet of tracing paper, make a time scale on which the dates are shown for the various sets of readings of the observation wells. Start the time scale near the top of the sheet with the initial set of readings. Draw horizontal constant-time lines across the sheet at the time values for the various sets of readings. Across the top of the sheet, draw a profile of the elevation of the soil surface along the line of observation wells. Use any convenient vertical scale and mark the location of the observation wells on the horizontal scale. Draw in horizontal lines representing convenient elevation intervals over the range of variation in the elevation of the water table and plot the water-table profile for the initial set of readings. Project the points of intersection of this profile curve with the elevation scale lines downward to the horizontal constant-time line of the initial set of readings. Place elevation numbers above these points on the constant-time line. Repeat this process, locating successive elevation points on successive constant-time lines for each set of well readings. Connect constant water-table elevation points on successive constant-time lines with smooth curves. These curves are called isopleths and show the variation with time of the points of equal water-table elevation along the line of water-table observation wells.

The sources of ground water as well as subsurface stratigraphy must be taken into account in the interpretation of isopleths. The method provides a convenient graphical summary of water-table observations and can be used to advantage in showing the rate of subsidence of the water table following an irrigation season. This information relates directly to the drainability of soils.

Physical Measurements

(37) Intrinsic Permeability

(37a) *Permeability of Soil to Air*

Apparatus

The apparatus for this measurement is shown in figure 31. Compressed air is admitted through a calcium chloride drying tube to an airtight tank of constant volume. An outflow tube leads to a water manometer and to the soil sample container. The soil sample container consists of a tinned iron can with an extension made from a 4-cm. section of brass tubing counter-bored to give a snug fit on the top of the can. Punch an outlet hole, approximately 5/32 in. in diameter in the bottom of the can. Use a disk of brass screen, 20- or 40-mesh, with 2 layers of fiberglass sheet

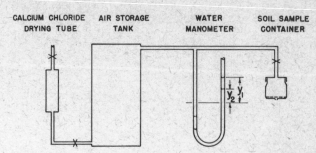

FIGURE 31.—Apparatus using air flow to measure the intrinsic permeability of soil by Method 37a. The manometer readings y_1 and y_2 represent successive heights of the free-water surface above the rest position.

as a filter in the bottom of each can. The soil-packing machine, mentioned below, is useful for this measurement.

Remarks

This method for measuring air permeability can be used for either disturbed or undisturbed samples. The following procedure is for disturbed soils. In order to get consistent results for comparing one soil with another and to determine the effect of various treatments, a standard procedure for preparing and packing the soil must be followed. Make determinations in triplicate.

Procedure

Pass air-dried soil through a wire-mesh sieve with 1-mm. openings. Obtain representative subsamples as outlined in Method 1. Attach the brass cylinder to the top of a can and fill the container about three-fourths full of soil. Dump the soil, which has been well mixed, into the container rather than by pouring or scooping. With a spring-load of 3-kg. wt. on top of the soil, drop the container 200 times on a solid block of wood from a height of 2.5 cm. A cam-operated mechanical dropper has been used for this purpose. Remove the brass cylinder from the can and use a spatula to strike the soil off level with the top of the can. Cover the soil with a disk of filter paper, place a lid on the can, and complete the seal with a tight rubber band or beeswax. Connection to the air source is made by means of a short piece of copper tubing soldered to the lid of the can. Pass compressed air through the drying tube to the tank until a manometer displacement of 40 to 50 cm. of water is attained. Record the air temperature in the tank and measure the rate of drop of the manometer level as air is allowed to flow from the tank through the soil sample. It is desirable to allow an initial 10-cm. drop of the manometer level before height and time readings are started.

Calculations

The intrinsic permeability of the soil using air is given by the equation:

$$k'_a = \frac{2.30\,LVS\,\eta}{A\,P_a}$$

in which

k'_a = Intrinsic permeability with air, cm.^{2}
L = Length of soil column, cm.
V = Volume of tank, cm.^{3}
η = Viscosity of air at the temperature at which the determination was made, dyne sec. cm.$^{-2}$ (poises).
A = Cross-sectional area of sample, cm.^{2}
P_a = Atmospheric pressure, dynes/cm.^{2}
S = Slope of log y vs. time curve =

$$\frac{\log_{10}y_1 - \log_{10}y_2}{\triangle t}$$

y = Displacement of the water surface in one arm of the manometer, cm.
$\triangle t$ = Time interval in seconds for the water surface in the manometer to drop from y_1 to y_2.

The time for a convenient and measurable drop in manometer level can be controlled by the volume of the tank used. For most soils prepared as outlined above, a 213-liter (55-gal.) drum gives a convenient time interval for a measurable manometer change. For soils of lower permeability, a 24-liter tank is used.

While c. g. s. units are suggested above, any consistent set of units can be used.

References

Kirkham (1947), Soil Science Society of America (1952).

(37b) Permeability of Soil to Water

Apparatus

Constant-level water-supply reservoir, glass siphon tubes, and rack for supporting samples; soil containers made from 3-oz. tinned iron soil cans with $\frac{5}{32}$-inch hole punched in bottom and brass cylinder extensions, 4-cm. high; 50- or 100-ml. graduates.

Procedure

The procedure for preparing and packing samples is as outlined in Method 37a. Water-permeability determinations may be made on the same samples used for air permeability. Care must be exercised to avoid disturbance of the sample in handling.

Following the air-permeability determination, place a brass cylinder extension on top of the can containing the soil sample and seal in place with an elastic band or beeswax. Place the soil sample on the rack, cover the soil surface with filter paper, and admit water to the sample from the supply reservoir with the siphon. The water level is adjusted so that the height of soil plus water column is 2 times the soil column, giving a hydraulic gradient of 2.

Record the water temperature, the time at which water is admitted to the container, and the time at which water first percolates through the sample. Measure the volume of percolate for a number of successive time intervals. The amount of water passed through the soil and the number of volume measurements made will depend upon the purpose of the determination. Usually 3 to 6 in. is used, a depth corresponding to an irrigation. For comparing one soil with another and for determining the effect of various treatments on a given soil, use a value obtained after the hydraulic conductivity has become more or less constant.

Calculations

Intrinsic permeability of the soil using water is given by the equation:

$$k'_w = \frac{\eta}{d_w g}\,k = \frac{\eta}{d_w g}\,\frac{VL}{A\triangle h\triangle t}$$

in which

k'_w = Intrinsic permeability with water, cm.^{2}
k = Hydraulic conductivity, cm./sec.
V = Volume of percolate in time, $\triangle t$, cm.^{3}
L = Length of soil column, cm.
$\triangle h$ = Difference in hydraulic head between the inflow and outflow ends of the soil column, cm.
A = Cross-sectional area of the soil column, cm.^{2}
$\triangle t$ = Time interval for volume of percolate V to pass through the soil, sec.
η = Viscosity of water at the recorded temperature, dyne sec. cm.$^{-2}$ (poises).
d_w = Density of water, gm./cm.^{3}
g = Acceleration of gravity, cm. sec.$^{-2}$

Intrinsic permeability is related to hydraulic conductivity as indicated by the above equation. If desired, hydraulic conductivity may first be calculated and then converted to intrinsic permeability by multiplying by the ratio $\eta/d_w g$. While c. g. s. units are suggested above, any consistent set of units can be used.

Remarks

Soils may be compared with respect to permeability on the basis of values obtained at a fixed time after wetting or after a specified amount of water has passed through the sample. For comparing changes in structure between different soils, the time basis has been found to be preferable.

Reference

Soil Science Society of America (1952).

(38) Bulk Density

Apparatus

Balance, drying oven, moisture boxes, and core sampler. The latter can be anything from an elaborate power-driven machine to a short section of thin-walled brass tubing with an internal closely fitting ring of clock spring soldered in place to form the cutting lip. (See drawing of soil sampler in Appendix.)

Procedure

Details of procedure will depend on the type of core sampler and soil conditions. Usually a flat soil surface, either horizontal or vertical, is prepared at the desired depth, and the core sampler is pressed or driven into the soil. Care should be taken to see that no compaction occurs during the process, so that a known volume of soil having field structure is obtained. The oven-dry weight of the sample is then determined.

Calculations

Bulk density (d_b) = (wt. of oven-dry soil core)/(field volume of sample). Bulk density is expressed as pounds per cubic foot or grams per cubic centimeter. For practical purposes, the latter is equal numerically to apparent specific gravity or volume weight.

(39) Particle Density

Apparatus

Balance, vacuum desiccator, and pycnometers.

Procedure

Weigh a pycnometer when filled with air (W_a), when filled with water (W_w), when partially filled with an oven-dried sample of soil (W_s), and when completely filled with soil and water (W_{sw}). To exclude air, pycnometers containing the soil with enough water to cover should be subjected to several pressure reductions in a vacuum desiccator and then allowed to stand for a number of hours under reduced pressure before completely filling with water for weighing W_{sw}. The particle density (d_p) of the soil in gm. cm.$^{-3}$, is then given by the formula:

$$d_p = d_w\ (W_s - W_a)/(W_w + W_s - W_a - W_{sw})$$

where d_w is the density of the water in gm. cm.$^{-3}$.

Slightly different and perhaps better values will be obtained for d_p if a nonpolar liquid such as kerosene, xylene, or acetylene tetrachloride is used for the displacing liquid.

(40) Porosity

The porosity of soil is the fraction of the soil space not occupied by soil particles. The porosity (n) may be calculated from the formula:

$$n = (d_p - d_b)/d_p$$

if the bulk density (d_b) and the particle density (d_p) are known. Solutions of this equation may be found graphically by use of the nomograms given at the right of figure 8 (ch. 2).

(41) Particle-Size Distribution

Remarks

The method as given is essentially that described by Kilmer and Alexander (1949), except that the 0.005-mm. determination has been omitted. The names used at present by the United States Department of Agriculture for the soil separates are as follows: The diameters 2.0 to 1.0, 1.0 to 0.5, 0.5 to 0.25, 0.25 to 0.1, and 0.1 to 0.05 mm., respectively, separate very coarse, coarse, medium, fine, and very fine sands; particles from 0.050 to 0.002 mm. are called silt, and particles with effective diameters less than 0.002 mm. are designated as clay. With the International System, the diameters 2.0, 0.2, and 0.02, respectively, separate the classes represented by the numerals I, II, and III, while particles of diameters less than 0.002 mm. are represented by IV.

Apparatus

Set of sieves; size openings, 2-, 1-, and 0.5-mm. round hole; 60-, 80-, 140-, and 300-mesh per in. Pyrex nursing bottles, 8-oz., with rubber stoppers; Lowy 25-ml. automatic pipet; haw pipet rack; Pasteur-Chamberland filters, short, "F" fineness. Analytical balance, drying oven, steam chest, motor stirrer, reciprocating shaker, desiccator, beakers, and evaporating dishes.

Reagents

A. Hydrogen peroxide, 30 percent solution.
B. Dispersing agent. Dissolve 35.7 gm. sodium metaphosphate and 7.94 gm. sodium carbonate in water and dilute to 1 liter. The sodium metaphosphate is prepared as follows: 125 gm. of monosodium phosphate $(NaH_2PO_4 \cdot H_2O)$ is slowly heated in a platinum dish to 650° C. This temperature is held for $1\frac{1}{2}$ hr. The platinum dish and its contents are removed from the furnace and the sodium metaphosphate is cooled rapidly by pouring it out in narrow strips on a clean marble slab. The sodium carbonate is used as an alkaline buffer to prevent the hydrolysis of the metaphosphate back to the orthophosphate which occurs in acidic solutions.

Procedure

GENERAL STATEMENT.—Samples are routinely run in sets of eight; the necessary equipment is designed accordingly. The sample is treated with hydrogen peroxide, washed, filtered, and dispersed. The sand is separated from the silt and clay by washing the dispersed sample through a 300-mesh sieve. The various sand fractions are obtained by sieving, while the 20-μ and 2-μ fractions are obtained by pipeting. Organic matter is determined on a separate sample by the dichromate reduction method (Peech and coworkers, 1947).

PREPARATION OF THE SAMPLE.—The air-dried sample is mixed and quartered. The quarter reserved for analysis is rolled with a wooden rolling pin to break up the clods. The sample is then passed through a sieve with 2-mm. round holes. Rolling and sieving of the coarse material are repeated until only pebbles are retained on the sieve. The material not passing the sieve is weighed and reported as a percentage of the air-dry weight of the whole sample.

REMOVAL OF ORGANIC MATTER.—A 10-gm. sample of the air-dry soil containing no particles larger than 2 mm. is weighed on a rough balance and placed in a 250-ml. electrolytic Pyrex beaker. About 50 ml. of water is added, followed by a few milliliters of 30 percent hydrogen peroxide. The beaker is then covered with a watch glass. If a violent reaction occurs, the cold hydrogen peroxide treatment is repeated periodically until no•more frothing occurs. The beaker is then heated to about 90° C. on an electric hot plate. Hydrogen peroxide is added in 5-ml. quantities at about 45-min. intervals until the organic matter is essentially removed as determined by visual inspection. Heating is then continued for about 30 min. to remove any excess hydrogen peroxide.

REMOVAL OF DISSOLVED MINERAL MATTER.—Following the hydrogen peroxide treatment, the beaker is placed in a rack and about 150 ml. of water is added by means of a jet strong enough to stir the sample well. The suspension is filtered by means of a short Pasteur-Chamberland filter of "F" fineness. Five such washings and filterings are usually sufficient except for soils containing much coarse gypsum. Soil adhering to the filter is removed by applying a gentle back-pressure and using the forefinger as a policeman. The beaker is then dried on a steam bath, placed overnight in an oven at 110° C., cooled in a desiccator, and then weighed to the nearest milligram. After the sample is transferred to a nursing bottle for dispersion, the oven-dry weight of the beaker is obtained. Weight of oven-dry organic-free sample is used as the base weight for calculating percentages of the various fractions.

DISPERSION OF THE SAMPLE.—To the oven-dry sample is added 10 ml. of sodium hexametaphosphate dispersing reagent B, and the sample is transferred to an 8-oz. Pyrex glass nursing bottle by means of a funnel, a rubber policeman, and a jet of water. The volume is made to 6 oz., and the bottle is stoppered and shaken overnight on a horizontal reciprocating shaker with 120 oscillations per minute. A similar volume of dispersing agent is placed in a liter cylinder, the volume made to 1,000 ml. and well mixed. A sample is taken with the pipet, dried, and weighed to obtain the weight correction referred to in the section on calculations. This weight correction is obtained for each new solution of sodium metaphosphate.

SEPARATION OF THE SANDS FROM SILT AND CLAY.—The dispersed sample is washed on a 300-mesh sieve, the silt and clay passing through the sieve into a 1-liter graduated cylinder. The sieve is held above the cylinder by means of a clamp and a stand. Jets of water should be avoided in washing the sample. The sieve clamp is tapped gently with the side of the hand to facilitate the washing procedure. Washing is continued until the volume in the cylinder totals about 800 ml. The sands and some coarse silt remain on the sieve. It is necessary that all particles of less than 20μ diam. be washed through the sieve. The sieve is removed from the holder, placed in an aluminum pan, and dried at 110° to 120° C. While the sands are drying, another sieve is used for the next sample. The material on the sieve is then brushed into a platinum dish and further dried for about 2 hr. The dish is then placed in a desiccator, the contents to be sieved and weighed when convenient. The silt and clay suspension in the cylinder is made up to 1 liter with distilled water, covered with a watchglass, and set aside until the pipetings are to be made.

PIPETING.—Pipetings are made for the 20μ and 2μ particles in the order named. The 20μ particles are pipeted at a 10-cm. depth, the sedimentation time varying according to the temperature. The 2μ fraction is pipeted after a predetermined settling time (usually 6 to 6½ hr.), the depth varying according to the time and temperature. A Lowy 25-ml. automatic pipet with a filling time of about 12 sec. is used. Prior to each sedimentation process, the material in the sedimentation cylinder is stirred for 6 min. with a motor-driven stirrer (8 min. if the suspension has stood for more than 16 hr.). After removal from the stirrer, the sedimentation cylinder is surrounded with insulating material and the suspension is stirred for 30 to 60 sec. with a hand stirrer, an up-and-down motion being used. This stirrer is made by fastening a circular piece of perforated brass sheeting to one end of a brass rod. A wide rubber band is placed around the edge of the brass sheeting to prevent abrasion. The time is noted at completion of the stirring. About 1 min. before the sedimentation is complete, the tip of the 25-ml. pipet is lowered slowly into the suspension to the proper depth by means of a Shaw pipet rack. The pipet is then filled and emptied into a 60-ml. weighing bottle having an outside cover. One rinse from the pipet is added. A vacuum is used to dry the pipet for use on the next sample. The weighing bottle is dried in an oven at 95° to 98° C. and then further dried for about 4 hr. at 110°. The initial drying is done at a lower temperature to prevent spattering of the suspension. The weighing bottle is then cooled in a desiccator containing phosphorus pentoxide as a desiccant and weighed.

SIEVING AND WEIGHING THE SAND FRACTIONS.—The dry sands, including some coarse silt, are weighed and brushed into a nest of sieves. Sieves and specifications are as follows:

Sieve Opening (mm.)	Specifications
1.0	Perforated brass plate, round holes, No. 3 straight, 0.04-in. diam. holes, 240 holes per in.²
0.5	Perforated brass plate, round holes, No. 00 staggered, 0.02-in. diam. holes, 714 holes per in.²
0.25	60-mesh, Bureau of Standards (Phosphor Bronze wire cloth)
0.177	80-mesh, Bureau of Standards (Phosphor Bronze wire cloth)
0.105	140-mesh, Bureau of Standards (Phosphor Bronze wire cloth)
0.047	300-mesh (Phosphor Bronze wire cloth), 0.0015-in. wire.

(An 80-mesh sieve is included in order to obtain International Society of Soil Sciences fraction I.) The sands are then shaken for 3 min. on a shaker having vertical and lateral movements of $\frac{1}{2}$ in., making 500 oscillations per minute. For a different shaker, the time of shaking would have to be determined by microscopic study. The summation method of weighing is used. The first sand fraction is weighed, the second fraction added to it, the total weight determined, and so on. If the sum of the weights of the fractions is equal to the total weight, it is assumed that no weighing error has been made.

Calculations

PIPETED FRACTIONS.—$(A-B)KD$=percent of pipeted fraction where A=weight in gm. of pipeted fraction, B=weight correction for dispersing agent in gm.),

$$K=\frac{1,000}{\text{volume contained by pipet}}$$

and

$$D=\frac{100}{\text{organic-free oven-dry weight of total sample}}$$

(The 20μ fraction) − (the 2μ fraction) = International Society of Soil Sciences fraction III. United States Department of Agriculture silt is obtained by subtracting the sum of the percentages of sand and clay from 100. International Society of Soil Sciences fraction II is obtained by subtracting the sum of the percentages of fractions I, III, and IV from 100.

SAND FRACTIONS.—

(Weight in grams of fraction on sieve × 100) ÷ (organic-free oven-dry weight of total sample) = percent of fraction

References

Kilmer and Alexander (1949), Peech and others (1947), and Tyner (1940).

(42) Aggregate-Size Distribution

(42a) Wet Sieving

Remarks

This is a modification of the mimeographed tentative method that was distributed in August 1951 by the Committee on Physical Analyses of the Soil Science Society of America. The method in brief consists of placing a sample of soil on a nest of sieves that is oscillated vertically under water. The amount of soil remaining on the individual screens is determined, and aggregation is expressed as the mean weight-diameter of the aggregates and primary particles. After weighing, the aggregate separates are combined and dispersed and washed through the nest of sieves. The resulting separates make it possible to correct the previous separates of aggregates for primary particles and to calculate the aggregation index. This is a single-value index of the aggregation of a soil.

Apparatus

Yoder-type wet-sieving apparatus, sieve holders, 4 sets of 5-inch sieves with 2-, 1-, 0.5-, 0.25-, and 0.10-mm. openings (corresponding to United States Screens Nos. 10, 18, 35, 60, and 140), drying oven, moisture cans, balance Pyrex watchglasses, and 6-in. diameter porcelain funnel.

Procedure

Collect the soil sample with spade or garden trowel, preferably when the soil is moist, avoiding excessive compaction or fragmentation of soil. Dry the sample slowly and, when sufficiently friable, pass it gently through an 8-mm. sieve and air-dry. If the soil is stony, pass the sample through a 4-mm. sieve and discard all primary material greater than 4 mm. in size. Mix the soil and take subsamples in accordance with Method 1. Make determinations in duplicate on 40- to 60-gm. subsamples. Weigh the subsamples to the closest 0.1 gm. and determine the moisture content by drying a separate subsample at 105° C.

Install the nests of sieves in the water slowly and at a moderate angle to avoid entrapping air bubbles below the sieves. Adjust the mechanism so that the top sieve makes contact with the water surface when the oscillation mechanism is at the top of its stroke. Distribute the sample on the top sieve so that wetting occurs by capillarity and wait 5 to 10 min. after the soil surface appears wet to insure saturation of the aggregates. Oscillate the sieves for 30 min. with a stroke of 3.8 cm. and a frequency of 30 cycles per minute, keeping soil submerged at all times. Some attention may be required during the first few minutes of operation, in order to prevent water from spilling over the top sieve, and later, to prevent the top sieve from rising above water level.

Remove the sieves from the water and drain for a few minutes in an inclined position. Remove excess water from the bottom of the screens with absorbent tissue and place the sieves on watchglasses. Dry in a circulating oven at not higher than 75° C. because high temperatures cause some soils to adhere. Then remove the soil from the sieves, dry at 105°, and weigh.

In order to determine how much of the soil retained on the individual sieves represents aggregates and how much is gravel and sand, the oven-dried soil taken from the five sieves is dispersed and washed through the sieves with a stream of water. The oven-dry weight of the primary particles remaining on each sieve is then determined.

Calculations

The amount of soil remaining on each sieve is expressed as percentage of the total sample. Prepare a graph, plotting the accumulated percentage of soil remaining on each sieve as ordinate against the upper limit of each fraction in millimeters as the abscissa, and measure the area shown by the curve connecting these points and by the ordinate and the abscissa. If 1 mm. (sieve size) represents 1 unit of the abscissa and 10 percent a unit on the ordinate, a square unit will represent 0.1 mm. mean weight-diameter of the aggregates of the sample. Multiplying the number of square units of the area by 0.1 gives the mean weight-diameter of the entire sample, including the material that has been washed through the smallest sieve.

The results from the wet sieving of the dispersed sample are plotted and calculated in the same way. The difference between the mean weight-diameters of the original and the dispersed samples gives the aggregation index.

Remarks

The water container in which the sieve nest is oscillated can be of any desired size or shape, providing its area is at least 1.6 times the area of the sieves. The temperature of the water should be in the range 20° to 24° C., and the water should not be excessively saline. Fresh water should be used for each set of determinations. Rubber bands cut from old inner tubes are convenient for holding loosely fitting sieves together.

References

Russell (1949), Van Bavel (1950).

(42b) Aggregation of Particles Less than 50 Microns

Remarks

This procedure measures the degree of aggregation of the silt and clay (less than 50μ) fraction for those soils that do not contain enough large aggregates to be adequately characterized by wet-sieving. The method involves measuring the concentration of two suspensions of the same soil, one of which is dispersed by any standard dispersion procedure to give total silt plus clay. The other suspension, prepared by mild (end-over-end) agitation of the sample in water, gives a measure of the unaggregated silt plus clay. The difference in concentration between the two suspensions provides a measure of the amount of silt plus clay particles that is bound into water-stable aggregates larger than 50μ in size.

This procedure may also be used as a rapid exploratory test to determine the effect of various soil-aggregating chemicals in producing water-stable aggregation.

Apparatus

Dispersion apparatus with high-speed stirring motor, metal cup, 1-liter hydrometer jars, thermometer, and Bouyoucos hydrometer or hydrometer-pipet. If the pipet procedure is used, a Lowy automatic pipet, a Shaw pipet rack, and tared moisture boxes are needed.

Procedure

Weigh two 50-gm. subsamples of air-dried soil prepared as in Method 42a. Make a moisture determination on a separate subsample.

TOTAL SILT PLUS CLAY.—Disperse one of the subsamples in the dispersion apparatus. Transfer to a hydrometer jar and dilute with distilled water to the required volume. For procedure a (below) the final volume is 1,130 ml., determined with the hydrometer in the suspension; for procedures b and c, the volume is 1,000 ml. (Note: If either procedure b or c is to be used, stopper and invert the cylinder 2 or 3 times and record the temperature. This is necessary in order to determine in advance the settling time used.) Stopper, invert, and shake the cylinder vigorously several times and determine the total silt plus clay in the suspension as directed under procedures a, b, or c, given below.

UNBOUND SILT PLUS CLAY.—Incline the hydrometer jar containing the second subsample to a nearly horizontal position and shake lightly to spread the sample over a distance of 10 or 12 cm. along the side of the jar. Add distilled water slowly and in such manner as to favor wetting by capillarity rather than by flooding. When soil is completely wetted, dilute to the appropriate volume, as given above, but do not allow water to fall directly on soil. Allow the soil to slake for at least 15 min. Record the temperature. Stopper the cylinder and gently invert it 20 times (do not shake) within a period of about 40 sec., requiring about 1 sec. for inversion with a 1-sec. interval between inversions. After the required settling period, determine the amount of unbound silt plus clay in suspension by the same procedure a, b, or c used for the total silt plus clay measurement.

PROCEDURES FOR MEASURING CONCENTRATION OF SUSPENSIONS.—(a) Hydrometer. After final mixing, insert the hydrometer and take a reading after 40 seconds, as prescribed by Bouyoucos (1936). Immediately record the suspension temperature in degrees F. and apply a temperature correction as follows: Add 0.2 to the hydrometer reading for each degree above 67° F.; subtract if below.

The corrected hydrometer reading gives the grams per liter of silt plus clay in suspension.

(b) Hydrometer-pipet. The hydrometer-pipet (Hellman and McKelvey, 1941) measures the concentration of soil particles in grams per liter of a suspension that has been pipeted from a known depth and that is uniform throughout when measured by the hydrometer contained within the pipet. The settling time and depth of sampling are the same as for the pipet procedure c, and the hydrometer readings require the same temperature corrections as for the hydrometer procedure a.

After final mixing and a few seconds prior to time of sampling, squeeze the bulb and insert the hydrometer-pipet into the suspension to a depth of 12.5 cm. Start filling the pipet after the prescribed time interval in seconds, as indicated under procedure c. Care should be taken to keep the suspension well mixed by occasionally allowing a bubble to rise through the suspension in the pipet. Read the hydrometer at the top of the meniscus and apply the proper temperature correction as prescribed for the Buoyoucos hydrometer.

The corrected hydrometer-pipet reading gives the grams per liter of silt plus clay in suspension.

(c) *Pipet*. After final mixing, insert the Lowy or other suitable pipet into the suspension to a depth of 12.5 cm. Start filling the pipet after the time-interval in seconds indicated by the accompanying data. Other depth-time-temperature relationships may be obtained from the nomograms of Tanner and Jackson (1948).

Temperature: °C. or °F.		Time to sample at 12.5-cm. depth (*seconds*)
20	(68)	57
22	(71.5)	54
24	(75)	51
26	(79)	49
28	(82.5)	46
30	(86)	44

The weight in grams of oven-dry (105° C.) material in the 25-ml. aliquot is multiplied by 40 to give grams per liter of silt plus clay in suspension.

Calculations

Percent aggregation = (wt. of total silt plus clay in dispersed suspension, gm., minus wt. of silt plus clay in undispersed suspension, gm.) × 100/(wt. of total silt plus clay in dispersed suspension, gm.).

References

Bouyoucos (1936), Hellman and McKelvey (1941), and Tanner and Jackson (1948).

(43) Modulus of Rupture

Remarks

In the following procedure, the maximum force required to break a small specially molded briquet of soil is measured, and from this breaking force the maximum fiber stress in the standard sample is calculated.

Shrinkage of soil material on drying is a pertinent property and can be determined from the dimensions before and after drying of the briquet samples used in this test.

Apparatus

The machine for breaking the sample makes use of 2 parallel bars 5 cm. apart for supporting the sample. The breaking force is supplied from a third overlying bar centrally located and parallel with respect to the supporting bars. The bar above and one bar below are self-alining to accommodate to any slight lack of parallelism in the line of bearing on the sample. The bars are coated with a strip of soft rubber with a cross section 0.16 cm. square. The breaking machine is mounted on the platform of a beam balance. The briquet sample is broken by upward motion of the two lower bars, which are supported by the platform of the balance. Upward motion of the upper bar is constrained by a cross frame above the balance. The breaking force is supplied by water accumulating in a vessel hung from the end of the balance beam. The breaking force is applied at the rate of 2,000 gm.-wt./min., and the beam motion that occurs when the sample breaks can be used to automatically stop the accumulation of water in the vessels.

The briquet molds are precision made from ⅜-in. brass strip with inside dimensions of 3½ cm. by 7 cm. by 0.952 cm. high. Rectangles of hard white photographic blotting paper are cut to the size 5 cm. by 8½ cm. A screen-bottomed tray, 50 cm. square, is made by pulling brass window screen taut and soldering it to a rigid ½-in. galvanized pipe frame. A pan or other water container slightly larger than 50 cm. square. Graduated cylinder. Tremie funnel with straight cylindrical tube 2 cm. diam. and 10 cm. high. (See drawing of apparatus in Appendix.)

Procedure

Make the determination on 6 replicate samples of soil that have been passed through a 2-mm. round-hole sieve, using the subsampling procedure outlined in Method 1. Samples should be just slightly larger than will fill the briquet molds. Cover the inside of the molds with a thin layer of vaseline so that the soil will not stick to the mold. Place the screen-bottomed tray in the pan. Place the molds on the blotting paper on the screen. Rest the tremie on the blotting paper at one end of the mold. Dump all of a soil subsample into the tremie. Move the funnel around inside the mold while raising continuously so as to give a uniform smooth filling of the mold.

Strike off excess soil level with the upper surface of the mold. Add water to the pan until free water surrounds every mold. Allow samples to stand for 1 hour after all the soil samples become wet. Raise the screen very carefully so as not to jar the samples and transfer to a forced-draft oven at 50° C. After drying the briquets to constant weight, remove from the molds and determine the breaking strength.

Calculations

Use the formula $s = (3FL)/(2bd^2)$, where s is the modulus of rupture (in dynes per sq. cm.), F is the breaking force in dynes (the breaking force in gm.-wt. × 980); L is the distance between the lower two supporting bars, b is the width of the briquet, and d is the depth or thickness of the briquet, all expressed in cm.

Methods of Plant Culture and Plant Analysis

Plant-Culture Techniques Adapted to Salt-Tolerance Investigations

There are certain aspects of salt-tolerance investigations involving extensive plant breeding and selection programs that are being conducted by crop specialists at a number of agricultural experiment stations. Furthermore, since salt tolerance of plants may be influenced profoundly by climatic conditions, investigators in a given region may find it desirable to undertake salt-tolerance studies under local climatic conditions in order to determine the crops best suited to their region. In anticipation of a continued interest in such breeding and testing programs, techniques used in such studies at the Salinity Laboratory are included in this handbook.

(50) Artificially Salinized Field Plots

Information is needed regarding the response of crop plants to adverse saline conditions as related to climatic factors, planting techniques, and cultural practices used in the field. However, field observations relating crop growth to the salinity of the soil are difficult to evaluate, because of the wide range of salt concentrations frequently encountered within a small area in the field. In order to obtain information on these aspects of salt tolerance, an artificially salinized field-plot technique may be employed (Wadleigh and Fireman, 1949). Small, 14-ft. square plots are used, and each crop is managed according to practices generally followed in the principal regions where it is grown under irrigation. Density of stand, spacing, fertilizer practice, irrigation methods, and other conditions are all reproduced as closely as possible. The salt tolerance of field, vegetables, forage, and tree crops may be studied by this technique.

In the preparation of plots, careful leveling is necessary to insure uniform distribution and penetration of the salinizing water, and all parts of a basin-irrigated plot should be brought to within $1/4$ in. of the mean plot level. Similar precautions should be used where furrow irrigation is to be practiced so that all bed surfaces and furrows will be at uniform levels. The salinizing waters can be restricted to the plots by borders; and, if the plots are closely spaced, the borders can be supplemented with 6-in. boards around the plot. Asphalt roofing paper 18 in. wide can be attached to the boards and buried to a 12-in. depth. If the soil is sufficiently permeable and adequate irrigations are applied, salt concentration in the plot tends to reach a steady value following the first several irrigations with a minimum of variability within the plot.

In order to avoid the development of alkali conditions in the soil, it has been standard practice to add salts to the irrigation water as equal parts of sodium chloride and calcium chloride. This is readily accomplished for small plots by dissolving the desired amount of salts in water in a galvanized tank and mixing with the aid of a circulating pump. Salinity levels commonly employed in salt-tolerance tests are 0, 3,000, 6,000, and 9,000 p. p. m. of added salts, although a more dilute series may be desirable for the more salt-sensitive crops, such as beans and fruit trees; and a more concentrated series for salt-tolerant crops, such as barley and beets. Salinization of the plots is begun after the seedlings or transplants are established because of the greater sensitivity of most crops to salinity during germination and immediately following transplanting. To avoid the shock, which too abrupt a change in soil salinity may induce in the plant, it is advisable to increase salinity stepwise during the first 3 or 4 salinizing irrigations. By applying relatively light irrigations at frequent intervals, the salinization of a series of plots may be completed in 7 to 10 days. However, owing to dilution of the salinizing water by residual soil moisture, a few additional salinizing irrigations may be required to establish a relatively constant concentration of salt in the plot.

Subsequent irrigations are usually applied at conventional frequencies, as judged by the condition of the control plot. The salt status of the salinized plots is determined periodically during the growth of the crop by taking soil samples at various depths in the beds and furrows and determining the conductivity of the saturation extract (EC_e). Yield data and observations on crop quality and composition can then be correlated with the salt status of the several plots in the series.

Plots treated in the above manner may be reused after leaching the salt from the soil. Although the plots remain nonalkali, recovery is facilitated by the addition of gypsum at the rate of 1 ton per acre. To insure continued uniformity of the plots with regard to soil structure (as measured by water penetration, aeration, and other properties), it is desirable to grow some salt-

127

tolerant grass following leaching and prior to reusing the plots.

The above procedure may be modified for certain purposes. For crops that may be specifically sensitive to high concentrations of soluble calcium or chloride, the composition of the added salt may be changed to vary the sodium : calcium ratio, or sulfate may be substituted for some or all of the chloride. The solubility of calcium sulfate is a limiting factor in making such substitutions, and the effect of high ratios of sodium to calcium on the exchangeable-sodium-percentage must be taken into account.

Inasmuch as this procedure does not include observations on the salt tolerance of the crop during germination, this must be determined separately, either by a laboratory technique (Ayers and Hayward, 1949) or by a modification of the artificially salinized field-plot technique. The plots may be salinized prior to planting with a series of waters of graded concentrations. Salinity levels are then determined by EC_e measurements, and the seeds are planted according to standard or experimental practice. Irrigating with water, usually much less saline than that used in salinizing the plots, will result in a redistribution of salt, especially where furrow irrigation is practiced. Germination counts will serve to delimit the critical level of salinity which can be tolerated by the crop at the time of planting under the specific cultural conditions employed.

(51) Drum Cultures

Drum cultures have been used extensively for studies of salt tolerance relating to the specific effects of various added salts and to the frequency of irrigation as it interacts with salinity in affecting the growth of plants (Wadleigh and coworkers, 1951; Wadleigh and Ayers, 1945). Since the number of treatments may be greatly increased with a minimum of space and effort by using drum cultures, this technique has a very definite place in salinity investigations.

Salinization of drum cultures requires a different technique from that employed with artificially salinized plots. Any salt added to the drums remains in the soil and is not moved downward past the root zone by subsequent irrigations as in field plots. It is, therefore, necessary to add the salt only in the initial irrigation of the drums or by mixing salt with the dry soil in amounts calculated to give the desired salinity levels. Thereafter, nonsaline water must be used in irrigating to avoid further increases in the salt concentration of the soil. However, repeated irrigations with nonsaline water will tend to leach the salt downward in the drum, and a very steep gradient in salt concentration will ensue.

In order to maintain a relatively uniform distribution of salt in the soil, it is necessary to irrigate alternately on the surface and by subirrigation. For subirrigation, provision is made for introducing the irrigation water into a layer of fine gravel in the bottom of the drum before filling with soil. With alternate surface and subirrigation the distribution of the salt in the soil can be maintained more nearly uniform. Frequency of irrigation may be determined by daily weighings of the drum cultures and calculation of mean soil-moisture content. It is important to avoid over-irrigation of the drums, since drainage, if permitted, will result in loss of salt; or, if drainage is prevented, the saturated soil condition will inhibit proper root activity.

(52) Sand and Water Cultures

Frequently, problems difficult to solve by soil-culture methods can be studied more satisfactorily by sand or water cultures, because the latter allow for a more precise control of the substrate. Salinity studies using sand or water cultures involve the addition of various salts to a base nutrient solution. The salts may be added in isosmotic concentration to facilitate comparisons of growth or in isoequivalent concentration to permit a readier comparison of accumulation of the elements in question. Occasionally, the two methods of adjusting salt concentration are combined to permit both isosmotic and isoequivalent comparisons, or a series of concentrations of each salt may be used, and the effect of osmotic pressure and equivalent concentration determined by graphical analysis of the data. By these techniques the effects of various ions, such as sodium, potassium, calcium, magnesium, chloride, sulfate, and bicarbonate, on the growth and composition of plants may be studied. In sand or water cultures the treatments are not altered as a result of cation exchange, nor is fluctuating moisture content a disturbing factor as it is in soil cultures.

For sand and water cultures, provision must be made for adequate nutrition by use of a base nutrient solution, proper control of the pH of the nutrient solution, and adequate aeration.

Methods of Plant Analysis

[See the introductory notes at the beginning of chapter 6]

(53) Sampling and Preparation of Plant Samples

In collecting plant samples for chemical analysis in connection with salinity studies, the usual care should be practiced to obtain material representative of the plant population. Since plant organs may differ markedly in their selectivity in accumulating various ions, it is frequently desirable to collect separate fractions of the various plant parts: leaves, stems, and roots. In taking leaf samples it is the usual practice to select mature, fully expanded leaves, avoiding senescent ones, since salt accumulation may vary with age of leaf. If some leaves are affected by leaf burn or other visual symptoms of salt injury, separate samples of affected and normal leaves may furnish data of diagnostic importance.

Remove surface contamination of the plant material by brushing and brief rinsing in distilled or demineralized water. If iron or other heavy metals are to be determined, rub the entire surface gently in 0.3 N hydrochloric acid and rinse. Dry the sample rapidly in a forced-draft oven at 70° C. Grind the sample in a Wiley mill, or by means of a mortar and pestle if metallic contamination is to be avoided. Mix well and store in tightly stoppered containers. Label each sample, giving information on species, plant part sampled, fresh weight, date, collector, and other pertinent data.

If soluble sap constituents are to be determined, freeze weighed amounts of fresh plant material in wide-mouthed jars and store at −10° C. To obtain sap, thaw the plant material quickly by immersing the container in running water, press at 10,000 to 15,000 lb. per sq. in. until the major portion of the sap has been released. Centrifuge the liquid 15 min. at $RCF = 1,500$, pour off the supernatant liquid, and save for analysis. The expressed sap may be kept for several days in a refrigerator if a few drops of toluene are added, but analysis of the fresh sap is preferred. When the determination of insoluble constituents is desired, combine the residue from the centrifuge tube with the press cake, determine moisture content, and analyze for desired constituents. Correct these results on the basis of moisture content of the press cake and the concentration of soluble constituents of the sap.

Procedures for chemical analyses of plant materials routinely employed in salt-tolerance studies are described under Methods 54 to 62. Additional determinations of various plant constituents are sometimes desirable, depending upon the specific problems under investigation. Methods employed in studies of bicarbonate-induced chlorosis have been described by Wadleigh and Brown (1952).

(54) Ashing

(54a) Wet Digestion

This procedure is preferable to dry ignition, because of the possibility of loss of mineral constituents at high temperatures during dry ignition.

Reagents

A. Nitric acid, conc.
B. Perchloric acid, 72 percent.

Procedure

Transfer 1.000 gm. of dried plant material or an equivalent volume of sap (usually 10 ml.) to a 50-ml. beaker and add 20 ml. of reagent A. Cover with a watchglass and allow to stand until initial reactions subside. Heat until solid particles have nearly disappeared, cool, add 10 ml. of B. *Caution: Perchloric acid is explosive in presence of easily oxidizable organic matter.* Heat gently at first, then heat more vigorously until a clear, colorless solution results. Do not take to dryness; discontinue heating when the volume is reduced to approximately 3 ml. Cool and transfer quantitatively to a 100-ml. volumetric flask, make to volume, mix, allow to stand overnight and filter through a dry filter paper without washing. Retain this solution and use for analyses as described under Methods 55 to 58 and 61.

Reference

Toth and associates (1948).

(54b) Magnesium Nitrate Ignition

Since the wet-digestion procedure does not quantitatively retain sulfur, magnesium nitrate ignition should be used in the determination of sulfur in plants. Total phosphorus may be determined in the ignited material as well, since phosphorus is quantitatively oxidized to phosphate by this ignition.

Reagents

A. Magnesium nitrate solution. Add 113 gm. of magnesium oxide to 300 ml. of water and stir to a paste. Add nitric acid (1+1) until the magnesium oxide is in solution. Add a little excess magnesium oxide and boil; filter and dilute to 1 liter.
B. Hydrochloric acid (1+1).

Procedure

Weigh 2.000 gm. of the sample and transfer into a large porcelain crucible or casserole. Add 10 ml. of reagent A, taking care that all the material is brought in contact with the solution, and heat gently on a hot plate to 180° C. until the reaction is complete. Transfer the crucible while hot to an electric muffle and allow to remain at low heat (muffle must not show any red) until the charge is thoroughly oxidized. No black particles should remain. (It may be necessary to break up the charge and return to the muffle.) Remove from the muffle and allow to cool. Moisten the ash with water and add 10 ml. of B, which should provide an excess of acid. Evaporate to dryness, moisten with B, and again evaporate to dryness to dehydrate silica. Add 5 ml. of B and sufficient water to bring the salts into solution. Allow to stand on the steam bath until solution is complete. Filter, wash, and make to 100 ml. with water. Retain this solution for analysis of sulfur and phosphorus according to Methods 60 and 61.

Reference

Association of Official Agricultural Chemists (1950, 2.8 (e), p. 8, and 6.35, p. 104)

(55) Calcium

(55a) Calcium by Flame Photometer

Apparatus

Perkin-Elmer model 52 flame photometer with acetylene or propane burner.

Reagents

A. Lithium chloride, 0.05 N. Dissolve 2.12 gm. of lithium chloride in water and make to 1 liter.

B. Sodium chloride, 5.00 meq./l. Dissolve 0.2922 gm. of dry sodium chloride in water and make to 1 liter.

C. Potassium chloride, 12.5 meq./l. Dissolve 0.9320 gm. of dry potassium chloride in water and make to 1 liter.

D. Calcium chloride, 50.0 meq./l. Dissolve 2.503 gm. of pure calcium carbonate (calcite crystals) in 50 ml. of 3 N hydrochloric acid and dilute to 1 liter.

E. Magnesium chloride, 50.0 meq./l. Dissolve 5.1 gm. of $MgCl_2 \cdot 6H_2O$ in approximately 900 ml. of water. Standardize by Method 78 and add the calculated amount of water to bring the magnesium concentration to 50.0 meq./l.

Remarks

The optimum concentration of lithium chloride for use as an internal standard varies with individual flame photometers but is usually 5 to 10 meq./l.

Interference by sodium, potassium, and magnesium is not an appreciable factor unless the concentration of the interfering element is at least 5 times the concentration of calcium. Interference may be compensated for by determining the concentration of the interfering element(s) in the unknown and by adding this concentration (± 20 percent) of the interfering element(s) to the standard solutions. In the determination of calcium in plant tissue, interference is seldom encountered.

Procedure

Prepare a series of standards containing 0, 1, 2, 3, and 4 meq./l. of calcium (0, 1, 2, 3, and 4 ml. of reagent D per 50 ml.) and the concentration of lithium chloride found to be optimum for the instrument.

Transfer an aliquot (usually 10 ml.) of the acid digest (Method 54a) containing 0.05 to 0.20 meq. of calcium to a 50-ml. volumetric flask and add the same concentration of lithium chloride used in the standard series. Add compensating solutions B, C, and E when necessary, and make to volume. Obtain instrument readings for standard solutions and unknowns with the wave-length indicator set at the point corresponding to the calcium emission maximum at 6,220 A.

Calculations

Milliequivalents of Ca per 100 gm. of dry material= (meq./l. of Ca from calibration curve) $\times 500$/ml. in aliquot.

(55b) Calcium by Oxalate Method

The acid digest (Method 54a) may be analyzed for calcium by Method 77, if a flame photometer is not available.

Calculations

Milliequivalents of Ca per 100 gm. of dry material= normality of $KMnO_4 \times 10,000 \times$ (ml. of $KMnO_4$ − ml. of blank) /ml. in aliquot of acid digest.

(56) Magnesium

Remarks

Methods for determining magnesium by the use of thiazole yellow or related dyes have not given acceptable results at this laboratory. The following method, while time-consuming, has proved to be reliable. The calcium is removed as the oxalate, and magnesium is precipitated as magnesium ammonium phosphate hexahydrate. The phosphate is determined colorimetrically, and magnesium is calculated by reference to a calibration curve.

Apparatus

Photoelectric colorimeter or spectrophotometer.

Reagents

A. Oxalic acid, 1 N. Dissolve 63 gm. of oxalic acid in water and make to 1 liter.

B. Methyl orange, 0.01 percent in 95 percent ethanol.

C. Ammonium hydroxide, conc.

D. Hydrochloric acid (1+1).

E. Magnesium chloride, 5.00 meq./l. Dissolve 0.51 gm. $MgCl_2 \cdot 6H_2O$ in approximately 900 ml. of water. Standardize by Method 78 and add the calculated amount of water to bring the magnesium concentration to 5.00 meq./l.

F. Ammonium chloride, 3 percent. Filter before use.

G. Ammonium dihydrogen phosphate, 5 percent. Filter before use.

H. Phenolphthalein, 1 percent in 60 percent ethanol.

I. Ammonium hydroxide in ethanol and ether. Mix 20 ml. of concentrated ammonium hydroxide with 980 ml. of a mixture of equal volumes of ethanol, ether, and water.

J. Sulfuric acid (1+6).

K. Ammonium vanadate, 0.25 percent. Dissolve 2.5 gm. of ammonium vanadate in 500 ml. of boiling water, cool somewhat, and then add 60 ml. of reagent J. Cool to room temperature and dilute to 1 liter. Store in a brown bottle.

L. Ammonium molybdate, 5 percent. Store in a brown bottle.

Procedure

Transfer an aliquot (usually 10 ml.) of the acid digest from Method 54a containing 0.01 to 0.05 meq. of magnesium to a 25-ml. volumetric flask. Prepare a series of standards in 25-ml. volumetric flasks containing 0, 0.01, 0.02, 0.03, 0.04, and 0.05 meq. of magnesium (0, 2, 4, 6, 8, and 10 ml. of reagent E). To all standards and unknowns, add 3 drops of B, acidify with D, if necessary, and add 1 ml. of D in excess. Add 1 ml. of A, heat to boiling, and neutralize with C. Cool and add more C if necessary to keep basic (yellow). Make to volume and filter through a dry filter paper; do not wash. Transfer a 5-ml. aliquot of the filtrate to a 15-ml. centrifuge tube and add 1 ml. each of F and G and 1 drop of H. Heat to about 90° C. in a water bath, and then add C until permanently pink. After 15 min., add an additional 2 ml. of C, stopper, mix, and let stand overnight.

Centrifuge at $RCF = 2,000$ for 10 min., decant carefully, drain on filter paper for 10 min., and wipe the mouth of the tube with a clean towel or lintless filter paper. Suspend the precipitate and rinse the sides of the tube with a stream of 5 ml. of reagent I from a pipet equipped with a rubber bulb. Centrifuge at $RCF = 2,000$, decant, drain for 5 min., and wipe the mouth of the tube. Repeat this washing procedure once.

Pipet 10 ml. of reagent J into the tube and twirl for a few seconds. After 5 min. transfer the contents quantitatively into a 100-ml. volumetric flask with a total of 50 ml. of water. Pipet 10 ml. each of K and L into the flask while swirling the solution rapidly. Make to volume and mix. After 10 min. measure the percent transmission of the unknown and standard solutions at 4,000 A. or by means of an appropriate blue filter.

Calculations

Milliequivalents of Mg per 100 gm. of dry material = (meq. of Mg from calibration curve) × 10,000/ml. in aliquot of acid digest.

(57) Sodium

(57a) Sodium by Flame Photometer

Apparatus

Perkin-Elmer model 52 flame photometer with acetylene or propane burner.

Reagents

A. Lithium chloride, 0.05 N. Dissolve 2.12 gm. of lithium chloride in water and make to 1 liter.

B. Sodium chloride, 5.00 meq./l. Dissolve 0.2922 gm. of dry sodium chloride in water and make to 1 liter.

C. Potassium chloride, 12.5 meq./l. Dissolve 0.9320 gm. of dry potassium chloride in water and make to 1 liter.

D. Calcium chloride, 50.0 meq./l. Dissolve 2.503 gm. of pure calcium carbonate (calcite crystals) in 50 ml. of 3 N hydrochloric acid and dilute to 1 liter.

E. Magnesium chloride, 50.0 meq./l. Dissolve 5.1 gm. of $MgCl_2 \cdot 6H_2O$ in approximately 900 ml. of water. Standardize by Method 78 and add the calculated amount of water to bring the magnesium concentration to 50.0 meq./l.

Remarks

The optimum concentration of lithium chloride for use as an internal standard varies with individual flame photometers, but is usually 5 to 10 meq./l.

Sodium is frequently found in relatively small amounts in plant material, so that interference often occurs. Potassium interferes if the potassium : sodium ratio is 5 or greater; and calcium, if the calcium : sodium ratio is 10 or greater. Since these ratios are frequently exceeded in plant materials, it is advisable to determine calcium and potassium first, so that the approximate concentrations of interfering elements may be added to the sodium standard solutions. Magnesium does not cause interference unless magnesium : sodium ratios are in excess of 100. Such magnesium : sodium ratios are very rarely encountered.

Procedure

Prepare a series of standards containing 0, 0.1, 0.2, 0.3, and 0.4 meq./l. of sodium (0, 1, 2, 3, and 4 ml. of reagent B per 50 ml.) and the concentration of lithium chloride found to be optimum for the instrument.

Transfer an aliquot (usually 10 ml.) of the acid digest (Method 54a) containing 0.005 to 0.020 meq. of sodium to a 50-ml. volumetric flask and add the same concentration of lithium chloride used in the standard series. Add compensating solutions C, D, and E when necessary and make to volume. Obtain instrument readings for standard solutions and unknowns with the wave-length indicator set at the point corresponding to the sodium emission maximum at 5,890 A.

Calculations

Milliequivalents of Na per 100 gm. of dry material = (meq./l. of Na from calibration curve) × 500/ml. in aliquot.

(57b) Sodium by Uranyl Zinc Acetate

Reagents

A. Uranyl zinc acetate. Weigh 300 gm. of uranium acetate dihydrate, 900 gm. of zinc acetate dihydrate, and 10 mg. of sodium chloride into a large flask. Add 82 ml. of glacial acetic acid and 2,618 ml. of water. Stir or shake until the salts are dissolved, leaving only a small amount of sodium uranyl zinc acetate precipitate. This may require several days. Filter before use.

B. Ethanol, saturated with *sodium* uranyl zinc acetate. Filter before use. Sodium uranyl zinc acetate may be prepared as follows: Add 125 ml. of reagent A to 5 ml. of 2 percent sodium chloride solution, stir, and after 15 min. collect the precipitate in a porous-bottomed porcelain crucible. Wash several times with glacial acetic acid, then several times with ether. Dry in a desiccator.

C. Ether, anhydrous.
D. Phenolphthalein, 1 percent in 60 percent ethanol.
E. Calcium chloride dihydrate, 10 percent in water.
F. Ammonium hydroxide $(1+1)$.
G. Acetic acid, 2 percent.
H. Acetic acid, glacial.

Procedure

Transfer an aliquot (usually 25 ml.) of the acid digest (Method 54a) sufficient to give 50 to 200 mg. of sodium uranyl zinc acetate to a 50-ml. sugar flask. Add 1 drop of reagent D and 5 ml. of E and make the solution basic (pink) with F to precipitate phosphate. Make to 55 ml. and filter through a dry paper; do not wash. Transfer a 50-ml. aliquot to a 100-ml. beaker, acidify with H, and evaporate to dryness on a steam bath. Cool, dissolve the residue in 2 ml. of G, and add 75 ml. of filtered reagent A. Stir the solution and allow to stand for 1 hr. Filter through a porous-bottomed porcelain filtering crucible, taking care to transfer all the sodium uranyl zinc acetate precipitate onto the filter by means of a small wash bottle filled with A. Wash the beaker 5 times with 2-ml. portions of A and pass the washings through the filter. Allow the crucible to drain completely, because it is important to have the filter and the precipitate free of the reagent before washing with the alcohol. Wash the crucible 5 times with 2-ml. portions of B and, after removing all the alcohol by suction, wash once or twice with C. The suction is continued until the precipitate is dry. Allow the crucible to stand in a desiccator for 2 hr. and weigh.

Return the crucible to a suction apparatus and wash with small portions of water until all the soluble material is dissolved and passes through the crucible. Wash with alcohol and ether as above. Dry and weigh. The difference between the first and last weight represents the weight of sodium precipitate. The precipitate is assumed to have the composition: $(UO_2)_3NaZn(CH_3COO)_9 \cdot 6H_2O$; molecular weight, 1538.079; percent sodium, 1.4952.

Calculations

Milliequivalents of Na per 100 gm. of dry material = (gm. of sodium uranyl zinc acetate precipitate) $\times$ 7,152/ml. in aliquot.

(58) Potassium

(58a) Potassium by Flame Photometer

Apparatus

Perkin-Elmer model 52 flame photometer with acetylene or propane burner.

Reagents

A. Lithium chloride, 0.05 N. Dissolve 2.12 gm. of lithium chloride in water and make to 1 liter.

B. Sodium chloride, 5.00 meq./l. Dissolve 0.2922 gm. of dry sodium chloride in water and make to 1 liter.
C. Potassium chloride, 12.5 meq./l. Dissolve 0.9320 gm. of dry potassium chloride in water and make to 1 liter.
D. Calcium chloride, 50.0 meq./l. Dissolve 2.503 gm. of pure calcium carbonate (calcite crystals) in 50 ml. of 3 N hydrochloric acid and dilute to 1 liter.
E. Magnesium chloride, 50.0 meq./l. Dissolve 5.1 gm. of $MgCl_2 \cdot 6H_2O$ in approximately 900 ml. of water. Standardize by Method 78 and add the calculated amount of water to bring the magnesium concentration to 50.0 meq./l.

Remarks

The optimum concentration of lithium chloride for use as an internal standard varies with individual flame photometers but is usually 5 to 10 meq./l.

Interference by sodium occurs if the sodium : potassium ratio is 5 or greater, and by calcium if the calcium : potassium ratio is 10 or greater. Magnesium does not cause interference until the magnesium : potassium ratio is in excess of 100. Interference in the determination of potassium is very rarely encountered.

Procedure

Prepare a series of standards containing 0, 0.25, 0.50, 0.75, and 1.00 meq./l. of potassium (0, 1, 2, 3, and 4 ml. of reagent C per 50 ml.) and the concentration of lithium chloride found to be optimum for the instrument.

Transfer an aliquot (usually 10 ml.) of the acid digest (Method 54a) containing 0.01 to 0.05 meq. of potassium to a 50-ml. volumetric flask and add the same concentration of lithium chloride used in the standard series. Add compensating solutions B, D, and E when necessary and make to volume. Obtain instrument readings for standard solutions and unknowns with the wavelength indicator set at the point corresponding to the potassium emission maximum at 7,680 A.

Calculations

Milliequivalents of K per 100 gm. of dry material = (meq./l. of K from calibration curve) $\times$ 500/ml. in aliquot.

(58b) Potassium by Cobaltinitrite

Reagents

A. Nitric acid $(1+15)$.
B. Trisodium cobaltinitrite, 20 percent. Store at about 5° C. and filter before use. The solution is stable for some time but should be prepared fresh at about biweekly intervals.
C. Nitric acid $(1+1,500)$. Dilute 10 ml. of reagent A to 1 liter.

D. Ethanol, 95 percent.

E. Potassium chloride, 0.0100 N. Dissolve 0.7456 gm. of dry potassium chloride in water and make to 1 liter.

Procedure

Evaporate to dryness in a 50-ml. beaker an aliquot (usually 25 ml.) of the acid digest (Method 54a) containing 0.05 to 0.35 meq. of potassium. Add 10 ml. of water, 1 ml. of reagent A, and stir to dissolve. Add 5 ml. of B, stir and allow to stand for 2 hr. at 15° to 20° C. Filter in a porous-bottomed porcelain filtering crucible, the tare weight of which is known, using C in a wash bottle to make the transfer. Wash 10 times with C and 5 times with 2-ml. portions of D. Aspirate until quite dry. Wipe the outside with a cloth, dry for 1 hr. at 110° C., cool in a desiccator, and weigh.

Prepare a series of standards containing 0, 0.05, 0.15, 0.25, and 0.35 meq. of potassium (0, 5, 15, 25, and 35 ml. of reagent E) in 50-ml. beakers and proceed as directed for the aliquots of the acid digests.

Calculations

Milliequivalents of K per 100 gm. of dry material = (meq. of K from calibration curve) × 10,000/ml. in aliquot.

(59) Chloride

Remarks

A modification of the method described by Clark and others (1942) has been found to give results in close agreement with those obtained by AOAC procedures with a considerable saving in time. The sample for chloride analysis together with a tube containing acid and a well containing base are placed in a tightly closed weighing bottle (fig. 32). The acid digests the filter-paper plug in the acid tube and reacts with the sample, volatilizing chloride as hydrogen chloride, which is absorbed by the potassium hydroxide. The absorbed chloride is then titrated with mercuric nitrate.

Apparatus

Make the following items from ordinary glass tubing:

1. Acid tube, approximately 1.0 cm. inside diameter, with one end drawn out to a capillary tip. Capacity, 2 ml.

2. Outer well, approximately 1.1 cm. inside diameter, 4 to 5 cm. long, sealed at one end.

3. Inner well, approximately 1.0 cm. outside diameter, 1 to 2 cm. long, sealed at one end.

4. Support for inner well of such length that when assembled, the top of inner well is at, or slightly above, the top of the outer well.

Clamp. Any screw-type clamp, equipped with rub-

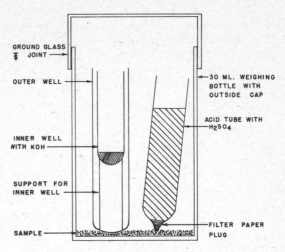

FIGURE 32.—Apparatus for the chloride determination (Method 59).

ber cushions which will hold the cap securely on the weighing bottle.

CAUTION.—After cleaning, rinse all glassware shown in figure 32 with nitric acid (1+100) and dry in oven. Use forceps, thereafter, in handling acid tubes, wells, and supports to avoid chloride contamination. Avoid contaminating the air with hydrogen chloride.

Reagents

A. Potassium hydroxide, 50 percent.

B. Sulfuric acid, conc.

C. Ethanol, 95 percent.

D. Diphenylcarbazone, 1 percent. Dissolve 1 gm. of diphenylcarbazone (Eastman No. 4459) in 100 ml. of 95 percent ethanol. Store at 5° C.

E. Mercuric nitrate, 0.01 N. Dissolve 1.7 gm. of $Hg(NO_3)_2 \cdot H_2O$ in water to which 10 ml. of nitric acid (1+7) have been added and make to 1 liter. Store in brown bottle in the dark.

F. Potassium chloride, 50.0 meq./l. Dissolve 3.728 gm. of dry potassium chloride in water and make to 1 liter.

G. Hydrogen peroxide, 30 percent.

H. Nitric acid (1+7).

I. Bromphenol blue, 0.05 percent in ethanol.

Procedure

Weigh accurately in a 30-ml. weighing bottle a sample (usually 0.1 gm.) of dried plant material containing 0.02 to 0.25 meq. of chloride. To determine chloride in expressed sap, evaporate a suitable aliquot (usually 1 ml.) to dryness in the weighing bottle at 70° C. Prepare a series of standards containing 0, 0.05, 0.10, 0.15, 0.20, and 0.25 meq. of chloride (0, 1, 2, 3, 4, and 5 ml. of reagent F) and evaporate to dryness in the weighing bottles.

Plug the acid tube with macerated filter paper and assemble the apparatus as shown in figure 32. Add 3 drops of reagent A and 1 drop of C to the inner well. Add 2 ml. of B to the acid tube and moisten the ground surface of the cap with B. Seal the weighing bottle by twisting the cap into position and clamp securely. Place the assembly in an oven at 110° C. overnight. Remove, cool, and open the weighing bottles, using rubber gloves.

Transfer the inner well with forceps to a porcelain casserole and add 5 ml. of water. Add 3 drops of reagent I, neutralize with H, dissolving all of the residue in the inner well, and add 1 drop of H in excess. Add 3 drops of G, 1 drop of D, and titrate with E to a purple or pink color, depending on volume. Prepare a standard curve; it is not linear over the entire range.

Calculations

Milliequivalents of Cl per 100 gm. dry material = (meq. of Cl in sample) × 100/gm. of sample.

Milliequivalents of Cl per liter of sap = (meq. of Cl in aliquot) × 1,000/ml. in aliquot.

References

Association of Official Agricultural Chemists (1950, 6.41–6.46, p. 105, 106), Clark and others (1942).

(60) Sulfur

Reagents

A. Hydrochloric acid, conc.
B. Barium chloride, 10 percent. Filter before use.
C. Methyl orange, 0.05 percent in ethanol.

Procedure

Transfer an aliquot (usually 50 ml.) of the digest (Method 54b) containing 0.1 to 2.0 meq. of sulfate to a 250-ml. beaker. Add 2 drops of reagent C, acidify with A if necessary, and then add 1 ml. of A. Make to approximately 100 ml. with water, heat to boiling, and add an excess of B, drop by drop, with constant stirring. Cover with a watchglass and allow to stand on a steam bath for several hours, until the volume is reduced to approximately 50 ml. After cooling, filter the precipitate of barium sulfate through an ignited and weighed Gooch crucible and wash with water until free of chloride. Dry, ignite in a muffle at low red heat, cool, and weigh. Ashless filter paper may be used in place of the Gooch crucible, but the muffle in which the ignition is made must be well ventilated.

Calculations

Milliequivalents of total S (expressed as sulfate) per 100 gm. of dry material = gm. BaSO$_4$ × 42,841/ml. in aliquot.

(61) Phosphorus

Phosphorus is retained quantitatively by both the magnesium nitrate ignition and wet digestion, provided the perchloric acid digest is not allowed to go to dryness.

Apparatus

A photoelectric colorimeter or spectrophotometer.

Reagents

A. Sulfuric acid (1+6).
B. Ammonium vanadate, 0.25 percent. Dissolve 2.5 gm. of ammonium vanadate in 500 ml. of boiling water, cool somewhat, and add 60 ml. of reagent A. Cool to room temperature and dilute to 1 liter. Store in a brown bottle.
C. Ammonium molybdate, 5 percent.
D. Potassium dihydrogen phosphate, 2.50 millimoles/l. Dissolve 0.3404 gm. of potassium dihydrogen phosphate in water and make to 1 liter.

Procedure

Transfer an aliquot (usually 5 ml.) of the solution prepared by Method 54a or 54b containing 0.002 to 0.020 millimoles of phosphate to a 50-ml. volumetric flask. Prepare a series of standards containing 0, 0.005, 0.010, 0.015, and 0.020 millimoles of phosphate (0, 2, 4, 6, and 8 ml. of reagent D). Add to each flask containing unknown or standard, 5 ml. each of A, B, and C successively, shaking the flask during each addition. Make to volume, allow to stand 15 to 30 min., and determine transmittance at 4,000 A., or by means of a suitable blue filter.

Calculations

Millimoles of phosphate per 100 gm. of dry material = (millimoles of phosphate from calibration curve) × 10,000/(ml. in aliquot × gm. of sample digested).

1 millimole of phosphate = 1 meq. of H$_2$PO$_4^-$.

(62) Boron

Remarks

Leaf samples, collected and prepared according to Method 53, are usually the best index to the boron status of the plant.

Apparatus

A spectrophotometer or photoelectric colorimeter.
Alkali-resistant (boron-free) glassware, porcelainware, platinum, or fused-quartz dishes. Avoid the use of borosilicate glassware.

Reagents

A. Calcium oxide, powdered.

B. Hydrochloric acid $(1+1)$.

C. Hydrochloric acid, conc.

D. Sulfuric acid, conc.

E. Carmine, 0.05 percent by weight in conc. sulfuric acid (0.920 gm./l.). Shake until completely dissolved.

F. Boric acid, 100 p. p. m. boron. Dissolve 0.5716 gm. of boric acid in water and make to 1 liter.

Procedure

Weigh a portion of the dry sample (usually 2.000 gm.) containing not more than 1.00 mg. of boron and transfer to a porcelain casserole or platinum dish. Add 0.1 gm. of reagent A per gram of sample and mix well. Ignite as completely as possible in a muffle at 500° to 550° C., cool, and moisten with water. Cover with a watchglass and introduce 3 ml. of B per gram of sample, which should make the solution strongly acid. Heat on a steam bath for 20 min. Transfer quantitatively to a 100-ml. volumetric flask, make to volume with water, and filter through a dry filter paper.

Prepare a series of standard solutions containing 0 to 10 p. p. m. boron (0 to 1.00 mg./100 ml.) by diluting 0, 2, 4, 6, 8, and 10 ml. of reagent F to 100 ml. Pipet 2 ml. of each of the standards and of the unknowns into Erlenmeyer flasks. Add 2 drops of C to each standard and 2 drops of water to each unknown. Add 10 ml. of D to each Erlenmeyer flask, mix, and cool. Add 10 ml. of E, mix, and allow to stand at least 45 min. for color development. Determine the transmittance at 5,850 A., or by means of a suitable yellow filter.

Calculations

Parts per million B in dry plant material = (p. p. m. B from calibration curve) $\times 100$/gm. of sample.

Reference

Hatcher and Wilcox (1950).

Chapter 8

Methods of Analysis of Irrigation Waters

[See the introductory notes at the beginning of chapter 6.]

(70) Collection of Irrigation Water Samples

The minimum quantity of water required for the ordinary chemical analysis is about one-half gallon (1.9 liters). In special cases, larger quantities may be necessary.

Care should be taken to obtain a representative sample. Satisfactory samples of some waters can be obtained only by mixing several portions collected at different times, the details as to collection and mixing depending on local conditions. Samples from wells should be collected after the pump has been running for some time, and samples from streams should be taken from running water.

In general the shorter the elapsed time between collection and analysis of a sample, the more reliable will be the analytical data. Changes resulting from chemical and biological activity may alter the composition of the sample. No satisfactory method for sterilizing a water sample to prevent bacterial action has been proposed.

References

American Public Health Association and American Water Works Association (1946, *p. 1*).

(71) Records, Reports, and Expression of Results

At the time of collection, a label, bearing a short identifying description, should be attached to the bottle. Additional information can be recorded on a "Collector's Description of Water Sample" form as shown. One item not specifically called for on this form, but often of importance, is the elevation above sea level of an appropriate reference point at the well. When this is known, it is possible to refer the water level in the well to sea level. This value may be useful in quality-of-water studies. The importance of an accurate and complete description, especially as regards location, cannot be overemphasized.

Two other blank forms used at the Laboratory in connection with the analyses of water samples are shown on pages 138 and 139. The laboratory work

sheet is used for recording the original data obtained from the chemical analysis. One such sheet is used for each sample. A laboratory number is assigned which, with the description from the "Collector's Description of Water Sample," is entered at the top of the page. Upon completing and recording each separate determination, the analyst enters his initials and the date.

For purposes of uniformity, the following rules for reporting analytical results are used:

pH.—Report to the nearest 0.1 unit.

ELECTRICAL CONDUCTIVITY ($EC \times 10^6$ at 25° C.).—Report to the nearest 0.1 when less than 100, and to 3 significant figures for values above 100.

DISSOLVED SOLIDS.—Report in parts per million (p. p. m.) to the nearest whole number, but not more than 3 significant figures.

BORON.—Electrometric titration method; report to the nearest 0.01 p. p. m. when less than 10 p. p. m. boron, and to 3 significant figures above 10 p. p. m. boron.

Colorimetric method; report to the nearest 0.1 p. p. m. boron but not more than 2 significant figures.

SILICA.—Report in p. p. m. SiO_2 to nearest whole number, but not more than 3 significant figures.

FLUORIDE.—Report to the nearest 0.1 p. p. m. fluoride or to the nearest 0.01 meq./l.

CATIONS AND ANIONS.—Report to the nearest 0.01 meq./l. up to 100, and to 4 significant figures if above 100 meq./l.

(72) Electrical Conductivity

Remarks

Electrical conductivity is commonly used for indicating the total concentration of the ionized constituents of a natural water. It is closely related to the sum of the cations (or anions) as determined chemically, and it usually correlates closely with the total dissolved solids. It is a rapid and reasonably precise determination that does not alter or consume any of the sample.

Apparatus

Wheatstone bridge, alternating current, suitable for conductivity measurements. This may be a 1,000-cycle a. c. bridge with telephone receivers, a 60-cycle a. c.

UNITED STATES DEPARTMENT OF AGRICULTURE

Agricultural Research Service
Soil and Water Conservation Research Branch
United States Salinity Laboratory
Riverside, California

COLLECTOR'S DESCRIPTION OF WATER SAMPLE

Collector's No. _____; Lab. No. _____; Date _____; Collector _____

Name and/or owner _____

_____

Spring, Stream, Lake, Well? (circle one)

_____

       County   Miles—distance nearest town   USGS sheet

Location _____ ¼, Sec. _____; T _____ _____; R _____ _____; _____

                                               Distance and direction from section corner
                                                  or landmark

Other description _____

Depth _____; Depth to upper perforation _____; Casing diameter _____

Discharge _____; Static level _____; Draws down to _____

Temp. _____; Odor _____; Gas _____; Color _____
      ° C. or °F.

Use: Irrig., Municipal, Ind., Stock, Domestic _____

Approximate acreage served, crops _____

Condition or symptoms of land or crops _____

Owner's opinion of water quality _____

Collector's remarks _____

_____

_____

Report to: _____

_____

_____

(Please draw a map on the reverse side, if necessary, to show the exact location of the sampling site).

259525 O - 54 - 10

Water sample No._____. Description:

pH [ ]	Dissolved Solids	Boron	Sum of Cations
Conductivity at 25°C.			Sum of Anions
T°C.			$\dfrac{ECx10^6}{Anions}$
$\dfrac{k}{R}$ = _____			Percent Na
$ECx10^6$ @ 25° C. [ ]	D.S. p.p.m. [ ]	B p.p.m. [ ]	
Calcium	**Magnesium**	**Sodium**	**Potassium**
Ca meq./l. [ ]	Mg meq./l. [ ]	Na meq./l. [ ]	K meq./l. [ ]
Carbonate and Bicarbonate	**Sulfate**	**Chloride**	**Nitrate**
CO_3 meq./l. [ ] HCO$_3$ meq./l. [ ]	SO$_4$ meq./l. [ ]	Cl meq./l. [ ]	NO$_3$ meq./l. [ ]
			Received laboratory:
			Analysis completed:
			Reported:
			Reported to:
[ ]	[ ]	[ ]	

UNITED STATES DEPARTMENT OF AGRICULTURE
Agricultural Research Service

Division of Soil and
Plant Relationships

U. S. Salinity Laboratory
Rubidoux Unit
Riverside, California

REPORT OF WATER ANALYSIS

Description

Conductivity, $EC \times 10^6$@25°C.
 	
Percent Sodium
 	
Boron (B) parts per million
		Dissolved Solids:
		    tons per acre-foot
		    parts per million
		
		Hydrogen-ion activity (pH)
		
		Silica (SiO_2) parts per million	

Cations	Milligram equivalents per liter	Parts per million	Anions	Milligram equivalents per liter	Parts per million
Calcium (Ca)			Carbonate (CO_3)		
Magnesium (Mg)			Bicarbonate (HCO_3)		
Sodium (Na)			Sulfate (SO_4)		
Potassium (K)			Chloride (Cl)		
			Fluoride (F)		
			Nitrate (NO_3)		
Sum		X X X	Sum		X X X

Analyzed by:

Reported by:

Reported to:

bridge with an a. c. galvanometer, or one of the newer bridges employing a cathode ray tube as the null indicator.

Conductivity cell, either pipet or immersion type, with platinized platinum electrodes. The cell constant should be approximately 1.0 reciprocal centimeter. New cells should be cleaned with chromic-sulfuric acid cleaning solution, and the electrodes should be platinized before use. Subsequently, they should be cleaned and replatinized whenever the readings become erratic or when an inspection shows that any of the platinum black has flaked off. The platinizing solution contains platinum chloride, 1 gm.; lead acetate, 0.012 gm.; in 100 ml. water. To platinize, immerse the electrodes in the above solution and pass a current from a 1.5-volt dry battery through the cell. The current should be such that only a small quantity of gas is evolved, and the direction of current flow should be reversed occasionally.

Reagents

A. Standard potassium chloride solution, 0.01 N. Dissolve 0.7456 gm. of potassium chloride in distilled water and make to 1 liter at 25° C. This is the standard reference solution and at 25° C. has an electrical conductivity of 1411.8×10^{-6} (0.0014118) mhos/cm.

Procedure

Place 4 tubes of reagent A in a water bath. (For subsequent sets of determinations, discard the first tube of potassium chloride solution, shift the others one place, and insert a tube of fresh solution.) Place 2 tubes of each sample in the bath, adjust the temperature to approximately 25° C., and hold at this temperature for 20 to 30 min. If the room temperature is not close to 25° C., it is better to adjust the temperature of the bath to approximately that of the room and hold it at that temperature until equilibrium is attained. The bath temperature is here represented by t. Rinse the electrode in three of the tubes of potassium chloride solution, transfer to the fourth, and measure the cell resistance (R'_t). Rinse the electrode several times in one tube of the water sample, transfer to the other tube, and read the resistance (R_t). The electrical conductivity (EC at 25° C.) of the sample is calculated from the equation:

$$EC = \frac{0.0014118 \times R'_t}{R_t}$$

This is multiplied by 1,000,000 (10^6) and reported as $EC \times 10^6$ at 25° C., or as EC, micromhos/cm. at 25°.

The expression "electrical conductivity" is synonymous with "specific electrical conductance." The standard unit for conductivity is the mho/cm. It is so large that most natural waters have a value of much less than 1 unit. For purposes of convenience in recording or expressing such results, the value in mhos/cm. is multiplied by 10^6 (decimal point moved 6 places to the right) and reported as $EC \times 10^6$ at 25° C. The several methods of reporting conductivity are shown below,

using as an example a western surface water with a conductivity of 0.00117 mho/cm.:

$$\begin{aligned} EC &= 0.00117 \text{ mho/cm.} \\ EC \times 10^3 &= 1.17 \text{ mmhos/cm.} \\ EC \times 10^5 &= 117 \ (= K \times 10^5) \\ EC \times 10^6 &= 1{,}170 \text{ micromhos/cm.} \end{aligned}$$

References

Wilcox (1950), National Research Council, International Critical Tables (1929, v. 6, p. 234).

(73) Boron

(73a) Boron, Electrometric Titration

Remarks

The addition of mannitol to a neutral, unbuffered solution of mixed salts containing boron causes the solution to become acid. The quantity of standard alkali required to titrate the solution back to the initial pH is an accurate measure of the boron present. Electrometric or direct methods of titration may be used.

The choice of apparatus for the electrometric titration of boron should be determined by the instruments available, the number of analyses to be made, and the frequency of use. Three sets of apparatus are described below, any one of which will give satisfactory results. The first requires a minimum of equipment. The operation depends on the fact that a 0.7 N calomel electrode and a quinhydrone electrode come to a null point (reversal of polarity) at approximately pH 7.0.

Apparatus

Galvanometer. An enclosed lamp and scale type sensitive to 0.025 microampere per scale division.

Quinhydrone electrode. A piece of platinum wire 7.5 cm. (3 in.) in length, with suitable contact above the surface of the solution. This type is preferable to an electrode of platinum sealed through glass and connected with mercury, as minute cracks develop in the glass and cause erratic results.

Calomel electrode, 0.7 N with respect to potassium chloride. A silver-silver chloride electrode can be used in place of the 0.7 N calomel electrode. For details see Wilcox (1932).

Motor-driven stirrer.

Switch, single-pole single-throw.

The electrodes are connected through the switch to the galvanometer. A shunt to protect the galvanometer is desirable but not essential.

The second apparatus is a simple potentiometer (fig. 33). In addition to the parts listed above, the following are required: resistance wire, 1,500 ohms tapped at 60 ohms; and a 1.5-volt dry cell. A calomel electrode, 0.1 N with respect to potassium chloride, is substituted for the 0.7 N electrode described above.

The third apparatus makes use of either a potentiometer or a pH meter as the indicating system. The

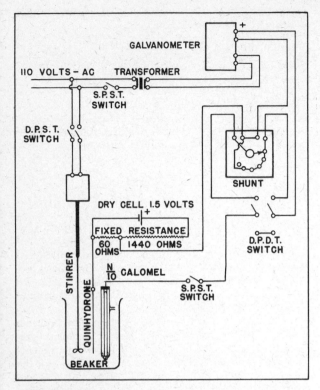

GALVANOMETER

110 VOLTS - AC   TRANSFORMER

S.P.S.T.
SWITCH

D.P.S.T.
SWITCH

SHUNT

DRY CELL 1.5 VOLTS

FIXED RESISTANCE
60   1440 OHMS
OHMS

D.P.D.T.
SWITCH

STIRRER

QUINHYDRONE

$\frac{N}{10}$ CALOMEL

S.P.S.T.
SWITCH

BEAKER

FIGURE 33.—Diagram of electrometric titration apparatus, showing electrical circuit. The 6 volt a. c. line from the transformer supplies the light in the reflecting galvanometer.

instrument is set so that, at balance, the solution under test will have a pH reading of 7.1. The following electrode pairs have been found satisfactory: quinhydrone and 0.1 N calomel; quinhydrone and saturated calomel; glass and saturated calomel.

Reagents

A. Quinhydrone, reagent quality, free from heavy metals.

B. Bromthymol blue indicator solution, 1 percent. Methyl red may be substituted.

C. Sulfuric acid. Approximately 1 N.

D. Sulfuric acid. Approximately 0.02 N.

E. Sodium hydroxide. Approximately 0.5 N, carbonate-free.

F. Sodium hydroxide. Standard 0.0231 N, carbonate-free (1 ml. is equivalent to 0.25 mg. boron).

G. Boric acid solution. Dissolve 0.5716 gm. dry H_3BO_3 in distilled water and dilute to 1 liter. The H_3BO_3 may be dried in a desiccator with calcium chloride. One ml. contains 0.1 mg. boron. This solution is used in standardizing reagent F.

H. Mannitol, neutral. Synthetic mannitol is preferable to the natural product. The "blank" titration for 5 gm. of mannitol should not exceed 0.1 ml. of reagent F.

Procedure

Transfer an aliquot of the sample, containing not more than 1 mg. boron, to a 400-ml. beaker and dilute, if necessary, to 250 ml. Add a few drops of reagent B and acidify with C, adding 0.5 to 1 ml. in excess. Bring to boil, stir, cautiously at first, then vigorously, to expel carbon dioxide. Cool to room temperature, preferably in a water bath. With the S. P. S. T. switch open and the shunt, if used, set at 0.1, introduce the electrodes and stirrer into the solution. Start the stirrer and add E to approximate neutrality as shown by B. Add about 0.2 gm. of A and close the switch in the electrode circuit. The galvanometer should indicate approximate balance. If it swings to the right, excess alkali is indicated, and if to the left, excess acid. Adjust with either F or D until the galvanometer shows no deflection.

If a shunt is used, reverse the switch, thus eliminating it from the circuit and permitting the galvanometer to function at its greatest sensitivity. Again adjust to balance with either dilute acid or alkali. The galvanometer should be steady, showing at most only a slow drift. This is the initial point of the titration. Bring the shunt into the circuit by reversing the D. P. D. T. switch or open the S. P. S. T. switch, if the shunt is omitted. Add 5 $\pm$ 0.1 gm. of mannitol. If boron is present, the indicator will change to the acid color and the galvanometer will swing to the left. Add reagent F until approximate balance is again attained; eliminate the shunt, if used, and complete the titration, bringing the galvanometer back to the original null point. This is the end point.

Note the number of milliliters of reagent F required after adding the mannitol at the initial point of the titration. From this, subtract a blank determined by substituting distilled water for the sample and proceed as indicated above. The net volume of F multiplied by the equivalency (mg. boron per ml. NaOH) gives milligrams of boron in the aliquot titrated. Report as parts per million boron. The equivalency of F is established by titrating an aliquot of G. The buret used should be of such accuracy that the volume of F can be read to 0.01 ml. Borosilicate glassware (Pyrex) can be used for this determination. New beakers should be cleaned by filling with acid and heating on the steam bath before use. If the concentration of phosphate exceeds 10 p. p. m., it should be precipitated with lead nitrate and the excess lead removed with sodium bicarbonate.

Calculations

Parts per million B = (ml. NaOH − blank) × mg. B equivalent to 1 ml. NaOH × 1,000/ml. in aliquot.

References

American Public Health Association and American Water Works Association (1946, *p. 87–90*), Association of Official Agricultural Chemists (1950, *31.52, p. 547*), Wilcox (1932).

(73b) Boron, Colorimetric, Using Carmine

Apparatus

A spectrophotometer with matched square cuvettes.[18]

Centrifuge tubes, flasks, beakers, pipets, and burets (boron-free glass). Alkali-resistant (boron-free) glassware, porcelainware, platinum, or fused quartz dishes are satisfactory. The use of borosilicate glassware is to be avoided. Convenient sizes are centrifuge tubes, 15-ml.; flasks, 125-ml.; beakers, 100-ml.; pipets, 2-ml.; burets, 10-ml. automatic.

Reagents

A. Sodium hydroxide, approximately 0.1 N, boron-free.

B. Hydrochloric acid, conc.

C. Hydrochloric acid, dilute (5 ml. conc.+95 ml. water).

D. Sulfuric acid, conc.

E. Carmine solution. A 0.05 percent solution by weight of carmine in conc. sulfuric acid (0.920 gm./l.). Shake until completely dissolved.

F. Standard boric acid solution. Stock solution. Dissolve 0.5716 gm. of recrystallized H_3BO_3 in distilled water and dilute to 1 liter. One ml. of this solution contains 0.100 mg. of boron.

Preparation of the Standard Curve

Dilute portions of reagent F to obtain standards over the range of 0 to 10 p. p. m. boron. Treat 2 ml. of each solution as described under *Procedure* and determine percent transmittance. For a reference, 2 ml. of distilled water is carried through the entire procedure and set at 100 percent transmittance.

Procedure

Pipet 2 ml. of the sample which should contain not more than 0.02 mg. boron into an Erlenmeyer flask. Add 2 drops of reagent B. Add 10 ml. of D. Mix and cool. Add 10 ml. of E, mix, and allow to stand at least 45 min. for color development. Determine the percent transmittance at 585 mμ against a reference solution of 2 ml. of distilled water carried through the entire procedure. For colored samples such as certain soil extracts, follow the procedure under paragraph headed "Boron Concentration Too Low," except ignite gently after evaporating the sample to dryness.

Calculations

Read the boron concentration from the concentration-transmittance calibration graph. Where the boron concentration is such that the measured transmittance value falls outside the recommended portion of the transmittance range (this method suggests 20 to 95

percent), the sample is either diluted or concentrated to meet these conditions.

BORON CONCENTRATION TOO GREAT.—Dilute the sample with distilled water to a known volume, mix, pipet 2 ml. into an Erlenmeyer flask, and proceed as directed above.

BORON CONCENTRATION TOO LOW.—Pipet a suitable aliquot of the sample into a beaker, a platinum dish, or other suitable vessel. Make alkaline with reagent A and add a slight excess. (The same amount should be added to all samples, including a reference.) Evaporate to dryness on a steam bath or in an oven at 95° C. Cool, add 5 ml. of C, and triturate with a rubber policeman. Pour the solution into a conical centrifuge tube and centrifuge at RCF=1,000 to 1,500. Pipet 2 ml. of the clear solution into an Erlenmeyer flask and follow the procedure shown above, correcting the reading from the standard curve to conform with the aliquot taken.

Reference

Hatcher and Wilcox (1950).

(74) Dissolved Solids

Procedure

Filter the sample to obtain a perfectly clear liquid. Evaporate a suitable aliquot containing not more than 1.0 gm. of residue to dryness in a weighed platinum dish. Dry to constant weight at 105° C. Cool in a desiccator and weigh. Reserve for the determination of silica under Method 76.

Calculations

Parts per million DS=gm. residue$\times$1,000,000/ml. in aliquot.

Reference

Association of Official Agricultural Chemists (1950, *31.3, p. 535*).

(75) pH of Waters

Procedure

See Method 21c.

(76) Silica

(76a) Silica, Gravimetric

Procedure

Acidify the sample or the residue from Method 74 with hydrochloric acid and evaporate to dryness on a steam bath in a platinum dish. Continue the drying for about an hour. Thoroughly moisten the residue

---

[18] A Coleman Model 14 Universal spectrophotometer with 13 by 13 by 105 mm. matched square cuvettes and filter PC–4 is quite satisfactory. Any good photoelectric colorimeter should be adequate, although perhaps somewhat less accurate.

with 5 to 10 ml. hydrochloric acid. Allow to stand 10 to 15 min. and add sufficient water to bring the soluble salts into solution. Heat on a steam bath until solution of salts is effected. Filter to remove most of the silica and wash thoroughly with hot water. Evaporate the filtrate to dryness and treat the residue with 5 ml. hydrochloric acid and sufficient water to effect solution of soluble salts, as before. Heat, filter, and wash with hot water. Transfer the 2 residues to a platinum crucible, ignite in a muffle furnace, cool, and weigh. Moisten the contents of the crucible with a few drops of water. Add a few drops of sulfuric acid and a few milliliters of hydrofluoric acid and evaporate on a steam bath under a hood. Repeat the treatment if all the silica is not volatilized. Dry carefully on a hot plate, ignite, cool, and weigh. The difference between the two weights is the weight of silica.

Calculations

Parts per million SiO_2 = gm. $SiO_2 \times 1,000,000$/ml. in aliquot.

Reference

Association of Official Agricultural Chemists (1950, *31.19, p. 539*).

(76b) Silica, Colorimetric [19]

Apparatus

Spectrophotometer or photoelectric colorimeter.

Reagents

A. Ammonium molybdate solution, 20 percent, stock solution. Dissolve 50 gm. $(NH_4)_6Mo_7O_{24} \cdot 4H_2O$ in 200 ml. water (do not heat), make to 250 ml. and filter.

B. Sulfuric acid, 10 N. Add 70.2 ml. conc. sulfuric acid with stirring to 185 to 190 ml. water, cool, transfer to 250-ml. volumetric flask, and dilute to the mark. Solutions A and B may be stored in glass because of the small amount used per determination.

C. Ammonium molybdate, sulfuric acid mixture. Add 1 ml. of reagent B and 2 ml. of A to 200 ml. of water. Use 10 ml. for each determination. A fresh lot of this reagent should be prepared for each set of samples.

D. Standard silica solution, 50 p. p. m. SiO_2. To prepare, dissolve more than the calculated amount of crystalline $Na_2SiO_3 \cdot 9H_2O$ in water, filter, and analyze gravimetrically, as described under Method 76a. Add the calculated amount of water necessary to dilute the solution to exactly 50 p. p. m. SiO_2. Store in a polyethylene bottle, not in glass.

Preparation of the Standard Curve

Dilute portions of reagent D to obtain standards over the range of 0 to 50 p. p. m. SiO_2. Treat 1 ml. of each solution as described under "Procedure" and determine percent transmittance.

Procedure

To 1 ml. of the sample add 10 ml. of reagent C and mix thoroughly. Determine the percent transmittance after standing 10 min., but not more than 45 min., at 350 mμ against a reference solution of 1 ml. of distilled water carried through the entire procedure. Read the silica concentration from the standard curve and report as p. p. m. SiO_2.

(77) Calcium

Reagents

A. Bromcresol green (sodium salt), 0.1 percent in water.

B. Hydrochloric acid, 6 N.

C. Oxalic acid solution, 1 N. Dissolve 63 gm. $(COOH)_2 \cdot 2H_2O$ in 1 liter of water.

D. Ammonium hydroxide solution $(1+1)$.

E. Sulfuric acid, dilute solution (45 ml. water plus 5 ml. conc. sulfuric acid).

F. Standard potassium permanganate, 0.05 N.

Procedure

Take an aliquot of the sample containing between 0.20 and 2.0 meq. of calcium and concentrate, if necessary, to a volume of approximately 200 ml. Add 2 to 3 drops of reagent A, acidify with B, and then add 0.5 ml. of B and 0.5 ml. of C for each 100 ml. of solution. Heat to boiling and neutralize with D. An excess of C is added gradually (5 ml. for each 100/ml. of solution) with constant stirring; the hot solution is made slightly alkaline with D and allowed to boil gently for several minutes. Cool and let stand until the precipitate of calcium oxalate settles. During the cooling, further additions of D may be necessary, in order to keep the solution faintly alkaline.

Filter through a good grade filter paper designed for fine precipitates, receiving the filtrate in a 400-ml. beaker. Reserve the filtrate for the determination of magnesium. Transfer the precipitate to the filter paper and wash both beaker and precipitate with water until free from soluble oxalates. Remove the beaker containing the filtrate and substitute the original beaker. Puncture the tip of the filter paper and wash the precipitate down into the beaker. Pour 50 ml. of reagent E through the funnel and rinse with water. The beaker is heated nearly to boiling and the liberated oxalic acid titrated with F until faintly pink. Add the filter paper and continue the titration until a very slight permanent pink color appears.

[19] This method was adapted for use with a spectrophotometer from a method proposed by Scripps Institution of Oceanography at La Jolla, California.

Calculations

Milliequivalents per liter of Ca$=1,000\times$normality of $KMnO_4 \times$ (ml. $KMnO_4$ —blank)/ml. in aliquot.

Reference

Blasdale (1909).

(78) Magnesium

Reagents

A. Hydrochloric acid (1+1).
B. Diammonium-hydrogen phosphate solution. Make up a 20 percent solution of diammonium-hydrogen phosphate in water. Filter before use. A fresh lot of this reagent should be prepared for each set of samples.
C. Ammonium hydroxide solution (1+1).
D. Ammonium hydroxide, conc.

Procedure

Acidify the filtrate from the calcium determination (Method 77) with reagent A then add 2 ml. in excess. Evaporate on a hot plate. If the weight of pyrophosphate is expected to be 0.0500 gm. or more, reduce the volume to 100 ml.; otherwise, evaporate to 50 ml. and allow to cool. Add 5 ml. of B for each 50 ml. volume, then C drop by drop with stirring, until the solution is strongly alkaline. After a few minutes add 10 ml. of D for each 100 ml. final volume. On the following day, filter on ashless paper and wash with dilute ammonium hydroxide (5+95). Transfer the paper with the precipitate to a weighed silica or porcelain crucible, dry, and ignite to whiteness in a muffle. Cool in a desiccator and weigh.

Calculations

Milliequivalents per liter of Mg$=$gm. $Mg_2P_2O_7\times$ 17,969/ml. in aliquot.

Reference

Association of Official Agricultural Chemists (1950, 31.26, p. 541).

(79) Calcium and Magnesium by the Versenate Method

Procedure

See Method 7.

(80) Sodium

(80a) Sodium by Uranyl Zinc Acetate, Gravimetric

The method of Barber and Kolthoff is the basis for the one here described. It has been modified in only minor details.

Reagents

A. Uranyl zinc acetate:
  Uranyl acetate, dihydrate_____ 300 gm.
  Zinc acetate, dihydrate_____ 900 gm.
  Acetic acid, 30 percent_____ 270 ml.
  Distilled water_____ 2,430 ml.

Weigh the salts and transfer to a large flask; add acetic acid and water; shake or stir occasionally until the salts are dissolved. This may take several days. Filter before use.
B. Ethyl alcohol, saturated with *sodium*-uranyl-zinc-acetate precipitate. Filter before use.
C. Ether, anhydrous.

Procedure

Evaporate an aliquot of water sufficient to give 50 to 200 mg. of the triple salt (usually 10 to 20 ml.) in a Pyrex beaker to a volume of 1 to 2 ml. Cool. Add 20 ml. of the filtered reagent A. Stir the solution and allow to stand for 1 hr. Filter through a porous-bottomed porcelain filtering crucible, taking care to transfer all the triple salt onto the filter by means of a small wash bottle filled with A. Wash the beaker 5 times with 2-ml. portions of A and pass the washings through the filter. Allow the crucible to drain completely, because it is important to have the filter and the precipitate free from the reagent before washing with the alcohol. Wash the crucible 5 times with 2-ml. portions of B and, after removing all the alcohol by suction, wash once or twice with C. The suction is continued until the precipitate is dry. Allow the crucible to stand in a desiccator 2 hr. and weigh.

Return the crucible to a suction apparatus and wash with small portions of water until all the soluble material is dissolved and passes through the crucible. Wash with alcohol and ether as above. Dry and weigh. The difference between the first and last weight represents the weight of sodium precipitate. The precipitate is assumed to have the composition $(UO_2)_3NaZn$ $(CH_3COO)_9 \cdot 6H_2O$; molecular weight, 1538.079; percent sodium, 1.4952.

Calculations

Milliequivalents per liter of Na$=$gm. sodium-uranyl-zinc-acetate precipitate$\times$650.16/ml. in aliquot.

Reference

Barber and Kolthoff (1928).

(80b) Sodium by Flame Photometer

Procedure

See Method 10a.

(81) Potassium

(81a) Potassium by Cobaltinitrite, Gravimetric

Reagents

A. Nitric acid, 1 N.

B. Trisodium cobaltinitrite solution. Prepare an aqueous solution containing 1 gm. of the salt of reagent quality in each 5 ml., allowing 5 ml. for each determination. Filter before use. The solution is stable for some time, but it is preferable to make up a fresh lot before each set of determinations.

C. Nitric acid, 0.01 N.

D. Ethyl alcohol, 95 percent.

Procedure

The aliquot for analysis should contain between 2 and 15 mg. of potassium in a neutral aqueous solution of 10-ml. volume. (Ammonia interferes and if present must be removed by evaporation with sodium hydroxide.) Add 1 ml. of reagent A and 5 ml. of B, mix, and allow to stand for 2 hr. at 15° to 20° C. Filter in a porous-bottomed porcelain filtering crucible, the tare weight of which is known, using C in a wash bottle to make the transfer. Wash 10 times with C and 5 times with 2-ml. portions of D. Aspirate until quite dry. Wipe the outside with a cloth, dry for 1 hr. at 105° C., cool in a desiccator, and weigh.

Modified Procedure

For very small quantities of potassium (0.2 meq./l. or less). Evaporate 200 ml. of the sample in a platinum dish and remove silica as under Method 76a. This aliquot may be used for the determination of dissolved solids as under Method 74 and silica as under Method 76a. After removal of silica, evaporate the filtrate to dryness to remove hydrochloric acid, add 10 ml. of water, 1 ml. of reagent A, and 5 ml. of B, and put the sample in the refrigerator at 5° to 15° C. overnight. When gypsum is high, add more of the reagents (10 ml. of water, 1 ml. of A, and 5 ml. of B for each 5 meq./l. of gypsum present). The following morning, remove the samples from the refrigerator, filter through a porous-bottomed porcelain crucible, and proceed as directed above.

If the sample is high in organic matter, such as a sewage effluent, evaporate the filtrate to dryness, take up in aqua regia (3 parts conc. hydrochloric acid+1 part conc. nitric acid), and evaporate again before potassium is precipitated.

The composition of the precipitate can be represented by the formula $K_2NaCo(NO_2)_6 \cdot H_2O$. K=17.216 percent.

Calculations

Milliequivalents per liter of K=gm. di-potassium sodium cobaltinitrite precipitate×4,403.4/ml. in aliquot.

Reference

Wilcox (1937).

(81b) Potassium by Cobaltinitrite, Volumetric

Reagents

In addition to the reagents listed under the gravimetric procedure, except 95 percent ethyl alcohol, the following are required:

A. Sodium hydroxide, approximately 0.5 N.

B. Sulfuric acid, conc.

C. Potassium permanganate solution, standard 0.05 N.

D. Sodium oxalate solution, standard 0.05 N.

Procedure

Follow the gravimetric procedure of Method 81a through the precipitation and washing with nitric acid. Omit washing with alcohol. Wash the precipitate into a 250-ml. beaker, place the crucible in the beaker, and make to about 100 ml. with water. Add 20 ml. of reagent A and boil for 3 min. Withdraw into another beaker a slight excess of C, make to 50 ml. with water, and add 5 ml. of B. Pour the hot potassium cobaltinitrite solution into the cold potassium permanganate solution, transfer the crucible, and wash the beaker with a small quantity of water. Add an excess of D, heat to boiling, and complete the titration with potassium permanganate.

Calculations

Milliequivalents per liter of K=normality of $KMnO_4$ × (ml. $KMnO_4$−blank) ×181.81/ml. in aliquot.

Reference

Wilcox (1937).

(81c) Potassium by Flame Photometer

Procedure

See Method 11a.

(82) Carbonate and Bicarbonate

Reagents

A. Phenolphthalein, 0.25 percent solution in 50 percent alcohol.

B. Sulfuric acid, standard 0.050 N.

C. Methyl orange, 0.1 percent in water.

Procedure

Take an aliquot of the sample containing not more than 1.0 meq. of carbonate plus bicarbonate and dilute to 50 ml., if less than that volume. Add a few drops of reagent A, and, if a pink color is produced, titrate with B, adding a drop every 2 or 3 seconds until the pink color disappears. To the colorless solution from this titration or to the original solution, if no color is produced with phenolphthalein, add 1 or 2 drops of C, continue the titration (without refilling the buret) to the methyl orange end point, and note the total reading. (Reserve the solution for the determination of chloride.) Blank determinations should be run with the reagents and carbon dioxide-free distilled water and corrections made, if necessary.

Remarks

To facilitate calculations a table similar to that shown in APHA Standard Methods (1946) is included (table 18).

TABLE 18—*The titration of hydroxide, carbonate, and bicarbonate ions in the presence of phenolphthalein and methyl orange indicators.*

Result of titration [1]	Titration value related to each ion—		
	Hydroxide	Carbonate	Bicarbonate
$P=0$	0	0	T
$P<\frac{1}{2} T$	0	2P	$T-2P$
$P=\frac{1}{2} T$	0	2P	0
$P>\frac{1}{2} T$	$2P-T$	$2(T-P)$	0
$P=T$	T	0	0

[1] P=Titration to the phenolphthalein end point; T=total titration to the methyl end point.

Calculations

Ion sought, milliequivalents per liter of either OH, CO_3, or HCO_3=1000×normality of the acid × [titration value (from table 18) in ml. acid−blank]/ml. in aliquot.

References

American Public Health Association and American Water Works Association (1946, *p. 9*), Association of Official Agricultural Chemists (1950, *31.18, p. 539*).

(83) Sulfate

Reagents

A. Hydrochloric acid, conc.
B. Barium chloride solution, 10 percent. Dissolve 100 gm. $BaCl_2 \cdot 2H_2O$ in 1 liter of water and filter.
C. Methyl orange, 0.1 percent in water.

Procedure

Take an aliquot of the sample containing between 0.2 and 5 meq. of sulfate and, if necessary, dilute to a volume of approximately 200 ml. Add a few drops of reagent C and 1 ml. of A. Heat to boiling and add an excess of B drop by drop with constant stirring. Allow to stand on the water bath until the volume is reduced to about 50 ml. After cooling, the precipitate of barium sulfate is filtered through an ashless filter paper and washed with water until free from chloride. The filter paper is then carefully folded, placed in a tared porcelain or silica crucible, ignited in a well-ventilated muffle at low red heat, and weighed.

Calculations

Milliequivalents per liter of SO_4=gm. $BaSO_4$× 8568.2/ml. in aliquot.

Reference

Association of Official Agriculture Chemists (1950, *31.27, p. 541*).

(84) Chloride

Reagents

A. Potassium chromate indicator. Dissolve 5 gm. of potassium chromate in water and add a saturated solution of silver nitrate until a slight permanent red precipitate is produced; filter and dilute to 100 ml.
B. Standard silver nitrate solution, 0.05 N. Dissolve 8.4944 gm. silver nitrate in water and dilute to 1 liter. Check by titration against pure sodium chloride or standard potassium chloride (reagent A, Method 72).

Procedure

To the solution from the carbonate and bicarbonate determination (Method 82), add 1 ml. of reagent A and titrate with B. Correct for the quantity of silver nitrate solution necessary to give, in 50 ml. of chloride-free water with 1 ml. potassium chromate indicator, the shade obtained at the end of the titration of the sample.
If the size of aliquot that is suitable for the carbonate-bicarbonate titration is too large for the chloride determination, a smaller aliquot must be taken and neutralized to methyl orange. The aliquot should contain not more than 2 meq. of chloride.

Calculations

Milliequivalents per liter of Cl=1000×normality of the $AgNO_3$× (ml. $AgNO_3$−blank)/ml. in aliquot.

Reference

Association of Official Agricultural Chemists (1950, *31.10, p. 536*).

(85) Fluoride

Remarks

Method suggested is given in Standard Methods, APHA (1946), substituting sulfuric acid for perchloric acid and silver sulfate for silver perchlorate.

It has been found reliable for potable waters of ordinary composition. Up to the following limits expressed as parts per million it is not interfered with by: Chloride ion (Cl)—500 ppm., sulfate ion (SO_4)—200 ppm., alkalinity (expressed as $CaCO_3$)—200 ppm., acidity (expressed as $CaCO_3$)—200 ppm., iron (Fe)—2 ppm., aluminum (Al)—0.5 ppm., phosphate ion (PO_4)—1 ppm., color 25, turbidity 25.

If limits are exceeded, separate fluoride by distillation.

Reagents

A. Acid zirconium alizarin reagent. Dissolve 0.3 gm. zirconium oxychloride ($ZrOCl_2 \cdot 8H_2O$) in 50 ml. distilled water contained in a 1-liter glass-stoppered flask. Dissolve 0.07 gm. alizarin sodium monosulfonate in 50 ml. distilled water and pour slowly into the zirconium oxychloride solution, while swirling the flask. This solution clears on standing for a few minutes. Prepare a mixed acid solution as follows: Dilute 112 ml. conc. hydrochloric acid to 500 ml. with distilled water. Dilute 37 ml. conc. sulfuric acid to 500 ml. with distilled water. After cooling, mix the two acids. To the zirconium alizarin solution in the 1-liter flask, add the mixed acid solution to the mark and mix. The reagent changes in color from red to yellow within an hour and is then ready for use. If stored in a refrigerator, it may be used for 60 to 90 days.

B. Standard sodium fluoride solution. Dissolve 0.221 gm. sodium fluoride in distilled water and make up to 1 liter. Dilute 100 ml. of the stock sodium fluoride solution to 1 liter with distilled water. One ml. is equivalent to 0.01 mg. of fluoride.

Procedure

To 100 ml. of sample containing not more than 0.14 mg. fluoride and to standards made up to 100 ml. with distilled water, contained in 100-ml. matched Nessler tubes, add 5 ml. of reagent A, accurately measured from a 5-ml. volumetric pipet. Mix and compare sample with standards after standing 1 hr. at room temperature. Recommended standards are 0, 0.01, 0.02, 0.03, 0.04, 0.05, 0.06, 0.08, 0.10, 0.12, and 0.14 mg. of fluoride. Since the color of the zirconium-alizarin lake varies with temperature, samples and standards should have the same temperature within 1° or 2° C., before adding the reagent.

Calculations

Parts per million F=mg. F×1,000/ml. in aliquot.

Reference

American Public Health Association and American Water Works Association (1946, *39A–2, p. 76*, and *39B–2, p. 77*).

(86) Nitrate

(86a) Nitrate, Phenoldisulfonic Acid

(For water of low chloride content.)

Procedure

See Method 15.

(86b) Nitrate, Devarda

(For water of high chloride content.)

Apparatus

Nitrogen distilling apparatus with scrubber bulbs.

Reagents

A. Devarda alloy.
B. Sodium hydroxide, saturated solution.
C. Boric acid, 2 percent solution.
D. Standard sulfuric acid, 0.05 N.
E. Bromcresol green-methyl red (BCG–MR) indicator solution.[20] Prepare a 0.1 percent bromcresol green solution, adding 2 ml. 0.1 N sodium hydroxide per 0.1 gm. of indicator. Prepare a 0.1 percent methyl red solution in 95 percent ethyl alcohol, adding 3 ml. 0.1 N sodium hydroxide per 0.1 gm. of indicator. Mix 75 ml. bromcresol green, 25 ml. methyl red, and 100 ml. of 95 percent ethyl alcohol. The indicator should be gray in a solution containing boric acid and ammonium sulfate in concentrations equal to those encountered in the Devarda procedure. It is often necessary to add a little of one or the other of the indicators until the proper shade is obtained. The color change is from green in alkali through gray at the end point to red in acid solution.

Procedure

Place 50 ml. of the sample, or such volume as will contain not less than 0.2 meq. nitrate, in a Kjeldahl flask and add 2 gm. Devarda alloy. Make up to 300 ml. with distilled water, then add 2 ml. of reagent B, allowing it to run down the side of the flask so that it does not mix with the contents at once. Connect with the distilling apparatus and rotate the flask to mix. Heat slowly at first and then at such a rate that the 200 ml. of distillate required will pass over in 1 hr. Collect the distillate in 50 ml. of C. The ammonia is titrated with D, using indicator E.

Calculations

Milliequivalents per liter of NO_3=1,000 × normality of acid × (ml. acid − blank)/ml. in aliquot.

Reference

Association of Official Agricultural Chemists (1950, *2.30, p. 14*).

[20] Chapman, H. D. Private communication.

Literature Cited

ALLISON, L. E.
  1952. EFFECT OF SYNTHETIC POLYELECTROLYTES ON THE STRUCTURE OF SALINE AND ALKALI SOILS. Soil Sci. 73: 443–454, illus.

AMERICAN PUBLIC HEALTH ASSOCIATION AND AMERICAN WATER WORKS ASSOCIATION.
  1946. STANDARD METHODS FOR THE EXAMINATION OF WATER AND SEWAGE. Ed. 9, 286 pp., illus. New York.

AMERICAN SOCIETY OF AGRONOMY.
  1952. SOIL PHYSICAL CONDITIONS AND PLANT GROWTH. Byron T. Shaw, Ed. 508 pp., illus. New York.

ASSOCIATION OF OFFICIAL AGRICULTURAL CHEMISTS.
  1950. OFFICIAL AND TENTATIVE METHODS OF ANALYSIS OF THE ASSOCIATION OF OFFICIAL AGRICULTURAL CHEMISTS. Ed. 7, 910 pp., illus. Washington.

AYERS, A. D.
  1950. SALT TOLERANCE OF AVOCADO TREES GROWN IN CULTURE SOLUTION. Calif. Avocado Soc. Yearbook 1950: 139–148, illus.

——
  1951. SEED GERMINATION AS AFFECTED BY SOIL MOISTURE AND SALINITY. Agron. Jour. 44: 82–84, illus.

—— ALDRICH, D. G., AND COONY, J. J.
  1951. SODIUM AND CHLORIDE INJURY OF FUERTE AVOCADO LEAVES. Calif. Avocado Soc. Yearbook 1951: 174–178, illus.

—— BROWN, J. W., AND WADLEIGH, C. H.
  1952. SALT TOLERANCE OF BARLEY AND WHEAT IN SOIL PLOTS RECEIVING SEVERAL SALINIZATION REGIMES. Agron. Jour. 44: 307–310.

—— AND CAMPBELL, R. B.
  1951. FREEZING POINT OF WATER IN SOIL AS RELATED TO SALT AND MOISTURE CONTENTS OF SOIL. Soil Sci. 72: 201–206, illus.

—— AND HAYWARD, H. E.
  1949. A METHOD FOR MEASURING THE EFFECTS OF SOIL SALINITY ON SEED GERMINATION WITH OBSERVATIONS ON SEVERAL CROP PLANTS. Soil Sci. Soc. Amer. Proc. (1948) 13: 224–226, illus.

BARBER, H. H., AND KOLTHOFF, I. M.
  1928. A SPECIFIC REAGENT FOR THE RAPID GRAVIMETRIC DETERMINATION OF SODIUM. Amer. Chem. Soc. Jour. 50: 1625–1631.

BAVEL, C. H. M. VAN.
  1950. MEAN WEIGHT-DIAMETER OF SOIL AGGREGATES AS A STATISTICAL INDEX OF AGGREGATION. Soil Sci. Soc. Amer. Proc. (1949) 14: 20–23, illus.

—— AND KIRKHAM, D.
  1949. FIELD MEASUREMENT OF SOIL PERMEABILITY USING AUGER HOLES. Soil Sci. Soc. Amer. Proc. (1948) 13: 90–96, illus.

BERG, C. VAN DEN.
  1950. THE INFLUENCE OF SALT IN THE SOIL ON THE YIELD OF AGRICULTURAL CROPS. Fourth Internatl. Cong. Soil Sci. Trans. 1: 411–413.

——
  1952. THE INFLUENCE OF ABSORBED SALTS ON GROWTH AND YIELD OF AGRICULTURAL CROPS ON SALTY SOILS. THE INUNDATIONS OF 1944–1945 IN THE NETHERLANDS AND THEIR EFFECT ON AGRICULTURE. XII. [Netherlands] Dir. van den Landbouw, Verslag. van Landbouwk. Onderzoek, 58.5, 118 pp., illus. [In Dutch. English summary, pp. 105–107.]

BERNSTEIN, L., AYERS, A. D., AND WADLEIGH, C. H.
  1951. THE SALT TOLERANCE OF WHITE ROSE POTATOES. Amer. Soc. Hort. Sci. Proc. 57: 231–236.

BILLINGS, W. D.
  1945. THE PLANT ASSOCIATIONS OF THE CARSON DESERT REGION. WESTERN NEVADA. Butler Univ. Bot. Studies 7: 89–123, illus.

BLASDALE, W. C.
  1909. THE QUANTITATIVE SEPARATION OF CALCIUM FROM MAGNESIUM. Amer. Chem. Soc. Jour. 31: 917–922.

BODMAN, G. B.
  1942. NOMOGRAMS FOR RAPID CALCULATION OF SOIL DENSITY, WATER CONTENT, AND TOTAL POROSITY RELATIONSHIPS. Amer. Soc. Agron. Jour. 34: 883–893, illus.

BOUYOUCOS, G. J.
  1936. DIRECTIONS FOR MAKING MECHANICAL ANALYSES OF SOILS BY THE HYDROMETER METHOD. Soil Sci. 42: 225–228, illus.

BOWER, C. A., AND GSCHWEND, F. B.
  1952. ETHYLENE GLYCOL RETENTION BY SOILS AS A MEASURE OF SURFACE AREA AND INTERLAYER SWELLING. Soil Sci. Soc. Amer. Proc. 16: 342–345, illus.

—— AND HUSS, R. B.
  1948. RAPID CONDUCTOMETRIC METHOD FOR ESTIMATING GYPSUM IN SOILS. Soil Sci. 66: 199–204.

—— AND PETERSEN, R. K.
  1950. TECHNIC FOR DETERMINING THE PERMEABILITY OF SOIL CORES OBTAINED WITH THE LUTZ SAMPLER. Agron. Jour. 42: 55–56, illus.

—— REITEMEIER, R. F., AND FIREMAN, M.
  1952. EXCHANGEABLE CATION ANALYSIS OF SALINE AND ALKALI SOILS. Soil Sci. 73: 251–261, illus.

—— SWARNER, L. R., MARSH, A. W., AND TILESTON, F. M.
  1951. THE IMPROVEMENT OF AN ALKALI SOIL BY TREATMENT WITH MANURE AND CHEMICAL AMENDMENTS. Oreg. Agr. Expt. Sta. Tech. Bul. 22, 37 pp., illus.

—— AND TURK, L. M.
  1946. CALCIUM AND MAGNESIUM DEFICIENCIES IN ALKALI SOILS. Amer. Soc. Agron. Jour. 38: 723–727.

—— AND WADLEIGH, C. H.
  1949. GROWTH AND CATIONIC ACCUMULATION BY FOUR SPECIES OF PLANTS AS INFLUENCED BY VARIOUS LEVELS OF EXCHANGEABLE SODIUM. Soil Sci. Soc. Amer. Proc. (1948) 13: 218–223, illus.

BOYNTON, D., AND BURRELL, A. B.
  1944. POTASSIUM-INDUCED MAGNESIUM DEFICIENCY IN THE MC INTOSH APPLE TREE. Soil Sci. 58: 441–454.

BREAZEALE, J. F., AND MCGEORGE, W. T.
  1932. NUTRITIONAL DISORDER IN ALKALINE SOILS AS CAUSED BY DEFICIENCY OF CARBON DIOXIDE. Ariz. Agr. Expt. Sta. Tech. Bul. 41, pp. 113–153, illus.

BRIGGS, L. J.
  1899. ELECTRICAL INSTRUMENTS FOR DETERMINING THE MOISTURE, TEMPERATURE, AND SOLUBLE SALT CONTENT OF SOILS. U. S. Dept. Agr., Div. Soils Bul. 15, 35 pp., illus.

BROWN, J. W., WADLEIGH, C. H., AND HAYWARD, H. E.
  1953. FOLIAR ANALYSIS OF STONE FRUIT AND ALMOND TREES ON SALINE SUBSTRATES. Amer. Soc. Hort. Sci. Proc. 61: 49–55.

CAMPBELL, R. B.
  1952. FREEZING POINT OF WATER IN PUDDLED AND UNPUDDLED SOILS AT DIFFERENT SOIL MOISTURE TENSION VALUES. Soil Sci. 73: 221–229, illus.

—— BOWER, C. A., AND RICHARDS, L. A.
  1949. CHANGE OF ELECTRICAL CONDUCTIVITY WITH TEMPERATURE AND THE RELATION OF OSMOTIC PRESSURE TO ELECTRICAL CONDUCTIVITY AND ION CONCENTRATION FOR SOIL EXTRACTS. Soil Sci. Soc. Amer. Proc. (1948) 13: 66–69, illus.

CAMPBELL, R. B., AND RICHARDS, L. A.
1950. SOME MOISTURE AND SALINITY RELATIONSHIPS IN PEAT SOILS. Agron. Jour. 42: 582–585, illus.

CHAPMAN, H. D.
1949. CITRUS LEAF ANALYSIS. Calif. Agr. Expt. Sta., Calif. Agr. 3 (11): 10, 12, 14.

CHENG, K. L., AND BRAY, R. H.
1951. DETERMINATION OF CALCIUM AND MAGNESIUM IN SOIL AND PLANT MATERIAL. Soil Sci. 72: 449–458.

CHILDS, E. C.
1940. THE USE OF SOIL MOISTURE CHARACTERISTICS IN SOIL STUDIES. Soil Sci. 50: 239–252, illus.

CHRISTIANSEN, J. E.
1943. GROUND-WATER STUDIES IN RELATION TO DRAINAGE. Agr. Engin. 24: 339–342, illus.

―― 1947. SOME PERMEABILITY CHARACTERISTICS OF SALINE AND ALKALI SOILS. Agr. Engin. 28: 147–150, 153, illus.

CLARK, W. G., LEVITAN, N. I., GLEASON, D. F., AND GREENBERG, G.
1942. TITRIMETRIC MICRODETERMINATION OF CHLORIDE, SODIUM, AND POTASSIUM IN A SINGLE TISSUE OR BLOOD SAMPLE. Jour. Biol. Chem. 145: 85–100, illus.

CLARKE, F. W.
1924. THE DATA OF GEOCHEMISTRY. U. S. Geol. Survey Bul. 770, 841 pp., Ed. 5.

COOIL, B. J.
1948. POTASSIUM DEFICIENCY AND EXCESS IN GUAYULE. I. GROWTH RESPONSES AND MINERAL CONTENT. Plant Physiol. 23: 286–308, illus.

COOPER, W. C.
1951. SALT TOLERANCE OF AVOCADOS ON VARIOUS ROOTSTOCKS. Tex. Avocado Soc. Yearbook 1951: 24–28.

―― AND GORTON, B. S.
1951. RELATION OF LEAF COMPOSITION TO LEAF BURN OF AVOCADOS AND OTHER SUBTROPICAL FRUITS. Tex. Avocado Soc. Yearbook 1950: 32–38, illus.

―― GORTON, B. S., AND EDWARDS, C.
1951. SALT TOLERANCE OF VARIOUS CITRUS ROOTSTOCKS. Rio Grande Valley Hort. Inst. Proc. 5: 46–52.

―― GORTON, B. S., AND OLSON, E. O.
1952. IONIC ACCUMULATION IN CITRUS AS INFLUENCED BY ROOTSTOCK AND SCION AND CONCENTRATION OF SALTS AND BORON IN THE SUBSTRATE. Plant Physiol. 27: 191–203.

DAVIDSON, J. M.
1940. INFILTRATION OF WATER INTO SOIL. U. S. Soil Conserv. Serv., Soil Conserv. Bibliog. 3, 77 pp. [Processed.]

DAVIS, L. E.
1945. SIMPLE KINETIC THEORY OF IONIC EXCHANGE FOR IONS OF UNEQUAL CHARGE. Jour. Phys. Chem. 49: 473–479.

DAVIS, R. O. E., AND BRYAN, H.
1910. THE ELECTRICAL BRIDGE FOR THE DETERMINATION OF SOLUBLE SALTS IN SOILS. U. S. Dept. Agr., Bur. Soils Bul. 61, 36 pp.

DIEHL, H., GOETZ, C. A., AND HACH, C. C.
1950. THE VERSENATE TITRATION FOR TOTAL HARDNESS. Amer. Water Works Assoc. Jour. 42: 40–48.

DISERENS, E.
1934. BEITRAG ZUR BESTIMMUNG DER DURCHLÄSSIGKEIT DES BODENS IN NATÜRLICHER BODENLAGERUNG. Schweiz. Landw. Monatsh. 12: 188–198, 204–212.

DONNAN, W. W., AND CHRISTIANSEN, J. E.
1944. GROUND WATER DETERMINATIONS. West. Construct. News 19 (11): 77–79, illus.

DORPH–PETERSEN, K., AND STEENBJERG, F.
1950. INVESTIGATIONS OF THE EFFECT OF FERTILIZERS CONTAINING SODIUM. Plant and Soil 2: 283–300, illus.

DYAL, R. S., AND HENDRICKS, S. B.
1950. TOTAL SURFACE OF CLAYS IN POLAR LIQUIDS AS A CHARACTERISTIC INDEX. Soil Sci. 69: 421–432, illus.

―― AND HENDRICKS, S. B.
1952. FORMATION OF MIXED LAYER MINERALS BY POTASSIUM FIXATION IN MONTMORILLONITE. Soil Sci. Soc. Amer. Proc. 16: 45–48, illus.

EATON, F. M.
1935. BORON IN SOILS AND IRRIGATION WATERS AND ITS EFFECT ON PLANTS WITH PARTICULAR REFERENCE TO THE SAN JOAQUIN VALLEY OF CALIFORNIA. U. S. Dept. Agr. Tech. Bul. 448, 131 pp., illus.

―― 1942. TOXICITY AND ACCUMULATION OF CHLORIDE AND SULFATE SALTS IN PLANTS. Jour. Agr. Res. 64: 357–399, illus.

―― 1944. DEFICIENCY, TOXICITY, AND ACCUMULATION OF BORON IN PLANTS. Jour. Agr. Res. 69: 237–277, illus.

―― 1950. SIGNIFICANCE OF CARBONATES IN IRRIGATION WATERS. Soil Sci. 69: 123–133.

―― AND WILCOX, L. V.
1939. THE BEHAVIOR OF BORON IN SOILS. U. S. Dept. Agr. Tech. Bul. 696, 57 pp., illus.

FIREMAN, M.
1944. PERMEABILITY MEASUREMENTS ON DISTURBED SOIL SAMPLES. Soil Sci. 58: 337–353, illus.

―― AND HAYWARD, H. E.
1952. INDICATOR SIGNIFICANCE OF SOME SHRUBS IN THE ESCALANTE DESERT, UTAH. Bot. Gaz. 114: 143–155, illus.

―― AND WADLEIGH, C. H.
1951. A STATISTICAL STUDY OF THE RELATION BETWEEN pH AND THE EXCHANGEABLE-SODIUM-PERCENTAGE OF WESTERN SOILS. Soil Sci. 71: 273–285, illus.

FLOWERS, S.
1934. VEGETATION OF THE GREAT SALT LAKE REGION. Bot. Gaz. 95: 353–418, illus.

FREVERT, R. K., AND KIRKHAM, D.
1949. A FIELD METHOD FOR MEASURING THE PERMEABILITY OF SOIL BELOW A WATER TABLE. Highway Res. Bd. Proc. (1948) 28: 433–442, illus.

FULLMER, F. S.
1950. METERING DRY FERTILIZERS AND SOIL AMENDMENTS INTO IRRIGATION SYSTEMS. Better Crops With Plant Food 34(3): 8–14, 40–41, illus.

GAPON, E. N.
1933. THEORY OF EXCHANGE ADSORPTION IN SOILS. Zhur. Obshch. Khim. (Jour. Gen. Chem.) 3: 144–152, illus.

GARDNER, R.
1945. SOME SOIL PROPERTIES RELATED TO THE SODIUM SALT PROBLEM IN IRRIGATED SOILS. U. S. Dept. Agr. Tech. Bul. 902, 28 pp., illus.

GAUCH, H. G., AND WADLEIGH, C. H.
1951. THE SALT TOLERANCE AND CHEMICAL COMPOSITION OF RHODES AND DALLIS GRASSES GROWN IN SAND CULTURE. Bot. Gaz. 112: 259–271, illus.

GEDROIZ, K. K.
1917. SALINE SOILS AND THEIR IMPROVEMENT. Zhur. Opytn. Agron. (Jour. f. Expt. Landw.) 18: 122–140. [In Russian. French summary, pp. 138–140.] [Translated by S. A. Waksman.]

GUGGENHEIM, E. A.
1945. STATISTICAL THERMODYNAMICS OF MIXTURES WITH ZERO ENERGIES OF MIXING. Roy. Soc. London Proc., Ser. A., 183: 203–213.

HAAS, A. R. C.
1950. EFFECT OF SODIUM CHLORIDE ON MEXICAN, GUATEMALAN AND WEST INDIAN AVOCADO SEEDLINGS. Calif. Avocado Soc. Yearbook 1950: 153–160, illus.

HARLEY, C. P., AND LINDNER, R. C.
1945. OBSERVED RESPONSES OF APPLE AND PEAR TREES TO SOME IRRIGATION WATERS OF NORTH CENTRAL WASHINGTON. Amer. Soc. Hort. Sci. Proc. 46: 35–44, illus.

HARMER, P. M., AND BENNE, E. J.
1941. EFFECTS OF APPLYING COMMON SALT TO A MUCK SOIL ON THE YIELD, COMPOSITION, AND QUALITY OF CERTAIN VEGETABLE CROPS AND ON THE COMPOSITION OF THE SOIL PRODUCING THEM. Amer. Soc. Agron. Jour. 33: 952–979, illus.

HARPER, H. J.
1946. EFFECT OF CHLORIDE ON PHYSICAL APPEARANCE AND CHEMICAL COMPOSITION OF LEAVES ON PECANS AND OTHER NATIVE OKLAHOMA TREES. Okla. Agr. Expt. Sta. Tech. Bul. 23, 30 pp., illus.

HARRIS, F. S.
1920. SOIL ALKALI, ITS ORIGIN, NATURE, AND TREATMENT. 258 pp., illus. New York and London.

HARRIS, J. A.
1925. A TABLE TO FACILITATE CORRECTION FOR UNDERCOOLING IN CRYOSCOPIC WORK. Amer. Jour Bot. 12: 499–501.

—— AND GORTNER, R. A.
1914. NOTES ON THE CALCULATION OF THE OSMOTIC PRESSURE OF EXPRESSED VEGETABLE SAPS FROM THE DEPRESSION OF THE FREEZING POINT, WITH A TABLE FOR THE VALUES OF P FOR $\triangle = 0.001°$ TO $\triangle = 2.999°$. Amer. Jour. Bot. 1: 75–78.

—— GORTNER, R. A., HOFFMAN, W. F., AND OTHERS.
1924. THE OSMOTIC CONCENTRATION, SPECIFIC ELECTRICAL CONDUCTIVITY, AND CHLORIDE CONTENT OF THE TISSUE FLUIDS OF THE INDICATOR PLANTS OF TOOELE VALLEY, UTAH. Jour. Agr. Res. 27: 893–924.

HATCHER, J. T., AND WILCOX, L. V.
1950. COLORIMETRIC DETERMINATION OF BORON USING CARMINE. Analyt. Chem. 22: 567–569, illus.

HAYWARD, H. E., LONG, E. M., AND UHVITS, R.
1946. THE EFFECT OF CHLORIDE AND SULFATE SALTS ON THE GROWTH AND DEVELOPMENT OF THE ELBERTA PEACH ON SHALIL AND LOVELL ROOTSTOCKS. U. S. Dept. Agr. Tech. Bul. 922, 48 pp., illus.

—— AND MAGISTAD, O. C.
1946. THE SALT PROBLEM IN IRRIGATION AGRICULTURE. U. S. Dept. Agr. Misc. Pub. 607, 27 pp., illus.

—— AND SPURR, W. B.
1944. EFFECTS OF ISOSMOTIC CONCENTRATIONS OF INORGANIC AND ORGANIC SUBSTRATES ON THE ENTRY OF WATER INTO CORN ROOTS. Bot. Gaz. 106: 131–139, illus.

—— AND WADLEIGH, C. H.
1949. PLANT GROWTH ON SALINE AND ALKALI SOILS. Advances in Agron. 1: 1–38, illus.

HEALD, W. R., MOODIE, C. D., AND LEAMER, R. W.
1950. LEACHING AND PRE-EMERGENCE IRRIGATION FOR SUGAR BEETS ON SALINE SOILS. Wash. Agr. Expt. Sta. Bul. 519, 16 pp., illus.

HELLMAN, N. N., AND McKELVEY, V. E.
1941. A HYDROMETER-PIPETTE METHOD FOR MECHANICAL ANALYSIS. Jour. Sedimentary Petrology 11: 3–9, illus.

HILGARD, E. W.
1906. SOILS, THEIR FORMATION, PROPERTIES, COMPOSITION, AND RELATIONS TO CLIMATE AND PLANT GROWTH. 593 pp., illus. New York and London.

HISSINK, D. J.
1933. DIE SALZTONBÖDEN UND DIE ALKALITONBÖDEN IN DEN NIEDERLANDEN. Internatl. Soc. Soil Sci. 2nd Com. (Copenhagen), Part A: 185–189.

HOOGHOUDT, S. B.
1936. BIJDRAGEN TOT DE KENNIS VAN EENIGE NATUURKUNDIGE GROOTHEDEN VAN DER GROND, NO. 4. [Netherlands] Dir. van den Landbouw, Verslag. van Landbouwk. Onderzoek. 42 (13) B: 449–541, illus.

——
1952. TILE DRAINAGE AND SUBIRRIGATION. Soil Sci. 74: 35–48, illus.

ILJIN, W. S.
1951. METABOLISM OF PLANTS AFFECTED WITH LIME-INDUCED CHLOROSIS (CALCIOSE) II. ORGANIC ACIDS AND CARBOHYDRATES. Plant and Soil 3: 339–351, illus.

——
1952. METABOLISM OF PLANTS AFFECTED WITH LIME-INDUCED CHLOROSIS (CALCIOSE) III. MINERAL ELEMENTS. Plant and Soil 4: 11–28, illus.

ISRAELSEN, O. W.
1950. IRRIGATION PRINCIPLES AND PRACTICES. Ed. 2, 405 pp., illus. New York.

JACOB, C. E.
1940. ON THE FLOW OF WATER IN AN ELASTIC ARTESIAN AQUIFER. Amer. Geophys. Union Trans. 1940: 574–586, illus.

——
1947. DRAWDOWN TEST TO DETERMINE THE EFFECTIVE RADIUS OF ARTESIAN WELL. Amer. Soc. Civ. Engin. Trans. 112: 1047–1064, illus.

JENNY, H., VLAMIS, J., AND MARTIN, W. E.
1950. GREENHOUSE ASSAY OF FERTILITY OF CALIFORNIA SOILS. Hilgardia 20: 1–8, illus.

JENSEN, M. C., LEWIS, G. C., AND BAKER, G. O.
1951. CHARACTERISTICS OF IRRIGATION WATERS IN IDAHO. Idaho Agr. Expt. Sta. Res. Bul. 19, 44 pp., illus.

JOHNSON, H. P., FREVERT, R. K., AND EVANS, D. D.
1952. SIMPLIFIED PROCEDURE FOR MEASUREMENT AND COMPUTATION OF SOIL PERMEABILITY BELOW THE WATER TABLE. Agr. Engin. 33: 283–286, illus.

KEARNEY, T. H., BRIGGS, L. J., SHANTZ, H. L., AND OTHERS.
1914. INDICATOR SIGNIFICANCE OF VEGETATION IN TOOELE VALLEY, UTAH. Jour. Agr. Res. 1: 365–417, illus.

—— AND SCOFIELD, C. S.
1936. THE CHOICE OF CROPS FOR SALINE LAND. U. S. Dept. Agr. Cir. 404, 24 pp.

KELLEY, O. J., HARDMAN, J. A., AND JENNINGS, D. S.
1948. A SOIL-SAMPLING MACHINE FOR OBTAINING TWO-, THREE- AND FOUR-INCH DIAMETER CORES OF UNDISTURBED SOIL TO A DEPTH OF SIX FEET. Soil Sci. Soc. Amer. Proc. (1947) 12: 85–87, illus.

KELLEY, W. P.
1948. CATION EXCHANGE IN SOILS. Amer. Chem. Soc. Monog. Ser. 109, 144 pp., illus. New York.

——
1951. ALKALI SOILS, THEIR FORMATION, PROPERTIES AND RECLAMATION. 176 pp., illus. New York.

—— AND BROWN, S. M.
1934. PRINCIPLES GOVERNING THE RECLAMATION OF ALKALI SOILS. Hilgardia 8: 149–177, illus.

KILMER, V. J., AND ALEXANDER, L. T.
1949. METHODS OF MAKING MECHANICAL ANALYSIS OF SOILS. Soil. Sci. 68: 15–24.

KIRKHAM, D.
1946. PROPOSED METHOD FOR FIELD MEASUREMENT OF PERMEABILITY OF SOIL BELOW THE WATER TABLE. Soil Sci. Soc. Amer. Proc. (1945) 10: 58–68, illus.

——
1947. FIELD METHOD FOR DETERMINATION OF AIR PERMEABILITY OF SOIL IN ITS UNDISTURBED STATE. Soil Sci. Soc. Amer. Proc. (1946) 11: 93–99, illus.

——
1948. REDUCTION IN SEEPAGE TO SOIL UNDERDRAINS RESULTING FROM THEIR PARTIAL EMBEDMENT IN, OR PROXIMITY TO, AN IMPERVIOUS SUBSTRATUM. Soil Sci. Soc. Amer. Proc. (1947) 12: 54–59, illus.

——
1949. FLOW OF PONDED WATER INTO DRAIN TUBES IN SOIL OVERLYING AN IMPERVIOUS LAYER. Amer. Geophys. Union Trans. 30: 369–385, illus.

—— AND BAVEL, C. H. M. VAN.
1949. THEORY OF SEEPAGE INTO AUGER HOLES. Soil Sci. Soc. Amer. Proc. (1948) 13: 75–82, illus.

KITSON, R. E., AND MELLON, M. G.
1944. COLORIMETRIC DETERMINATION OF PHOSPHORUS AS MOLYBDIVANADOPHOSPHORIC ACID. Indus. and Engin. Chem., Analyt. Ed. 16: 379–383, illus.

KRISHNAMOORTHY, C., AND OVERSTREET, R.
1950. AN EXPERIMENTAL EVALUATION OF ION-EXCHANGE RELATIONSHIPS. Soil Sci. 69: 41–53.

LEHR, J. J.
1942. THE IMPORTANCE OF SODIUM FOR PLANT NUTRITION. III. THE EQUILIBRIUM OF CATIONS IN THE BEET. Soil Sci. 53: 399–411, illus.

——
1949. EXPLORATORY POT EXPERIMENTS ON SENSITIVENESS OF DIFFERENT CROPS TO SODIUM. A. SPINACH. Plant and Soil 2: 37–48, illus.

LILLELAND, O., BROWN, J. G., AND SWANSON, C.
1945. RESEARCH SHOWS EXCESS SODIUM MAY CAUSE LEAF TIP BURN. Almond Facts 9 (2) : 1, 5, illus.
LUTHIN, J. N., AND KIRKHAM, D.
1949. A PIEZOMETER METHOD FOR MEASURING PERMEABILITY OF SOIL IN SITU BELOW A WATER TABLE. Soil Sci. 68: 349–358, illus.
MCGEORGE, W. T.
1949. A STUDY OF LIME-INDUCED CHLOROSIS IN ARIZONA ORCHARDS. Ariz. Agr. Expt. Sta. Tech. Bul. 117, pp. 341–388, illus.
—— AND BREAZEALE, J. F.
1938. STUDIES ON SOIL STRUCTURE: EFFECT OF PUDDLED SOILS ON PLANT GROWTH. Ariz. Agr. Expt. Sta. Tech. Bul. 72, pp. 413–447, illus.
—— AND BREAZEALE, E. L.
1951. ABSORPTION OF GYPSUM BY SEMIARID SOILS. Ariz. Agr. Expt. Sta. Tech. Bul. 122, pp. 1–49, illus.
—— AND GREENE, R. A.
1935. OXIDATION OF SULPHUR IN ARIZONA SOILS AND ITS EFFECT ON SOIL PROPERTIES. Ariz. Agr. Expt. Sta. Tech. Bul. 59, pp. 297–325, illus.
MAGISTAD, O. C.
1945. PLANT GROWTH RELATIONS ON SALINE AND ALKALI SOILS. Bot. Rev. 11: 181–230.
—— AND CHRISTIANSEN, J. E.
1944. SALINE SOILS, THEIR NATURE AND MANAGEMENT. U. S. Dept. Agr. Cir. 707, 32 pp., illus.
MARSH, A. W., AND SWARNER, L. R.
1949. THE COLLECTION AND STUDY OF NATURAL SOIL CORES FOR DETERMINING IRRIGATION PROPERTIES. Soil Sci. Soc. Amer. Proc. (1948) 13: 515–518.
MARTIN, W. P., TAYLOR, G. S., ENGIBOUS, J. C., AND BURNETT, E.
1952. SOIL AND CROP RESPONSES FROM FIELD APPLICATIONS OF SOIL CONDITIONERS. Soil Sci. 73: 455–471, illus.
MASAEWA, M.
1936. ZUR FRAGE DER CHLOROPHOBIE DER PFLANZEN. Bodenk. u. Pflanzenernähr. 1:39–56.
MATTSON, S., AND WIKLANDER, L.
1940. THE LAWS OF COLLOIDAL BEHAVIOR: XXI. A. THE AMPHOTERIC POINTS, THE pH, AND THE DONNAN EQUILIBRIUM. Soil Sci. 49: 109–134, illus.
MIDDLETON, H. E.
1930. PROPERTIES OF SOILS WHICH INFLUENCE SOIL EROSION. U. S. Dept. Agr. Tech. Bul. 178, 16 pp.
MILLER, M. R.
1950. THE QUALITY OF THE WATER OF THE HUMBOLDT RIVER. Nev. Agr. Expt. Sta. Bul. 186, 31 pp.
MORTLAND, M. M., AND GIESEKING, J. E.
1951. INFLUENCE OF THE SILICATE ION ON POTASSIUM FIXATION. Soil Sci. 71: 381–385.
MUSGRAVE, G. W.
1935. THE INFILTRATION CAPACITY OF SOILS IN RELATION TO THE CONTROL OF SURFACE RUNOFF AND EROSION. Amer. Soc. Agron. Jour. 27: 336–345, illus.
NATIONAL RESEARCH COUNCIL.
1929. INTERNATIONAL CRITICAL TABLES OF NUMERICAL DATA, PHYSICS, CHEMISTRY AND TECHNOLOGY. vol. 6, 471 pp., illus. New York.
PEECH, M., ALEXANDER, L. T., DEAN, L. A., AND REED, J. F.
1947. METHODS OF SOIL ANALYSIS FOR SOIL-FERTILITY INVESTIGATIONS. U. S. Dept. Agr. Cir. 757, 25 pp.
PETERSON, D. F., JR., ISRAELSON, O. W., AND HANSEN, V. E.
1952. HYDRAULICS OF WELLS. Utah Agr. Expt. Sta. Tech. Bul. 351, 48 pp., illus.
PILLSBURY, A. F., AND CHRISTIANSEN, J. E.
1947. INSTALLING GROUND-WATER PIEZOMETERS BY JETTING FOR DRAINAGE INVESTIGATIONS IN COACHELLA VALLEY, CALIFORNIA. Agr. Engin. 28: 409–410, illus.
RATNER, E. I.
1935. THE INFLUENCE OF EXCHANGEABLE SODIUM IN THE SOIL ON ITS PROPERTIES AS A MEDIUM FOR PLANT GROWTH. Soil Sci. 40: 459–471, illus.

RATNER, E. I.
1944. PHYSIOLOGICAL EFFECT OF ALKALINITY OF SOILS AND THE AMELIORATIVE ROLE OF PLANT ROOT SYSTEMS ON SOLONETZ (ALKALI SOILS). POCHVOVEDENIE. (PEDOLOGY) : 205–227, illus. [In Russian. English summary, pp. 226–227.]
RAVIKOVITCH, S., AND BIDNER, N.
1937. THE DETERIORATION OF GRAPE-VINES IN SALINE SOILS. Empire Jour. Expt. Agr. 5: 197–203, illus.
REED, H. S., AND HAAS, A. R. C.
1924. NUTRIENT AND TOXIC EFFECTS OF CERTAIN IONS ON CITRUS AND WALNUT TREES WITH SPECIAL REFERENCE TO THE CONCENTRATION AND pH OF THE MEDIUM. Calif. Agr. Expt. Sta. Tech. Paper 17, 75 pp., illus.
REEVE, R. C., ALLISON, L. E., AND PETERSON, D. F., JR.
1948. RECLAMATION OF SALINE-ALKALI SOILS BY LEACHING—DELTA AREA, UTAH. Utah Agr. Expt. Sta. Bul. 335, 52 pp., illus.
—— AND JENSEN, M. C.
1949. PIEZOMETERS FOR GROUND-WATER FLOW STUDIES AND MEASUREMENT OF SUBSOIL PERMEABILITY. Agr. Engin. 30: 435–438, illus.
—— AND KIRKHAM, D.
1951. SOIL ANISOTROPY AND SOME FIELD METHODS FOR MEASURING PERMEABILITY. Amer. Geophys. Union Trans. 32: 582–590, illus.
REGER, J. S., PILLSBURY, A. F., REEVE, R. C., AND PETERSEN, R. K.
1950. TECHNIQUES FOR DRAINAGE INVESTIGATIONS IN THE COACHELLA VALLEY, CALIFORNIA. Agr. Engin. 31: 559–564, illus.
REITEMEIER, R. F.
1943. SEMIMICROANALYSIS OF SALINE SOIL SOLUTIONS. Indus. and Engin. Chem., Analyt. Ed. 15: 393–402, illus.

1946. EFFECT OF MOISTURE CONTENT ON THE DISSOLVED AND EXCHANGEABLE IONS OF SOILS OF ARID REGIONS. Soil Sci. 61: 195–214, illus.
—— CHRISTIANSEN, J. E., MOORE, R. E., AND ALDRICH, W. W.
1948. EFFECT OF GYPSUM, ORGANIC MATTER AND DRYING ON INFILTRATION OF A SODIUM WATER INTO A FINE SANDY LOAM. U. S. Dept. Agr. Tech. Bul. 937, 36 pp., illus.
—— AND FIREMAN, M.
1944. PREVENTION OF CALCIUM CARBONATE PRECIPITATION IN SOIL SOLUTIONS AND WATERS BY SODIUM HEXAMETAPHOSPHATE. Soil Sci. 58: 35–41, illus.
—— AND RICHARDS, L. A.
1944. RELIABILITY OF THE PRESSURE-MEMBRANE METHOD FOR EXTRACTION OF SOIL SOLUTION. Soil Sci. 57: 119–135, illus.
—— AND WILCOX, L. V.
1946. A CRITIQUE OF ESTIMATING SOIL SOLUTION CONCENTRATION FROM THE ELECTRICAL CONDUCTIVITY OF SATURATED SOILS. Soil Sci. 61: 281–293, illus.
RICHARDS, L. A.
1947. PRESSURE-MEMBRANE APPARATUS CONSTRUCTION AND USE. Agr. Engin. 28: 451–454, 460, illus.

1948. POROUS PLATE APPARATUS FOR MEASURING MOISTURE RETENTION AND TRANSMISSION BY SOIL. Soil Sci. 66: 105–110, illus.

1949a. FILTER FUNNELS FOR SOIL EXTRACTS. Agron. Jour. 41: 446, illus.

1949b. METHODS FOR MOUNTING POROUS PLATES USED IN SOIL MOISTURE MEASUREMENTS. Agron. Jour. 41: 489, illus.

1952. WATER CONDUCTING AND RETAINING PROPERTIES OF SOILS IN RELATION TO IRRIGATION. Internatl. Symposium on Desert Res. Proc., pp. 1–22, illus. (Res. Council of Israel in coop. with UNESCO.)

RICHARDS, L. A., AND CAMPBELL, R. B.
1948. USE OF THERMISTORS FOR MEASURING THE FREEZING POINT OF SOLUTIONS AND SOILS. Soil Sci. 65: 429–436, illus.
—— AND CAMPBELL, R. B.
1949. THE FREEZING POINT OF MOISTURE IN SOIL CORES. Soil Sci. Soc. Amer. Proc. (1948) 13: 70–74, illus.
—— AND WADLEIGH, C. H.
1952. SOIL WATER AND PLANT GROWTH. In Soil Physical Conditions and Plant Growth. Byron T. Shaw, Ed., 491 pp., illus. New York.
—— AND WEAVER, L. R.
1944. MOISTURE RETENTION BY SOME IRRIGATED SOILS AS RELATED TO SOIL-MOISTURE TENSION. Jour. Agr. Res. 69: 215–235, illus.
ROBERTS, R. C.
1950. CHEMICAL EFFECTS OF SALT-TOLERANT SHRUBS ON SOILS. Fourth Internatl. Cong. Soil Sci. Trans. 1: 404–406.
RUSSELL, M. B.
1949. METHODS OF MEASURING SOIL STRUCTURE AND AERATION. Soil Sci. 68: 25–35.
SAMPSON, A. W.
1939. PLANT INDICATORS—CONCEPT AND STATUS. Bot. Rev. 5: 155–206, illus.
SCHOFIELD, R. K.
1947. A RATIO LAW GOVERNING THE EQUILIBRIUM OF CATIONS IN THE SOIL SOLUTION. Internatl. Cong. Pure and Appl. Chem. (London) Proc. (11) 3: 257–261, illus.
—— AND BOTELHODA COSTA, J. V.
1938. THE MEASUREMENT OF PF IN SOIL BY FREEZING-POINT. Jour. Agr. Sci. [England] 28: 644–653, illus.
SCHOLLENBERGER, C. J.
1945. DETERMINATION OF CARBONATES IN SOIL. Soil Sci. 59: 57–63, illus.
SCOFIELD, C. S.
1936. THE SALINITY OF IRRIGATION WATER. Smithsn. Inst. Ann. Rpt. 1935: 275–287, illus.
——
1940. SALT BALANCE IN IRRIGATED AREAS. Jour. Agr. Res. 61: 17–39, illus.
—— AND HEADLEY, F. B.
1921. QUALITY OF IRRIGATION WATER IN RELATION TO LAND RECLAMATION. Jour. Agr. Res. 21: 265–278.
SCHANTZ, H. L., AND PIEMEISAL, R. L.
1924. INDICATOR SIGNIFICANCE OF THE NATURAL VEGETATION OF THE SOUTHWESTERN DESERT REGION. Jour. Agr. Res. 28: 721–802, illus.
SIGMOND, A. A. J. DE.
1924. THE ALKALI SOILS IN HUNGARY AND THEIR RECLAMATION. Soil Sci. 18: 379–381.
——
1928. THE CLASSIFICATION OF ALKALI AND SALTY SOILS. First Internatl. Cong. Soil Sci. Proc. (1927) 1: 330–344, illus.
——
1938. THE PRINCIPLES OF SOIL SCIENCE. 362 pp., illus. London.
SMITH, H. V.
1949. BORON AS A FACTOR IN ARIZONA'S AGRICULTURE. Ariz. Agr. Expt. Sta. Tech. Bul. 118, pp. 391–435, illus.
—— CASTER, A. B., FULLER, W. H., AND OTHERS.
1949. THE CHEMICAL COMPOSITION OF REPRESENTATIVE ARIZONA WATERS. Ariz. Agr. Expt. Sta. Bul. 225, pp. 1–76, illus.
SNELL, F. D., AND SNELL, C. T.
1936. COLORIMETRIC METHODS OF ANALYSIS. Ed. 2, v. 1, illus. New York.
SOIL SCIENCE SOCIETY OF AMERICA.
1952. REPORT OF SUBCOMMITTEE ON PERMEABILITY AND INFILTRATION, COMMITTEE ON TERMINOLOGY. Soil Sci. Soc. Amer. Proc. 16: 85–88.
SOIL SURVEY STAFF.
1951. SOIL SURVEY MANUAL. U. S. Dept. Agr. Handb. No. 18. 503 pp., illus. Washington.

STEWART, G., COTTAM, W. P., AND HUTCHINGS, S. S.
1940. INFLUENCE OF UNRESTRICTED GRAZING ON NORTHERN SALT DESERT PLANT ASSOCIATIONS IN WESTERN UTAH. Jour. Agr. Res. 60: 289–316, illus.
TANNER, C. B., AND JACKSON, M. L.
1948. NOMOGRAPHS OF SEDIMENTATION TIMES FOR SOIL PARTICLES UNDER GRAVITY OR CENTRIFUGAL ACCELERATION. Soil Sci. Soc. Amer. Proc. (1947) 12: 60–65, illus.
TEAKLE, L. J. H.
1937. THE SALT (SODIUM CHLORIDE) CONTENT OF RAINWATER. West. Austral. Dept. Agr. Jour., Ser. 2, 14: 115–123, illus.
THEIS, C. V.
1935. THE RELATION BETWEEN THE LOWERING OF THE PIEZOMETRIC SURFACE AND THE RATE AND DURATION OF DISCHARGE OF A WELL USING GROUND-WATER STORAGE. Amer. Geophys. Union Trans. 16: 519–524, illus.
THOMAS, J. E.
1934. THE DIAGNOSTIC VALUE OF THE CHLORINE CONTENT OF THE VINE LEAF. Austral. Council Sci. & Indus. Res., Jour. 7: 29–38, illus.
THORNE, D. W.
1945. GROWTH AND NUTRITION OF TOMATO PLANTS AS INFLUENCED BY EXCHANGEABLE SODIUM, CALCIUM, AND POTASSIUM. Soil Sci. Soc. Amer. Proc. (1944) 9: 185–189, illus.
—— WANN, F. B., AND ROBINSON, W.
1951. HYPOTHESES CONCERNING LIME-INDUCED CHLOROSIS. Soil Sci. Soc. Amer. Proc. (1950) 15: 254–258.
THORNE, J. P., AND THORNE, D. W.
1951. THE IRRIGATION WATERS OF UTAH. Utah. Agr. Expt. Sta. Bul. 346, 64 pp., illus.
TOTH, S. J., PRINCE, A. L., WALLACE, A., AND MIKKELSEN, D. S.
1948. RAPID QUANTITATIVE DETERMINATION OF EIGHT MINERAL ELEMENTS IN PLANT TISSUE BY A SYSTEMATIC PROCEDURE INVOLVING USE OF A FLAME PHOTOMETER. Soil Sci. 66: 459–466.
TYNER, E. H.
1940. THE USE OF SODIUM METAPHOSPHATE FOR DISPERSION OF SOILS FOR MECHANICAL ANALYSIS. Soil Sci. Soc. Amer. Proc. (1939) 4: 106–113.
UNITED STATES BUREAU OF RECLAMATION.
1948. LAND CLASSIFICATION REPORT. Wellton-Mohawk Division, Gila Project, Arizona. 32 pp., illus. [Processed.]
UNITED STATES GEOLOGICAL SURVEY.
1945. QUALITY OF SURFACE WATERS OF THE UNITED STATES, 1943. U. S. Geol. Survey Water-Supply Paper 970, 180 pp.
——
1949. QUALITY OF SURFACE WATERS OF THE UNITED STATES, 1945. U. S. Geol. Survey Water-Supply Paper 1030, 335 pp.
——
1950. QUALITY OF SURFACE WATERS OF THE UNITED STATES, 1946. U. S. Geol. Survey Water-Supply Paper 1050, 486 pp.
[UNITED STATES] NATIONAL RESOURCES COMMITTEE.
1938. REGIONAL PLANNING: PART VI—THE RIO GRANDE JOINT INVESTIGATION IN THE UPPER RIO GRANDE BASIN IN COLORADO, NEW MEXICO, AND TEXAS. 1936–1937. 566 pp., illus. Washington.
[UNITED STATES] NATIONAL RESOURCES PLANNING BOARD.
1942. THE PECOS RIVER JOINT INVESTIGATION: REPORTS OF PARTICIPATING AGENCIES. 407 pp., illus. Washington.
VEIHMEYER, F. J., AND HENDRICKSON, A. H.
1946. SOIL DENSITY AS A FACTOR IN DETERMINING THE PERMANENT WILTING PERCENTAGE. Soil Sci. 62: 451–456, illus.
—— AND HENDRICKSON, A. H.
1948. THE PERMANENT WILTING PERCENTAGE AS A REFERENCE FOR THE MEASURING OF SOIL MOISTURE. Amer. Geophys. Union Trans. 29: 887–896, illus.

WADLEIGH, C. H.
1946. THE INTEGRATED SOIL MOISTURE STRESS UPON A ROOT SYSTEM IN A LARGE CONTAINER OF SALINE SOIL. Soil Sci. 61: 225–238, illus.
—— AND AYERS, A. D.
1945. GROWTH AND BIOCHEMICAL COMPOSITION OF BEAN PLANTS AS CONDITIONED BY SOIL MOISTURE TENSION AND SALT CONCENTRATION. Plant Physiol. 20: 106–132, illus.
—— AND BROWN, J. W.
1952. THE CHEMICAL STATUS OF BEAN PLANTS AFFLICTED WITH BICARBONATE-INDUCED CHLOROSIS. Bot. Gaz. 113: 373–392, illus.
—— AND FIREMAN, M.
1949. SALT DISTRIBUTION UNDER FURROW AND BASIN IRRIGATED COTTON AND ITS EFFECT ON WATER REMOVAL. Soil Sci. Soc. Amer. Proc. (1948) 13: 527–530, illus.
—— AND GAUCH, H. G.
1944. THE INFLUENCE OF HIGH CONCENTRATIONS OF SODIUM SULFATE, SODIUM CHLORIDE, CALCIUM CHLORIDE, AND MAGNESIUM CHLORIDE ON THE GROWTH OF GUAYULE IN SAND CULTURE. Soil Sci. 58: 399–403, illus.
—— GAUCH, H. G., AND KOLISCH, M.
1951. MINERAL COMPOSITION OF ORCHARD GRASS GROWN ON PACHAPPA LOAM SALINIZED WITH VARIOUS SALTS. Soil Sci. 72: 275–282, illus.
WALKLEY, A.
1935. AN EXAMINATION OF METHODS FOR DETERMINING ORGANIC CARBON AND NITROGEN IN SOILS. Jour. Agr. Sci. [England] 25: 598–609, illus.
——
1947. A CRITICAL EXAMINATION OF A RAPID METHOD FOR DETERMINING ORGANIC CARBON IN SOILS—EFFECT OF VARIATIONS IN DIGESTION CONDITIONS AND OF INORGANIC SOIL CONSTITUENTS. Soil Sci 63: 251–264, illus.
WALSH, T., AND CLARKE, E. J.
1942. A CHLOROSIS OF TOMATOES. (Abstract) Éire Dept. Agr. Jour. 39: 316–325, illus.
WENZEL, L. K.
1942. METHODS FOR DETERMINING PERMEABILITY OF WATER-BEARING MATERIALS WITH SPECIAL REFERENCE TO DISCHARGING-WELL METHODS. U. S. Geol. Survey Water-Supply Paper 887, 192 pp., illus.

WHITE, L. M., AND ROSS, W. H.
1937. INFLUENCE OF FERTILIZERS ON THE CONCENTRATION OF THE SOIL SOLUTION. Soil Sci. Soc. Amer. Proc. (1936) 1: 181–186, illus.
WHITNEY, M., AND BRIGGS, L. J.
1897. AN ELECTRICAL METHOD OF DETERMINING THE TEMPERATURE OF SOILS. U. S. Dept. Agr., Div. Soils Bul. 7, 15 pp., illus.
—— AND MEANS, T. H.
1897. AN ELECTRICAL METHOD OF DETERMINING THE SOLUBLE SALT CONTENT OF SOILS. U. S. Dept. Agr., Div. Soils Bul. 8, 30 pp., illus.
WILCOX, L. V.
1932. ELECTROMETRIC TITRATION OF BORIC ACID. Indus. and Engin. Chem., Analyt. Ed. 4: 38–39.
——
1937. DETERMINATION OF POTASSIUM BY MEANS OF AN AQUEOUS SOLUTION OF TRISODIUM COBALTINITRITE IN THE PRESENCE OF NITRIC ACID. Indus. and Engin. Chem., Analyt. Ed. 9: 136–138.
——
1948. THE QUALITY OF WATER FOR IRRIGATION USE. U. S. Dept. Agr. Tech. Bul. 962, 40 pp., illus.
——
1950 ELECTRICAL CONDUCTIVITY. Amer. Water Works Assoc. Jour. 42: 775–776.
——
1951. A METHOD FOR CALCULATING THE SATURATION PERCENTAGE FROM THE WEIGHT OF A KNOWN VOLUME OF SATURATED SOIL PASTE. Soil Sci. 72: 233–237, illus.
WILLIAMS, D. E.
1949. A RAPID MANOMETRIC METHOD FOR THE DETERMINATION OF CARBONATE IN SOILS. Soil Sci. Soc. Amer. Proc. (1948) 13: 127–129, illus.
WILLIAMS, W. O.
1941. RAPID DETERMINATION OF POTASSIUM WITH DIPICRYLAMINE. Amer. Soc. Hort. Sci. Proc. 39: 47–50.
YODER, R. E.
1936. A DIRECT METHOD OF AGGREGATE ANALYSIS OF SOILS AND A STUDY OF THE PHYSICAL NATURE OF EROSION LOSSES. Amer. Soc. Agron. Jour. 28: 337–351, illus.
ZUUR, A. J.
1952. DRAINAGE AND RECLAMATION OF LAKES AND OF THE ZUIDERZEE. Soil Sci. 74: 75–89, illus.

ABSORPTION.—The process by which a substance is taken into and included within another substance, i. e., intake of water by soil, or intake of gases, water, nutrients, or other substances by plants.

ADSORPTION.—The increased concentration of molecules or ions at a surface, including exchangeable cations and anions on soil particles.

AGGREGATE.—A group of soil particles cohering so as to behave mechanically as a unit.

AGGREGATION.—The act or process of forming aggregates, or the state of being aggregated.

ALKALI SOIL.—A soil that contains sufficient exchangeable sodium to interfere with the growth of most crop plants, either with or without appreciable quantities of soluble salts. *See* Nonsaline-Alkali Soil and Saline-Alkali Soil.

ALKALINE.—A chemical term referring to basic reaction where the pH reading is above 7, as distinguished from acidic reaction where the pH reading is below 7.

ALKALINE SOIL.—A soil that has an alkaline reaction, i. e., a soil for which the pH reading of the saturated soil paste is higher than 7.

ALKALIZATION.—The process whereby the exchangeable-sodium content of a soil is increased.

ATMOSPHERE.—*See* Standard Atmosphere.

BASE-EXCHANGE CAPACITY.—*See* Cation-Exchange-Capacity.

BULK DENSITY.—The ratio of the mass of water-free soil to its bulk volume. Bulk density is expressed in pounds per cubic foot or grams per cubic centimeter and is sometimes referred to as "apparent density." When expressed in grams per cubic centimeter, bulk density is numerically equal to apparent specific gravity or volume weight.

CATION EXCHANGE.—The interchange of a cation in solution with another cation on a surface-active material.

CATION-EXCHANGE-CAPACITY.—The total quantity of cations which a soil can adsorb by cation exchange, usually expressed as milliequivalents per 100 grams. Measured values of cation-exchange-capacity depend somewhat on the method used for the determination.

CELL CONSTANT.—*See* Conductivity-Cell Constant.

COEFFICIENT OF CORRELATION.—A statistic used in linear correlation that provides a measure of the proportion of variation in one variable that is associated with variation in another variable.

COEFFICIENT OF DETERMINATION.—A statistic used in linear correlation that gives the fraction of the variance in one variable which is associated with variance in another variable. It is the square of the coefficient of correlation and is usually expressed in percent.

COEFFICIENT OF VARIATION.—Standard deviation expressed as percentage of the mean.

CONDUCTIVITY.—*See* Electrical Conductivity and Hydraulic Conductivity.

CONDUCTIVITY-CELL CONSTANT (k).—The product of the known electrical conductivity (EC) of a standard solution in a conductivity cell and the corresponding measured resistance (R) of the cell containing the standard solution. That is: $k = EC \times R$. The value of the cell constant is determined by the geometry of the cell and so is nearly independent of the temperature, but EC and R must be evaluated at the same temperature. Rearranging the equation and indicating temperatures by a subscript gives: $EC_t = k/R_t$. In this form, the equation may be used for evaluating the conductivity EC_t of an unknown solution in the cell at temperature (t), where R_t is the measured resistance of the cell containing the solution at the temperature t and k is the cell constant as evaluated from a previous measurement of a standard solution.

CONSUMPTIVE USE.—The water used by plants in transpiration and growth, plus water vapor loss from adjacent soil or snow or from intercepted precipitation in any specified time. Usually expressed as equivalent depth of free water per unit of time.

DARCY'S LAW.—1. Historical. The volume of water passing downward through a sand filter bed in unit time is proportional to the area of the bed and to the difference in hydraulic head and is inversely proportional to the thickness of the bed. 2. Generalization for three dimensions. The effective rate of viscous flow of water in isotropic porous media is proportional to, and in the direction of, the hydraulic gradient. 3. Generalization for other fluids. The effective rate of viscous flow of homogeneous fluids through isotropic porous media is proportional to, and in the direction of, the driving force.

DISPERSED SOIL.—Soil in which the clay readily forms a colloidal sol. Dispersed soils usually have low permeability. They tend to shrink, crack, and become hard on drying and to slake and become plastic on wetting.

DRAINAGE.—1. The processes of the discharge of water from an area of soil by sheet or stream flow (surface drainage) and the removal of excess water from within soil by downward flow through the soil (internal drainage). 2. The means for effecting the removal of water from the surface of soil and from within the soil, i. e., sloping topography or stream channels (surface drainage) and open ditches, underground tile lines, or pumped wells (artificial drainage).

DRAINAGE REQUIREMENTS.—Performance and capacity specifications for a drainage system, i. e., permissible depths and modes of variation of the water table with respect to the root zone or soil surface, and the volume of water that the drains must convey in a given time.

EFFICIENCY OF IRRIGATION.—The fraction of the water diverted from a river or other source that is consumed by the crop, expressed as percent. *See* Consumptive Use. Often applied to whole irrigation systems and takes account of conveyance losses.

EFFICIENCY OF WATER APPLICATION.—The fraction of the water delivered to the farm that is stored in the root zone for use by the crop, expressed as percent.

ELECTRICAL CONDUCTIVITY.—The reciprocal of the electrical resistivity. The resistivity is the resistance in ohms of a conductor, metallic or electrolytic, which is 1 cm. long and has a cross-sectional area of 1 cm.^{2} Hence, electrical conductivity is expressed in reciprocal ohms per centimeter, or mhos per centimeter. The terms "electrical conductivity" and "specific electrical conductance" have identical meaning.

EQUIVALENT; EQUIVALENT WEIGHT.—The weight in grams of an ion or compound that combines with or replaces 1 gm. of hydrogen. The atomic weight or formula weight divided by its valence.

EQUIVALENT PER MILLION.—An equivalent weight of an ion or salt per 1 million gm. of solution or soil. For solutions, equivalents per million (e. p. m.) and milliequivalents per liter (meq./l.) are numerically identical if the specific gravity of the solution is 1.0.

ETHYLENE GLYCOL RETENTIVITY.—Weight of ethylene glycol adsorbed per unit weight of soil under specified equilibrium or quasi-equilibrium conditions. *See* Method 25.

EXCHANGE CAPACITY.—*See* Cation-Exchange-Capacity.

EXCHANGE COMPLEX.—The surface-active constituents of soils (both inorganic and organic) that are capable of cation exchange.

EXCHANGEABLE CATION.—A cation that is adsorbed on the exchange complex and which is capable of exchange with other cations.

EXCHANGEABLE-SODIUM-PERCENTAGE.—The degree of saturation of the soil exchange complex with sodium. It may be calculated by the formula:

$$ESP = \frac{\text{Exchangeable sodium (meq./100 gm. soil)}}{\text{Cation-exchange-capacity (meq./100 gm. soil)}} \times 100$$

FIELD CAPACITY.—The moisture content of soil in the field 2 or 3 days after a thorough wetting of the soil profile by rain or irrigation water. Field capacity is expressed as moisture percentage, dry-weight basis.

FIFTEEN-ATMOSPHERE PERCENTAGE.—The moisture percentage, dry-weight basis, of a soil sample which has been wetted and brought to equilibrium in a pressure-membrane apparatus at a pressure of 221 p. s. i. This characteristic moisture value for soils approximates the lower limit of water available for plant growth.

FIFTY PERCENT YIELD-DECREMENT VALUE.—The measured value of the soil salinity or alkali that decreases crop yield 50 percent as compared with yields of the same crop on nonsaline and nonalkali soils under similar growing conditions.

GROUND WATER.—Water in soil beneath the soil surface, usually under conditions where the pressure in the water is greater than the atmospheric pressure, and the soil voids are substantially filled with the water.

HYDRAULIC CONDUCTIVITY.—The proportionality factor in the Darcy flow law, which states that the effective flow velocity is proportional to the hydraulic gradient. Hydraulic conductivity, therefore, is the effective flow velocity at unit hydraulic gradient and has the dimensions of velocity (LT^{-1}).

HYDRAULIC GRADIENT.—The decrease in hydraulic head per unit distance in the soil in the direction of the greatest rate of decrease of hydraulic head.

HYDRAULIC HEAD.—The elevation with respect to a standard datum at which water stands in a riser or manometer connected to the point in question in the soil. This will include elevation head, pressure head, and also the velocity head, if the terminal opening of the sensing element is pointed upstream. For nonturbulent flow of water in soil the velocity head is negligible. In unsaturated soil a porous cup must be used for establishing hydraulic contact between the soil water and water in a manometer. Hydraulic head has the dimensions of length (L).

INDICATOR PLANT.—A native plant that indicates, in general, and often in a specific manner, the nature of soil conditions with regard to moisture and salinity. Dominant species are the most important indicators of such conditions.

INFILTRATION.—The downward entry of water into soil.

INFILTRATION RATE; INFILTRATION CAPACITY.—The maximum rate at which a soil, in a given condition at a given time, can absorb rain. Also, the rate at which a soil will absorb water ponded on the surface at a shallow depth when the ponded area is infinitely large or when adequate precautions are taken to minimize the effect of divergent flow at the borders. It is the volume of water passing into the soil per unit of area per unit of time, and has the dimensions of velocity (LT^{-1}).

INTAKE RATE; INFILTRATION VELOCITY.—The rate of water entry into the soil expressed as a depth of water per unit of time. This term involves no restrictions on area of application or divergence of flow in the soil; therefore, the measuring procedure should be specified. It has the dimensions of velocity (LT^{-1}).

INTRINSIC PERMEABILITY.—The factor k' in the equation,

$$v = \frac{k' dgi}{\eta} = \frac{k'}{\eta} (dF_g - \nabla p)$$

where v=flow velocity, d=density, g=scalar value for acceleration of gravity, i=hydraulic gradient, η=viscosity, F_g=gravitational force per unit of mass, and ∇p=pressure gradient. Intrinsic permeability has the dimensions of length squared (L^2). See Permeability (Quantitative).

ISOBATH.—1. Having constant depth. 2. A line connecting points of equal depth to water table.

ISOPLETH.—1. A graph showing the occurrence or frequency of any phenomenon as a function of two variables. 2. A line showing the variation in time and position along a field profile of the point of intersection of a water-table contour line and the profile.

LEACHING.—The process of removal of soluble material by the passage of water through soil.

LEACHING REQUIREMENT.—The fraction of the water entering the soil that must pass through the root zone in order to prevent soil salinity from exceeding a specified value. Leaching requirement is used primarily under steady-state or long-time average conditions.

LIME.—Strictly, calcium oxide (CaO), but as commonly used in agriculture terminology calcium carbonate ($CaCO_3$) and calcium hydroxide ($Ca(OH)_2$) are included. Agricultural lime refers to any of these compounds, with or without magnesia, used as an amendment for acid soils.

MILLIEQUIVALENT.—One thousandth of an equivalent.

MILLIEQUIVALENT PER LITER.—A milliequivalent of an ion or a compound in 1 liter of solution.

MOISTURE PERCENTAGE.—1. Dry-weight basis. The weight of water per 100 units of weight of material dried to constant weight at a standard temperature. 2. Depth basis. The equivalent depth of free water per 100 units of depth of soil. Numerically this value approximates the volume of water per 100 units of volume of soil.

NONSALINE-ALKALI SOIL.—A soil that contains sufficient exchangeable sodium to interfere with the growth of most crop plants and does not contain appreciable quantities of soluble salts. The exchangeable-sodium-percentage is greater than 15 and the electrical conductivity of the saturation extract is less than 4 millimhos per centimeter (at 25° C.). The pH reading of the saturated soil paste is usually greater than 8.5.

ONE-THIRD-ATMOSPHERE PERCENTAGE.—The moisture percentage, dry-weight basis, of a soil sample that has been air-dried, screened, wetted, and brought to hydraulic equilibrium with a permeable membrane at a soil-moisture tension of 345 cm. of water. This retentivity value closely approximates the moisture equivalent value of many soils.

OSMOTIC PRESSURE.—The equivalent negative pressure that influences the rate of diffusion of water through a semipermeable membrane. Its direct experimental value for a solution is the pressure difference required to equalize the diffusion rates between the solution and pure water across a semipermeable membrane. Osmotic pressure in atmospheres may be calculated from the freezing-point depression ΔT in °C. by the formula $OP = 12.06\Delta T - 0.021\Delta T^2$.

PARTICLE DENSITY.—The average density of the soil particles. Particle density is usually expressed in grams per cubic centimeter and is sometimes referred to as "real density" or "grain density."

PERCOLATION.—A qualitative term applying to the downward movement of water through soil. Especially, the downward flow of water in saturated or nearly saturated soil at hydraulic gradients of one or less.

PERMANENT WILTING PERCENTAGE.—The moisture percentage of soil at which plants wilt and fail to recover turgidity. It is usually determined with dwarf sunflowers. The expression has significance only for nonsaline soils.

PERMEABILITY.—1. Qualitative. The quality or state of a porous medium relating to the readiness with which such a medium conducts or transmits fluids. 2. Quantitative. The specific property governing the rate or readiness with which a porous medium transmits fluids under standard conditions. The equation used for expressing the flow should take into account the properties of the fluid so that proper measurements on a given medium give the same permeability value for all fluids that do not alter the medium. The physical dimensions of the permeability unit are determined by the equation used to express the flow. See Intrinsic Permeability.

PLANT COMMUNITY.—An assemblage of plants living together under the same environmental conditions.

POROSITY.—The fraction of the soil volume not occupied by soil particles, i. e., the ratio of the sum of the volumes of the liquid and gas phases to the sum of the volumes of the solid, liquid, and gas phases of the soil.

POTASSIUM-ADSORPTION-RATIO.—A ratio for soil extracts and irrigation waters used to express the relative activity of potassium ions in exchange reactions with soil.

$$PAR = \frac{K^+}{\sqrt{(Ca^{++} + Mg^{++})/2}}$$

where the ionic concentrations are expressed in milliequivalents per liter.

RECLAMATION.—The process of removing excess soluble salts or excess exchangeable sodium from soils.

REGRESSION COEFFICIENT.—A statistic used in linear correlation that gives the change in one variable that is associated with unit change in another variable.

SALINE-ALKALI SOIL.—A soil containing sufficient exchangeable sodium to interfere with the growth of most crop plants and containing appreciable quantities of soluble salts. The exchangeable-sodium-percentage is greater than 15, and the electrical conductivity of the saturation extract is greater than 4 mmhos per centimeter (at 25° C.). The pH reading of the saturated soil is usually less than 8.5.

SALINE SOIL.—A nonalkali soil containing soluble salts in such quantities that they interfere with the growth of most crop plants. The electrical conductivity of the saturation extract is greater than 4 mmhos per centimeter (at 25° C.), and the exchangeable-sodium-percentage is less than 15. The pH reading of the saturated soil is usually less than 8.5.

SALINIZATION.—The process of accumulation of soluble salts in soil.

SATURATED SOIL PASTE.—A particular mixture of soil and water. At saturation the soil paste glistens as it reflects light, flows slightly when the container is tipped, and the paste slides freely and cleanly from a spatula for all soils except those with high clay content.

SATURATION EXTRACT.—The solution extracted from a soil at its saturation percentage.

SATURATION PERCENTAGE.—The moisture percentage of a saturated soil paste, expressed on a dry-weight basis.

SEMIPERMEABLE MEMBRANE.—A membrane that permits the diffusion of one component of a solution but not the other. In biology, a septum which permits the diffusion of water but not of the solute.

SODIUM-ADSORPTION-RATIO.—A ratio for soil extracts and irrigation waters used to express the relative activity of sodium ions in exchange reactions with soil.

$$SAR = \frac{Na^+}{\sqrt{(Ca^{++} + Mg^{++})/2}}$$

where the ionic concentrations are expressed in milliequivalents per liter.

SOIL EXTRACT.—The solution separated from a soil suspension or a soil at a particular moisture content.

SOIL-MOISTURE STRESS.—The sum of the soil-moisture tension and the osmotic pressure of the soil solution. It is the suction or negative pressure to which water must be subjected to be at equilibrium through a semipermeable membrane with the solution in soil.

SOIL-MOISTURE TENSION.—The equivalent negative pressure or suction of water in soil. Experimentally, the suction of water in soil is the pressure difference required across a permeable membrane to produce hydraulic equilibrium between the soil water and free water.

SOLUBLE-SODIUM PERCENTAGE.—A term used in connection with irrigation waters and soil extracts to indicate the proportion of sodium ions in solution in relation to the total cation concentration. It may be calculated by the formula:

$$SSP = \frac{\text{Soluble sodium concentration (meq./l.)}}{\text{Total cation concentration (meq./l.)}} \times 100$$

SPECIFIC ION EFFECT.—Any effect of a salt constituent in the substrate on plant growth that is not caused by the osmotic properties of the substrate.

SPECIFIC SURFACE.—The surface area, per unit weight of soil, commonly expressed as square meters per gram of soil (m.²/gm.).

STANDARD ATMOSPHERE.—A unit of pressure defined as follows: 1 atmosphere = 1.013×10^6 dynes per sq. cm. = 14.71 pounds per sq. in. = 76.39 cm. of mercury column = 1,036 cm. of water column = 34.01 ft. of water column. (Water and mercury at 20° C.).

STANDARD DEVIATION.—A statistic used to measure the dispersion of a set of values around their mean.

SUCTION.—See Soil-Moisture Tension.

WATER TABLE.—The upper boundary for ground water. The upper surface of the locus of points at which the pressure in the ground water is equal to atmospheric pressure.

Appendix

Symbols and Abbreviations

EC _____ Electrical conductivity in mhos/cm. unless otherwise specified.

$EC \times 10^3$ _____ Electrical conductivity in millimhos/cm. (value in mhos/cm. $\times 10^3$).

$EC \times 10^6$ _____ Electrical conductivity in micromhos/cm. (value in mhos/cm. $\times 10^6$).

EC_e _____ Electrical conductivity of saturation extract.

EC_1, EC_5, EC_{50} _____ Electrical conductivity of extract from a suspension having the proportions of 1 gm. of dry soil to 1, 5, or 50 gm. of water.

EC_{iw} _____ Electrical conductivity of irrigation water.

EC_{dw} _____ Electrical conductivity of drainage water or soil solution at the bottom of the root zone.

EC_s _____ Electrical conductivity of saturated soil paste.

R_s _____ Resistance of soil paste in Bureau of Soils cup.

mho _____ Reciprocal ohm; (ohm spelled backward).

mmho _____ Millimho.

μmho _____ Micromho.

ESP _____ Exchangeable-sodium-percentage.

SAR _____ Sodium-adsorption-ratio.

EPP _____ Exchangeable-potassium-percentage.

PAR _____ Potassium-adsorption-ratio.

CEC _____ Cation-exchange-capacity.

meq. _____ Milliequivalent.

mg./l. _____ Milligrams of solute per liter of solution.

p. p. m. _____ Parts per million. As commonly measured and used parts per million is numerically equivalent to milligrams per liter.

pH_s; pH_e; pH_1; pH_5 _____ pH reading of saturated soil paste; saturation extract; 1 : 1 or 1 : 5 soil-water suspension. Measured with glass electrode unless otherwise specified.

LR _____ Leaching requirement.

HC _____ Hydraulic conductivity.

PWP _____ Permanent-wilting percentage.

FAP _____ Fifteen-atmosphere percentage.

SP _____ Saturation percentage.

SMT _____ Soil-moisture tension.

OP _____ Osmotic pressure.

OP_e _____ Osmotic pressure of saturation extract.

$\triangle T$ _____ Freezing-point depression, °C.

P_w _____ Percentage water, dry-weight basis.

P_d _____ Percentage water, depth basis.

d_w _____ Density of water.

d_b _____ Bulk density of soil.

d_p _____ Particle density of soil.

k _____ Hydraulic conductivity; conductivity-cell constant.

k' _____ Intrinsic permeability.

D_{iw} _____ Depth of irrigation water applied to soil.

D_{dw} _____ Depth (equivalent free depth) of drainage water.

D_{cw} _____ Consumptive use expressed as equivalent free depth of water in a specified time.

E _____ Efficiency of irrigation water application.

n _____ Porosity.

$C2-S3$ _____ Example of classification of irrigation water; C denotes conductivity (electrical); S denotes sodium (SAR); numbers denote respective numerical quality classes. (See ch. 5.)

m _____ Meter.

cm _____ Centimeter.

mm _____ Millimeter.

mμ _____ Millimicron.

μ _____ Micron (10^{-6} meter); also prefix micro.

A _____ Angstrom (10^{-10} meter).

RCF _____ Relative centrifugal force.

r. p. m. _____ Revolutions per minute.

η _____ Viscosity.

Conversion Formulas and Factors

Conductivity to milliequivalent per liter:

meq./l. $= 10 \times EC \times 10^3$, for irrigation waters and soil extracts in the range from 0.1 to 5.0 millimhos per cm. *See* figures 4 and 20.

Conductivity to osmotic pressure in atmospheres:

$OP = 0.36 \times EC \times 10^3$ for soil extracts in the range from 3 to 30 millimhos/cm.

Conductivity to parts per million:

p. p. m. $= 0.64 \times EC \times 10^6$ for irrigation waters in the range 100 to 5,000 micromhos/cm.

Parts of salt per million parts of irrigation water to tons of salt per acre-foot of water:

Tons per acre-foot (t. a. f.) $= 0.00136 \times$ p. p. m.

Grains per gallon to parts per million:

p. p. m. $= 17.1 \times$ grains per gallon.

Milliequivalents per liter (from chemical analyses) to parts per million:

Multiply meq./l. for each ion by its equivalent weight and obtain the sum.

Gypsum ($CaSO_4 \cdot 2H_2O$) equivalent weight $= 86.09$ gm.

Saturated gypsum solution at 25° C. contains:

30.5 meq./l.; 2.63 gm./l.; 2,630 p. p. m.; 3.5 tons of gypsum per acre-foot of water. One milliequivalent of gypsum per 100 gm. of soil corresponds to 1.72 tons of gypsum per acre-foot of soil (4,000,000 lb.). In other words, tons of gypsum per acre-foot of soil $= 1.72 \times$ (milliequivalents gypsum per 100 gm. of soil). $EC \times 10^3 = 2.205$ at 25° C.

1 standard atmosphere $= 1.013 \times 10^6$ dynes cm.$^{-2}$; 14.71 lb. in.^{2}; 76.39 cm. of mercury column; 1,036 cm. of water column; 34.01 ft. of water column. (Mercury and water at 20° C.)

1 bar $= 10^6$ dynes cm.$^{-2} = 1,023$ cm. of water column.

1 millibar $=$ one thousandth of a bar.

1 mile $= 5,280$ feet.

1 inch $= 2.54$ cm.

1 foot $= 30.48$ cm.

1 pound $= 453.59$ gm.

1 acre $= 43,560$ sq. ft.

1 acre-foot soil weighs 4,000,000 pounds (approximate).
1 acre-foot water weighs 2,720,000 pounds (approximate).
Gallons per minute to cubic feet per second:
    c. f. s.=0.002228×g. p. m.
1 cubic foot per second (c. f. s.) =
    50 miner's inches in: Idaho, Kansas, Nebraska, Nevada, New Mexico, North Dakota, South Dakota, Utah, and southern California.
    40 miner's inches in: Arizona, California (statute), Montana, and Oregon.
    38.4 miner's inches in: Colorado.

1 c. f. s. for 24 hours=1.98 acre-feet.
1 U. S. gallon=231 cubic inches,
    8.345 pounds of water.
    0.1337 cubic foot.
    58,417 grains of water.
1 cubic foot=7.48 gallons.
1 cubic foot of water weighs 62.43 lbs.
1 cubic foot of soil in place weighs 68 to 112 pounds. Bulk density 1.1 to 1.8 gm. cm.$^{-3}$.
Average particle density=2.65 gm. cm.$^{-3}$, approximately. (For soils which are low in organic matter.)

Chemical symbols, equivalent weights, and common names

Chemical symbol or formula—	Equivalent weight	Common name
	Grams	
Ions:		
Ca^{++}	20.04	Calcium ion.
Mg^{++}	12.16	Magnesium ion.
Na^+	23.00	Sodium ion.
K^+	39.10	Potassium ion.
Cl^-	35.46	Chloride ion.
SO_4^{--}	48.03	Sulfate ion.
CO_3^{--}	30.00	Carbonate ion.
HCO_3^-	61.01	Bicarbonate ion.
Salts:		
$CaCl_2$	55.50	Calcium chloride.
$CaSO_4$	68.07	Calcium sulfate.
$CaSO_4 \cdot 2H_2O$	86.09	Gypsum.
$CaCO_3$	50.04	Calcium carbonate.
$MgCl_2$	47.62	Magnesium chloride.
$MgSO_4$	60.19	Magnesium sulfate.
$MgCO_3$	42.16	Magnesium carbonate.
$NaCl$	58.45	Sodium chloride.
Na_2SO_4	71.03	Sodium sulfate.
Na_2CO_3	53.00	Sodium carbonate.
$NaHCO_3$	84.01	Sodium bicarbonate.
KCl	74.56	Potassium chloride.
K_2SO_4	87.13	Potassium sulfate.
K_2CO_3	69.10	Potassium carbonate.
$KHCO_3$	100.11	Potassium bicarbonate.
Chemical amendments:		
S	16.03	Sulfur.
H_2SO_4	49.04	Sulfuric acid.
$Al_2(SO_4)_3 \cdot 18H_2O$	111.07	Aluminum sulfate.
$FeSO_4 \cdot 7H_2O$	139.01	Iron sulfate (ferrous).

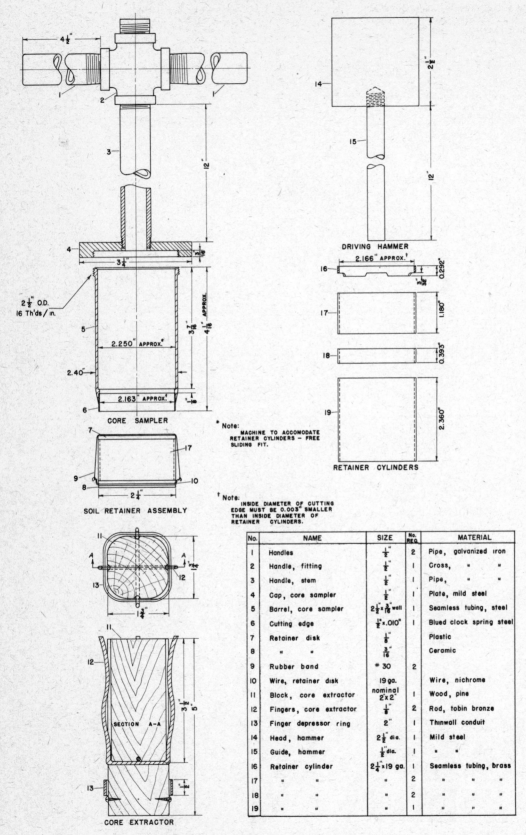

* Note:
MACHINE TO ACCOMODATE
RETAINER CYLINDERS — FREE
SLIDING FIT.

† Note:
INSIDE DIAMETER OF CUTTING
EDGE MUST BE 0.003" SMALLER
THAN INSIDE DIAMETER OF
RETAINER CYLINDERS.

DRIVING HAMMER

RETAINER CYLINDERS

CORE SAMPLER

SOIL RETAINER ASSEMBLY

SECTION A-A

CORE EXTRACTOR

No.	NAME	SIZE	No. REQ	MATERIAL
1	Handles	$\frac{1}{2}$"	2	Pipe, galvanized iron
2	Handle, fitting	$\frac{1}{2}$"	1	Cross, " "
3	Handle, stem	$\frac{1}{2}$"	1	Pipe, " "
4	Cap, core sampler	$\frac{1}{2}$"	1	Plate, mild steel
5	Barrel, core sampler	$2\frac{1}{2}$" x $\frac{3}{16}$" wall	1	Seamless tubing, steel
6	Cutting edge	$\frac{1}{2}$" x .010"	1	Blued clock spring steel
7	Retainer disk	$\frac{1}{8}$"		Plastic
8	" "	$\frac{3}{16}$"		Ceramic
9	Rubber band	# 30	2	
10	Wire, retainer disk	19 ga.		Wire, nichrome
11	Block, core extractor	nominal 2"x 2"	1	Wood, pine
12	Fingers, core extractor	$\frac{1}{8}$"	2	Rod, tobin bronze
13	Finger depressor ring	2"	1	Thinwall conduit
14	Head, hammer	$2\frac{1}{2}$" dia.	1	Mild steel
15	Guide, hammer	$\frac{1}{2}$" dia.	1	" "
16	Retainer cylinder	$2\frac{1}{4}$" x 19 ga.	1	Seamless tubing, brass
17	" "	"	2	" " "
18	" "	"	2	" " "
19	" "	"	1	" " "

Soil sampler and core retainer.

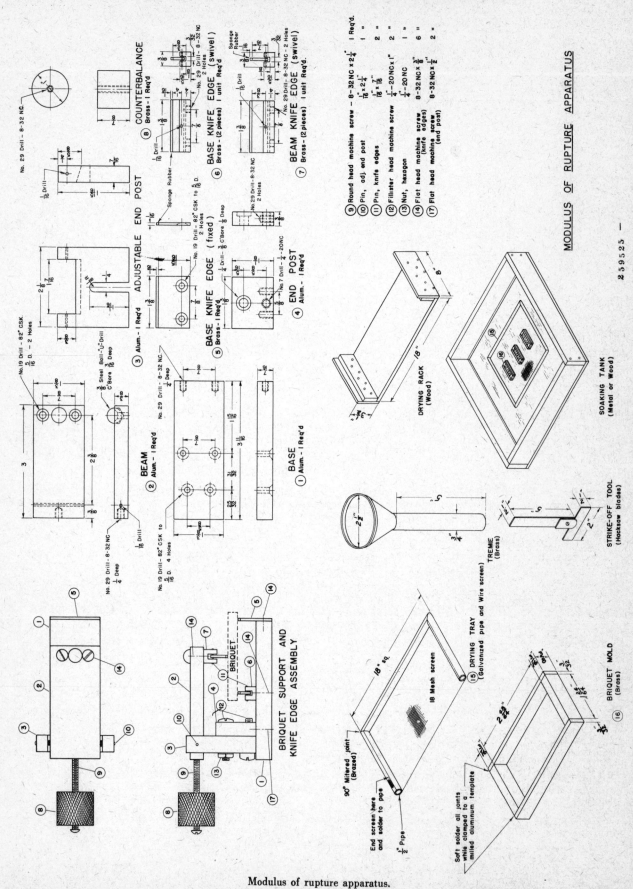

Modulus of rupture apparatus.